HANDBOOK OF SOVIET
MANNED SPACE FLIGHT

PUBLICATIONS OF THE AMERICAN ASTRONAUTICAL SOCIETY

Following are the principal publications of the American Astronautical
Society:

JOURNAL OF THE ASTRONAUTICAL SCIENCES (1954-)

Published quarterly and distributed by AAS Business Office, 6212-B Old
Keene Mill Court, Springfield, VA 22152. Back issues available from
Univelt, Inc., P.O. Box 28130, San Diego, CA 92128.

SPACE TIMES (1986-)

Published bi-monthly and distributed by AAS Business Office, 6212-B Old
Keene Mill Court, Springfield, VA 22152., Virginia 22152

AAS NEWSLETTER (1962-1985)

Incorporated in *Space Times*. Back issues available from AAS Business
Office, 6212-B Old Keene Mill Court, Springfield, VA 22152.

ASTRONAUTICAL SCIENCES REVIEW (1959-1962)

Incorporated in *Space Times*. Back issues still available from Univelt,
Inc., P.O. Box 28130, San Diego, CA 92128.

ADVANCES IN THE ASTRONAUTICAL SCIENCES (1957-)

Proceedings of major AAS technical meetings. Published and distributed
for the American Astronautical Society by Univelt, Inc., P.O. Box 28130,
San Diego, CA 92128.

SCIENCE AND TECHNOLOGY SERIES (1964-)

Supplement to *Advances in the Astronautical Sciences*. Proceedings and
monographs, most of them based on AAS technical meetings. Published and
distributed for the American Astronautical Society by Univelt, Inc., P.O.
Box 28130, San Diego, CA 92128

AAS HISTORY SERIES (1977-)

Supplement to *Advances in the Astronautical Sciences*. Selected works in
the field of aerospace history under the editorship of R. Cargill Hall.
Published and distributed for the American Astronautical Society by
Univelt, Inc., P.O. Box 28130, San Diego, CA 92128.

AAS MICROFICHE SERIES (1968-)

Supplement to *Advances in the Astronautical Sciences*. Consists princi-
pally of technical papers not included in the hard-copy volume. Published and distributed for the American Astronautical Society by Univelt,
Inc., P.O. Box 28130, San Diego, CA 92128.

Subscriptions to the *Journal* and the *Space Times* should be ordered from
the AAS Business Office. Back issues of the *Journal* and all books and
microfiche should be ordered from Univelt, Inc.

OTHER BOOKS BY THE SAME AUTHOR

Soviet Space Programs 1980-1985, Volume 66, Science
& Technology Series, 298p, 1987

Handbook of Soviet Lunar and Planetary Exploration, Volume
47, Science & Technology Series, 276p, 1979

Soviet Military Strategy in Space, Published by Jane's,
288p, 1987

Artificial Space Debris, Published by Orbit Book Co.,
124p, 1988

Available from Univelt, Inc., P.O. Box 28130, San Diego, CA 92128

Front Cover Illustration:

Photograph of Soyuz as seen from Apollo taken during the Apollo-Soyuz
mission. (Courtesy of NASA, Photo No. 75-H-891)

Frontispiece:

Artist's concept of launch of Soyuz spacecraft from Baykonur launch
complex near Aral Sea in Kazakhstan, USSR. (Courtesy of NASA,
Photo No. 75-H-251)

AN AMERICAN *Astronautical* SOCIETY PUBLICATION

HANDBOOK OF SOVIET MANNED SPACE FLIGHT

Nicholas L. Johnson

Volume 48
SCIENCE AND TECHNOLOGY SERIES

A Supplement to Advances in the Astronautical Sciences

Published by Univelt, Inc., P.O. Box 28130
San Diego, California 92128

First Printing 1980

Second Edition 1988

ISBN 0-87703-115-0 (Hard Cover)
ISBN 0-87703-116-9 (Soft Cover)

Published for the American Astronautical Society
by Univelt, Inc., P. O. Box 28130, San Diego, California 92128

Printed and Bound in the U.S.A.

FOREWORD

"Mankind will not forever remain on earth, but in the
pursuit of light and space will first timidly emerge
from the bounds of the atmosphere, and then advance
until he has conquered the whole of circumsolar space."

K. E. Tsiolkovskiy, 1911

Six years before the great October Revolution was to spawn the Union of
Soviet Socialist Republics, these words were penned by K. E. Tsiolkovskiy,
the founder and prophet of Soviet astronautics. Although the principles
of rocket propulsion had been known for hundreds of years, not until the
1903 publication of Tsiolkovskiy's *Investigation of Cosmic Spaces by
Reactive Devices* was there a scientific analysis of the obstacles to be
overcome if man were to leave his island in space. Fifty-four years later,
relying on the groundwork set forth by Tsiolkovskiy, the Soviet Union
launched another October revolution, the space revolution. On October 4,
1957, the beep-beep-beep of Sputnik 1 thrust a reluctant world into the
Space Age.

Like a modern day Columbus, Yuri Gagarin fulfilled Tsiolkovskiy's prophecy
a scant three and one-half years later by becoming the first of mankind
to "emerge from the bounds of the atmosphere" into earth orbit. But there
was nothing timid in the Soviet Union's drive to conquer space. Since the
launching of Sputnik 1 in 1957 one space spectacular has followed another
in an astounding Soviet effort designed to reach that stellar destiny of
the Soviet people.

The first earth satellite, the first manned spacecraft, the first lunar
and planetary probes all carried the familiar hammer and sickle emblem.
Soviet cosmonauts were the first to walk in space, conduct crew transfers
between spaceships, and operate scientific space stations for extended
periods. The first spacecraft to land on the moon, Mars, and Venus were
built by Soviet craftsman. Although no Soviet cosmonauts have yet traversed

the lunar surface, automatic Soviet robots have roved the lunar seas for periods exceeding one year and have returned soil samples from topographically diverse regions.

It was, of course, the unexpectedness of the Soviet Union's sudden prowess in space exploration which sent the rest of the world reeling. Almost a decade passed before the United States could recover from this cosmic Pearl Harbor and gain that elusive and ill-defined "lead" in space. Although the space race officially ended on July 20, 1969, when an American flag, not a Soviet banner, was erected by the first men on the moon, the competition in outer space continues today. Manned Soviet space stations now orbit overhead while the United States prepares to enter a new age of exploration with the reusable Space Shuttle.

What then may be the future role of the Soviet Union in space? Will the Soviets continue their broad space programs at presently high levels while the United States is reducing her own involvement in space exploration? Unfortunately, the answers to these questions must be deferred until such a time as the Soviet Union feels that the need for the secrecy surrounding her space activities has diminished. However, to appreciate the motives behind the Soviet Union's relentless drive to the moon and planets, and perhaps to catch a glimpse of what may lie in the future, one must first analyze her past accomplishments and goals in the proper perspective.

Since the dawn of the Space Age over twenty-two years ago hundreds of volumes have chronicled the United States' efforts to reach the moon and beyond. Whereas there have been also numerous attempts to construct a similar history of Soviet space exploration, until recently no single source had examined in depth the Soviet programs for manned and planetary exploration. The present work in two volumes is designed to fill that void. This volume reviews not only the exploits of Soviet manned space flights, but also the machines behind the men. Volume 47 of this series, *Handbook of Soviet Lunar and Planetary Exploration*, performed a similar survey of Soviet robot lunar and planetary missions.

Any work purporting to portray accurately the evolution of Soviet space exploration is immediately beset by a question of credibility. Although Soviet space scientists and journalists have the advantage of first-hand knowledge of Soviet intentions and goals, seldom are these reflected in Soviet publications or at international conferences. While technical information pertaining to spacecraft and other hardware has been found with few exceptions to be accurate, the same cannot be said of Soviet announced programs prior to or after their implementation. Here the record is littered by misleading and sometimes false statements. Even more glaring in Soviet authored accounts are the omissions of fact and purpose.

On the other hand, many Western documents concerned with the Soviet space program are largely a reflection of Soviet propaganda and of their author's beliefs and deductions which may or may not adhere to reality. In addition, the purpose of many of these publications is to condemn or praise the achievements of the USSR rather than to report them objectively. This serves merely to confuse further the true picture. However, scholarly studies are conducted in the West by individuals and groups, and these studies have proved invaluable to Soviet space watchers.

This then is the basis from which every author must begin. To ensure the most complete and reliable investigation thousands of books, pamphlets, articles, and documents have been examined. Whenever possible Russian language publications were obtained through the National Technical Information Service of the US Department of Commerce for historical purposes and to verify scientific data. Domestic and foreign periodicals and English-language Soviet publications also were reviewed for informative articles by Soviet space scientists. Finally, a wide range of Western works was consulted and personal correspondence was conducted with acknowledged experts in the field.

In particular, mention must be made of the efforts and publications of the British Interplanetary Society, who in addition to its prominent role in the support of space exploration is the acknowledged leader of Soviet space-flight analysis.

Great care has been taken to present in this volume only the facts as they now appear. When minor inconsistencies in data due to the continuing refinement of telemetry occurred, the most recent and widely accepted figures have been incorporated. Rarely are conjectures brought forth, but when appropriate they are always labeled as such. To this end the

application of footnotes and references has been widely adopted. The
cited reference is important not only to judge its own reliability, but
also as a source for further information on the topic in question.

This volume examines the evolution of Soviet manned space flight from the
brief and heroic flight of Yuri Gagarin aboard Vostok 1 to the latest
Soyuz-Salyut marathon space ventures. Each program -- Vostok, Voskhod,
and Soyuz -- is reviewed from the standpoint of spacecraft design, development and operation. Appendices are included to provide a brief summary
of launch vehicles, launch facilities, and manned missions. The bibliography lists major sources of Soviet space activities literature.

A work of this magnitude is only possible with the help of many individuals
and organizations. Special thanks are due the staff of the Smithsonian
Institution's National Air and Space Museum, the National Aeronautics and
Space Administration, and the Foreign Technology Division at Wright-
Patterson AFB, Ohio. My personal gratitude is extended to Anthony Kenden,
Phillip S. Clark, and Ralph Gibbons whose criticisms and contributions
have been invaluable.

But most of all I wish to thank my wife, Beth, for her enduring love and
support without which these volumes could never have been written.

                              Nicholas L. Johnson

ADDENDUM (April 1988)

In his second edition of the Handbook of Soviet Manned Flight the main
part of the book has remained essentially unchanged. However, the
appendices have been updated to incorporate information obtained since
the first edition was published, to reflect more recent missions and
to provide a more extensive account of Soviet cosmonauts. For an
update of Soviet missions through 1985, please refer to Soviet Space
Programs 1980-1985, Volume 66, Science and Technology Series.

CONTENTS

CONTENTS (Cont'd)

Section I

VOSTOK

INTRODUCTION TO VOSTOK

Before Soviet scientists could seriously dream of sending men into space and safely retrieving them, much experience with simpler biological payloads was needed. These experimental programs began in earnest in 1951 with the first launching of two dogs to an altitude of 100 km in a modified German A-4 (V-2) rocket. The Soviets as well as the Americans had captured these German rockets and plans for the intercontinental A-9/A-10 rocket in the waning days of World War II. Immediately this captured hardware along with many German scientists and technicians was transported to the Soviet Union where testing and experimentation began.

Starting in 1951 the Soviets began a three-phase program of testing animal reactions to short, high-altitude flights in geophysical rockets. The first series consisting of six flights was conducted between 1951 and 1952. Lift-off accelerations were maintained below 5.5 g while the rockets climbed to altitudes of 100 km. Each flight tested the pulse rate and temperature of the two dog passengers as well as recording their behavior on film. The results of complete physical examinations before and after the flights were compared. The hermetically sealed cabin in which the dogs rode had a 0.28 m^3 volume pressurized to 680-760 mm Hg with a 70% air/30% oxygen atmospheric mixture. A canine contingent of nine was utilized during this initial phase, resulting in double flights for three of the dogs.[1]

The second phase of experimentation lasting between 1955 and 1956 and consisting of nine flights also involved sending two dogs to altitudes in the 100-110 km range. However, the cabin layout and mission profile were substantially altered. The passenger compartment was no longer hermetically sealed, requiring each animal to wear special pressure suits with removable helmets. Each dog was secured to a separate ejectable chassis within the nose-cone compartment. As the rocket reached its programmed altitude the compartment carrying both dogs was separated. The dogs were ejected separately at different stages of the descent: the right-hand animal at 80-90 km with a separation velocity of 700 m/sec and the left-hand animal at 35-50 km with a 1000-1150 m/sec velocity. The subsequent flight paths of each dog differed significantly. The descent parachute of the first animal opened within three seconds at an altitude of 75-85 km, allowing for a long, gentle drop lasting from 50-65 minutes. The second animal underwent free fall to an altitude of 3.8-4.0 km at which point the parachute was deployed. Touchdown for both dogs occurred at a velocity of 6 m/sec and a separation distance of approximately 20-50 km. Figure 1 shows the flight profile of the 1955-1956 geophysical rocket experiments.

One of the important aspects of this second phase of testing was the thorough evaluation of the method of ejection from a descending cabin. The success of these flights undoubtably influenced the final design of the Soviet Union's first manned spacecraft, Vostok.

The final phase of animal experimentation with geophysical rockets was carried out between May 1957 and September 1960. In this series seven flights of the Soviet V-2-A rocket lifted payloads to an altitude of 212 km (Figure 2). Again the usual payload consisted of two dogs; however, on two A-2 flights a rabbit also tagged along for the ride. Although a total of 14 dogs made flights, one intrepid canine was a veteran of six missions.

The emphasis of these last biomedical flights was on increased understanding of the rigors of space flight on living organisms. Pulse, respiration, arterial pressure, EKG, and visual observation via photography were all monitored during the flights. Pre- and post-flight examinations were extensive. For these higher altitudes the special pressure suits were retained, but the 0.46 m^3 compartment was again hermetically sealed.[2]

The experience gained in these flights conducted from 1951 to 1960 provided the basic knowledge necessary to design vehicles capable of sustaining life during a true orbital mission.

Six months following the beginning of the third stage of the animal carrying geophysical rocket flights, the first orbital flight to carry a living payload took place on the second artificial earth satellite, Sputnik 2. Coming only one month after the historic launch of Sputnik 1,

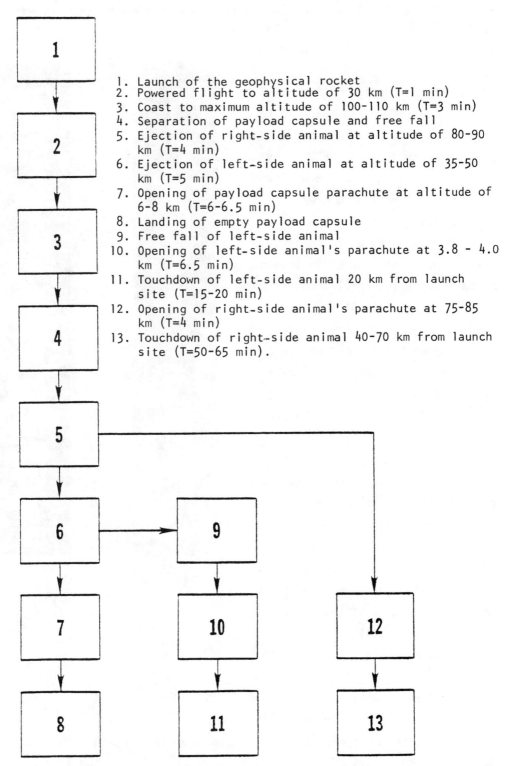

1. Launch of the geophysical rocket
2. Powered flight to altitude of 30 km (T=1 min)
3. Coast to maximum altitude of 100-110 km (T=3 min)
4. Separation of payload capsule and free fall
5. Ejection of right-side animal at altitude of 80-90 km (T=4 min)
6. Ejection of left-side animal at altitude of 35-50 km (T=5 min)
7. Opening of payload capsule parachute at altitude of 6-8 km (T=6-6.5 min)
8. Landing of empty payload capsule
9. Free fall of left-side animal
10. Opening of left-side animal's parachute at 3.8 - 4.0 km (T=6.5 min)
11. Touchdown of left-side animal 20 km from launch site (T=15-20 min)
12. Opening of right-side animal's parachute at 75-85 km (T=4 min)
13. Touchdown of right-side animal 40-70 km from launch site (T=50-65 min).

Figure 1   Flight profile of the 1955-1956 geophysical rocket experiments

Sputnik 2 amazed the world by its
weight of 508.3 kg and its passenger,
a dog named Laika. Figures 3 and 4
illustrate the design of Sputnik 2
and the compartment in which Laika
rode. Launched on 3 November 1957
into an earth orbit of 1670 km by
225 km at 65.3°, Sputnik 2 was cone-
shaped with a maximum diameter of
1.2 m and a length of 5.8 m and was
comprised of three basic compartments. Uppermost was an instrument
compartment which carried experiments
for detecting solar ultraviolet and
X-ray emissions and cosmic radiation. Beneath this section was a
spherical compartment identical to
Sputnik 1 containing instruments,
chemical batteries, and radio transmitters.[3]

Finally came the cylindrical
compartment which housed Laika. Such
physiological parameters as pulse,
respiration, blood pressure, and
movement were monitored. Active
chemicals provided oxygen and ab-
sorbed carbon dioxide and water
vapor. A forced ventilation system
was employed for this purpose as
well as to maintain a proper cabin
temperature.

Figure 2   The V-2-A (left) and the
V-5-V Soviet geophysical
rockets

The capsule containing Laika was designed for an operation of only
seven days, and since reentry vehicles would not be perfected for another
three years, no plans were made to recover the dog. At the end of seven
days an automatic system put Laika to sleep. Thus ended the life of the
world's first space traveler.

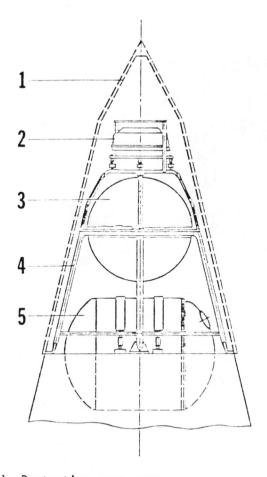 

1. Protective nose cone
2. Instrument for investigating short-wave solar radiation
3. Spherical container with radio transmitters
4. Frame for instrumentation
5. Pressurization cabin for dog Laika.

Figure 3   Design of Sputnik 2 which carried the world's first biological payload into orbit on 3 Nov 1957

Sputnik 2 which remained attached to the last stage of the carrier rocket for observational purposes was destroyed on 14 April 1958 during reentry into the earth's atmosphere after 2370 revolutions. Not only were valuable biomedical data obtained concerning the effects of prolonged exposure to weightlessness but also information regarding the radiation belts, atmospheric density, and ionospheric characteristics was returned.[4]

Figure 4   Layout of Laika's pressurized cabin on board Sputnik 2

    During this week in orbit Laika did not exhibit any adverse effects
of weightlessness. Soviet scientists were greatly encouraged and began
serious plans to develop a spaceship capable of carrying a human cargo
into earth orbit and return him safely to earth.

Chapter 1

VOSTOK SPACECRAFT DESIGN

The rocket used to launch Sputnik 1 and 2 was not capable of putting a much heavier spacecraft carrying a man into orbit. Hence an additional stage was developed to lift the proposed Vostok capsule into space (Figures 5-7). Figure 8 illustrates the modified spacecraft launcher and of the Vostok vehicle itself. Although most Soviet photographs and descriptions are of the combination, the actual Vostok vehicle separated from the final stage immediately upon reaching orbit.

A great deal of speculation and misinformation surrounded the design of the Vostok spacecraft for years after the flight of Vostok 1 with Yuri Gagarin since very few details were released at that time. In July 1961, a mock-up of a Vostok spacecraft was flown to a Soviet air display at Tushino. However, to permit ease of transportation the rocket shroud was left on and aerodynamic flairings were attached at the rear. This, combined with a painting done by future Cosmonaut Aleksey Leonov, led to depictions of Vostok which were highly exaggerated. These illustrations even found their way onto postage stamps from the USSR and other countries until as late as 1965 when Leonov performed the first space walk from Voskhod 2[5] (Figure 9). The actual Vostok* spacecraft was first put on display in April 1965.

The first drawings of Vostok were apparently conceived in the spring of 1959. After finalization of plans in the summer of that year the hardware was built and tested on two flights in May and August of 1960. Following these missions the spacecraft was redesigned from September to December 1960, and test flights were resumed.[6] In its final form Vostok consisted of two compartments: the spherical return capsule in which the cosmonaut sat during the entire flight and the instrument/retro-engine

---

* Vostok means "east" in Russian.

Figure 5   Soviet exhibition model of Vostok-type Launch facilities
(photograph courtesy of R.F. Gibbons)

compartment which was jettisoned immediately prior to reentering the earth's
atmosphere. Vostok weighed approximately 4730 kg and was 4.0 m long.

The spherical return capsule measured 2.3 m in diameter and weighed
2400 kg. A spherical design was chosen over the roughly conical shapes
of other manned spacecraft for several reasons. It was a shape whose aerodynamic properties for a wide range of velocities were well known. By
choosing an appropriate center of gravity the capsule would naturally orient itself in the proper attitude during reentry and landing. Also, maximum volume was obtained for a given outside surface area. There were three
large circular hatches in the capsule: the entrance hatch, the auxiliary
access hatch, and the parachute hatch. Three portholes with adjustable
shutters were arranged to allow the cosmonaut a view of space and the earth
below.[7]

The cosmonaut rode in a semi-reclining position in a powerful ejection
seat which could be used during an abortive launch or during landing. With
the spacecraft attached to the rocket launcher, the ejection seat was inclined 65° to the horizontal to ensure the proper attitude in the event
of ejection and to minimize the effects of acceleration forces during

Figure 6   Display of Vostok spacecraft and the final rocket stage at the
Kosmos Pavilion in Moscow (photograph courtesy of R.F. Gibbons)

11

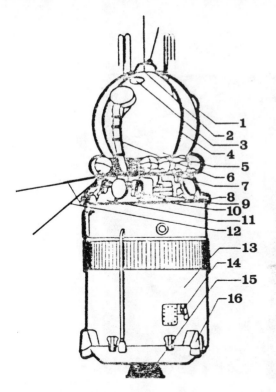

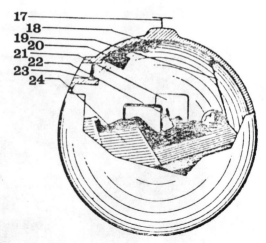

(1) Porthole with "Vzor" optical orienting device; (2) antennas of command
radio link system; (3) porthole; (4)
coupling bands; (5) descent capsule;
(6) cable-mast; (7) cylinders of pneumatic system; (8) solar orientation
transducer; (9) components of pneumatic system; (10) control nozzles; (11)
instrument compartment; (12) ribbon
antennas; (13) last stage of carrier-rocket; (14) loop antenna; (15) nozzle
of last stage engine; (16) control engines; (17) antenna; (18) instrument
panel with globe; (19) entrance hatch; (20) television camera; (21) food
container; (22) control wheel; (23) porthole with "Vzor" optical orienting
device; (24) pilot's seat.

Figure 7a   Diagram of Vostok spacecraft with last rocket stage

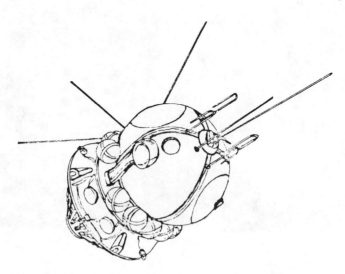

Figure 7b   The Vostok spacecraft in orbit   (drawing by R.F. Gibbons)

Figure 8   The Vostok launch vehicle on display outside the Kosmos
            Pavilion in Moscow (photograph courtesy of R.F. Gibbons)

launch. Figure 10 illustrates the design of the ejection seat. After the
entrance hatch was blown away by pyrotechnic devices, two solid fuel rockets under the seat would catapult the cosmonaut away from the capsule. The
seat contained a number of devices essential for the cosmonaut's survival.
In addition to the parachutes and pressure sensors of the landing system,
the ejection seat provided temporary oxygen and life support during the
descent. Upon landing, the cosmonaut had at his disposal an inflatable
dinghy (in the event of a water landing), emergency food and water supplies,
radio communications equipment, and flares.[8]

    As mentioned previously, the cosmonaut could either eject from the
capsule during the landing sequence or remain in the capsule. In practice,
though, all Vostok cosmonauts (with the possible exception of Gagarin) did
leave the capsule and landed like an ordinary parachutist. At this stage

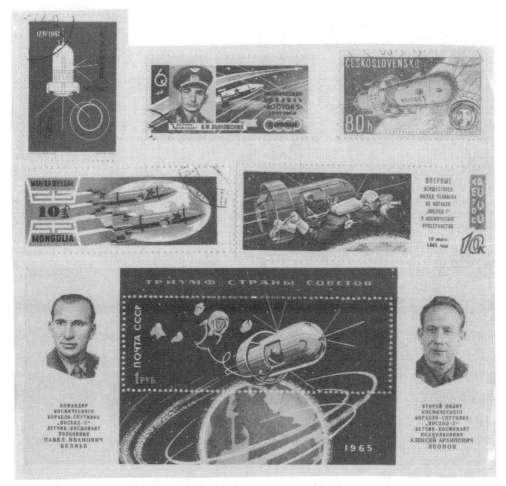

Figure 9   Soviet and foreign postage stamps erroneously depicting the
design of the Vostok and Voskhod spacecraft
(Courtesy of Beth Johnson)

of space exploration this would seem to be an undesirable strain to place
on a cosmonaut who had spent several days in the weightlessness of outer
space and who had just undergone the crushing forces of reentry. However,
some reports indicate this was a necessary procedure due to the high velocity with which the Vostok capsule landed. See the Vostok 1 and Voskhod
sections of this book for a further discussion of this problem.[9]

The instrumentation within the capsule was minimal (Figure 11). Unlike the Soviet Soyuz spacecraft to follow and American spacecraft, Vostok
largely performed automatically with little or no help required from the
cosmonaut. Directly in front of the cosmonaut was the austere main instrument panel (Figure 12). Slightly to the left of center on the panel

14

Figure 10   Drawing of a Soviet cosmonaut in the Vostok ejection seat

was a rotating globe similar to that used in conventional aircraft. With
it the cosmonaut could locate his position above the earth at any time.
To the right of the center of the panel was a digital readout of the number of revolutions which had been made. A series of indicator lights on
the panel's right side showed the operating condition of the spacecraft
systems. Other instruments monitored temperature, humidity, and pressure
(bottom row, second from left) and oxygen and carbon dioxide content (bottom row, third from left) of the capsule's atmosphere. In addition there
were gages indicating the pressure of gas in the attitude-control system
(bottom row, far right) and other on-board system parameters. In the bottom left corner was a clock activated at the moment of launch to be used
for reference with ground-control instructions.[10]

Below the instrument panel was a television camera which provided a
frontal view of the cosmonaut. This camera was used by ground controllers
to monitor the status of the cosmonaut. Below the camera was one of the
three portholes. These portholes were made of refractory glass and were
highly heat-resistant. This particular window was also the heart of

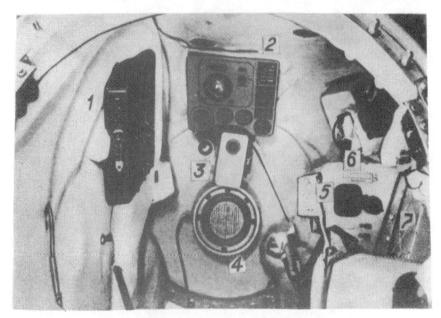

1. Pilot's control panel
2. Main instrument panel
3. TV camera
4. Porthole with optical orientator
5. Manual orientation control lever
6. Radio receiver
7. Food container

Figure 11   Interior of the Vostok cabin

Figure 12   Main Vostok instrument panel

16

the Vzor optical orientation system. Should manual orientation of the
spacecraft become necessary, the cosmonaut could determine his attitude
through a system of mirror reflectors and a grid etched into the viewing
window (Figure 13). A control stick on the pilot's right could then be
used to activate the compressed gas attitude-control jets and bring the
capsule to the proper position for retro-fire (Figure 14).[11]

In addition to the control stick the right side of the cosmonaut's
cabin contained the food storage container, the regeneration and air-con-
ditioning system, a second television camera, a radio receiver, an electric
clock, the sanitation system, and electrical storage batteries. Also on
the right was a second observation porthole. The third and final porthole
was located directly behind the cosmonaut's head in the entrance hatch.
On the left side were the cosmonaut control panel for activating the various systems in the spacecraft, the water supply, a tape recorder which was
activated by the sound of the cosmonaut's voice, the landing system direction finder, and the emergency heat regulation system. Behind the left wall
was the spacecraft parachute compartment and external parachute hatch.[12]

The interior atmosphere of the Vostok capsule was maintained at a pressure of between 755 and 775 mm Hg, a relative humidity of 51-57%, an oxygen
content of 21-25%, and a temperature of +13° to +26°C. Figure 15 is a
schematic diagram of the air regeneration and conditioning system. Elec-
trically driven fans forced the cabin air across an alkali metal superoxide
which would absorb cabin carbon dioxide and release oxygen. The air was
subsequently purged of noxious odors and excess moisture. Temperature
was regulated via a heat exchanger in the capsule to a heat radiator on
the outer portion of the instrument compartment. Human wastes were collected and stored on board. The entire life-support system, including food
and water supplies, was designed to maintain one cosmonaut for at least ten
days. This limit was set as a precaution due to the fact that the Vostok
spacecraft would naturally decay in that period even if the retro-system
malfunctioned.[13]

As pointed out, television observation of the cosmonaut was provided
by two TV cameras, allowing both a frontal and profile view. In addition,
medical data were obtained from sensors attached to the cosmonaut's body.
These included pulse rate, respiration, blood pressure, electrocardiograms,

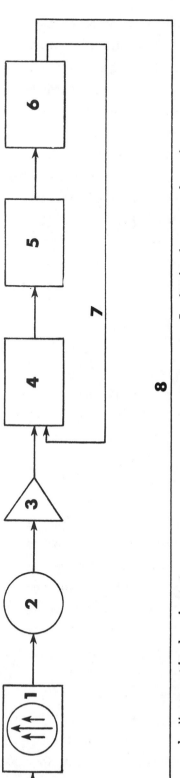

1. Vzor optical orientator
2 Cosmonaut
3 Control handle (roll, pitch, and yaw)
4 Angular-rate sensor

5. Attitude-control engine
6. Controlled object
7. Angular-rate feedback
8. Angular-position feedback

Figure 13   Vostok Manual Orientation System Diagram

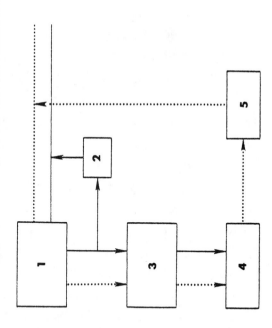

1. Controlled object
2. Automatic Control System (ACS)
3. Instrument panel
4. Cosmonaut
5. Controller

The solid line indicates the automatic system whereas the dotted line indicates cosmonaut interface when needed.

Figure 14   Vostok Control System

18

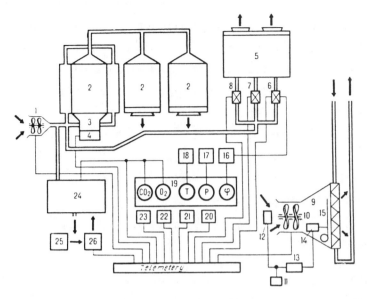

(1, 10) Electrically-driven fan; (2, 3, 4) adjustable regulators,
dust filter and contaminant filter; (5) moisture absorber unit;
(6) automatic valve; (7, 8) manually operated valves; (9) air-liq-
uid heat exchanger with condensed moisture collector; (11, 12, 13,
14, 15) automatic temperature regulators (controller, pick-up, am-
plifier, actuator, and adjustable screen); (16, 20, 21) humidity
gauges; (17, 23) pressure gauges; (18, 22) temperature gauges; (19)
control console; (24, 25, 26) automatic gas analyzers measuring oxygen and CO_2 content.

Figure 15   Air regeneration and conditioning on Vostok spaceship

etc. Radiation levels were constantly monitored by ground personnel through
telemetric readings from dosimetric apparatus in the Vostok capsule. The
cosmonaut was largely protected from excess radiation by the structure of
the spacecraft itself. Chemical serums were also available in the event
of solar outbursts before the cosmonaut could land.[14]

The attitude of the spacecraft could be controlled around the yaw,
pitch, and roll axes. With the aid of the Vzor optical device the cosmonaut could fire compressed gas microjets to bring the spacecraft around to
the proper orientation. Ordinarily the orientation system worked automatically with the aid of a solar sensor. However, Vostok did not have the
capability to change orbits as did the later Soyuz spacecraft. Telemetry
associated with the spacecraft orientation and a radio signal used for location of the spacecraft in orbit were transmitted on a frequency of 19.995
Mhz. For communications with Soviet ground stations within 2000 km a

frequency of 143.625 Mhz was used. For longer range communications two channels of 9.019 and 20.006 Mhz were employed. All tape recordings performed by the cosmonaut could be replayed at an accelerated rate on these frequencies when the spacecraft came within range of a tracking station. In all, the instrumentation within the Vostok capsule weighed 800 kg and contained over 6000 transistors, 56 electric motors, and 800 relays and switches.[15]

While in the spacecraft the cosmonaut wore his spacesuit at all times. This provided the cosmonaut with the following:

1. Insulation from the atmosphere of the cabin if harmful impurities appeared in it

2. Protection from supercooling in case of landing, or water landing by parachute in desert regions of the earth with low temperature of air and water

3. Decrease in the probability of injury in case of landing with parachute in a woody or mountainous site

4. Protection during catapulting from the escape hatch during an accident

5. Improvement of ventilation due to equal distribution of air over the entire surface of the body

6. The possibility of regulating heat exchange due to changes of ventilation of the pressure suit and the heat-insulating properties of the material.

The pressure suits worn by the Vostok cosmonauts were not spacesuits as defined today and were not designed for extravehicular activity. During the normal course of the flight the helmet visor was opened and the cosmonaut breathed the capsule atmosphere. A pair of bright orange overalls was worn over the three-layer pressure suit (Figure 16).[16]

The entire outside of the Vostok capsule was covered in a heavy ablative material needed to dissipate the intense heat generated during reentry. The three portholes were recessed to avoid the high temperatures encountered when the capsule returned to earth. Four paperclip antennae and two 3.6 m long aerial antennae protruded from the forward end of the capsule for communications. A large adapter plug and conduit carrying cables between the capsule and the instrument module ran from near the cosmoanut's right-hand porthole to the forward end of the instrument module. Four large metal tie plates encircled the cosmonaut's sphere and held it in place relative to the instrument module. After the retro-rockets

Figure 16   Flight suit worn
             by the Vostok
             cosmonauts

had fired, these bands would be released by explosive locks and the return capsule could separate from the instrument module. Aerodynamic weighting of the capsule ensured that the cosmonaut would remain in an attitude in which he could best endure the deceleration forces of reentry.[17]

The instrument module resembled two cones placed base to base with the forward end encompassed by a ring of spherical compressed gas containers. The overall length of the instrument module was approximately 2.6 m with an equal maximum diameter and a volume of about 1.5 m^3. The rear end of the instrument module was covered with the shutters of the heat regulation system. Four antennae for telemetry transmissions also extended from the rear, and at the extreme back end was located the retro-engine nozzle. The instrument module contained most of the storage batteries needed for a ten-day flight, the retro-rocket, the majority of the radio transmitters, the temperature-control system, and the attitude-control system.[18]

The shroud had a circular cutout directly opposite the Vostok entrance hatch, which permitted easy insertion of the cosmonaut into the vehicle and a clear path for ejection of the cosmonaut in the event of a booster malfunction.

After manufacture and check-out the Vostok spacecraft was mated to its rocket launcher in a horizontal position and then transported by rail to the launch site. (See Figures 17-20). Here the completed 38-m tall rocket assembly was raised into a vertical position and the final check-out was performed. When the launch countdown reached zero the 20 engine nozzles in the central unit and the four strap-on units were ignited. As soon as the combined thrust reached slightly more than the weight of the

Figure 17   Vostok spacecraft under construction
(TASS from Sovfoto)

Figure 18   Mating of the Vostok spacecraft with its protective shroud

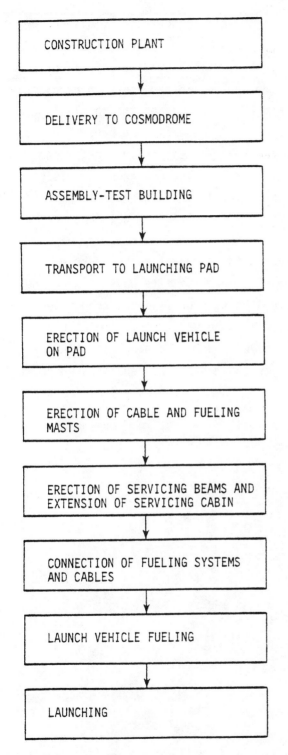

CONSTRUCTION PLANT

↓

DELIVERY TO COSMODROME

↓

ASSEMBLY-TEST BUILDING

↓

TRANSPORT TO LAUNCHING PAD

↓

ERECTION OF LAUNCH VEHICLE
ON PAD

↓

ERECTION OF CABLE AND FUELING
MASTS

↓

ERECTION OF SERVICING BEAMS AND
EXTENSION OF SERVICING CABIN

↓

CONNECTION OF FUELING SYSTEMS
AND CABLES

↓

LAUNCH VEHICLE FUELING

↓

LAUNCHING

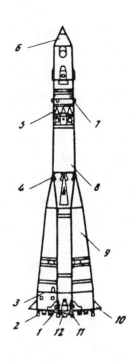

1. Engine of strap-on unit
2. Vernier engine of strap-on unit
3. Strap-on unit engine housing
4. Attachment of strap-on unit to
   main launch vehicle
5. Upper stage engine
6. Nose cone
7. Upper stage
8. Launch vehicle central unit
9. Strap-on unit
10. Stabilizer
11. Vernier engine of central unit
12. Engine of central unit

Figure 19   Launch vehicle movement
            and preparation diagram

Figure 20   Diagram of Vostok
            launch vehicle

23

rocket, the balanced supports which held the launch vehicle rigid on the
pad were pushed free and the launcher slowly lifted upward (Figure 21).
At a prescribed altitude the rocket began to pitch over to a more horizontal flight path. When the fuel for the engines in the four strap-on stages
was exhausted they were jettisoned and the four core engine nozzles continued to burn. A few moments later when the assembly had penetrated most
of the dense atmosphere the nose cone shroud was ejected. First stage
shutdown and separation came shortly after with the subsequent ignition
of the final stage. Upon reaching orbit the last stage was extinguished
and separated from the Vostok spacecraft. The entire flight sequence is
shown in Figure 22.[19]

Once in orbit the Vostok spacecraft with cosmonaut aboard carried out
the flight program which ranged from 90 minutes to five days. When the
time for the return to earth had come, the spacecraft was turned around
with its retro-engine pointed in the direction of flight. At the preset
moment the retro-engine was ignited, slowing down the spaceship. After
completion of the retro-burn the instrument module was separated where it
was later destroyed upon hitting the atmosphere. The spherical reentry

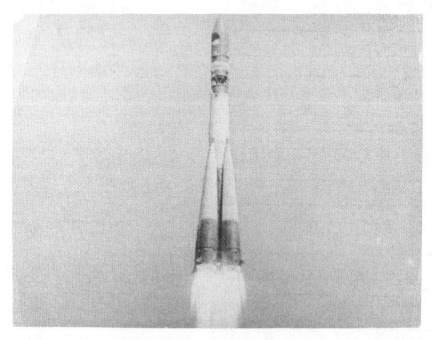

Figure 21   Launch of the Vostok launch vehicle (TASS from Sovfoto)
*Note cutout in launch shroud for ejection of cosmonaut
in the event of an emergency.*

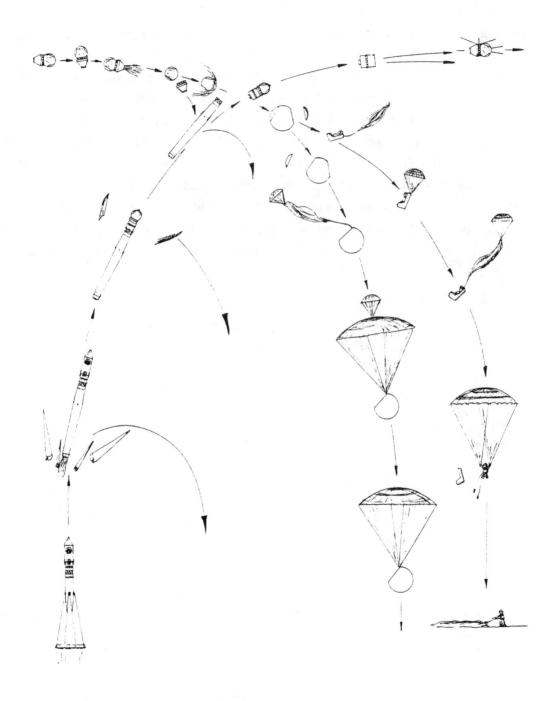

Figure 22   Launch sequence and reentry for the Vostok
launch vehicle (Drawing by R.F. Gibbons)

capsule then began its searing return. The cosmonaut was protected by the ability of the ablation covering the capsule to dissipate the intense heat generated as the spacecraft entered the dense atmosphere at a high velocity. The deceleration force exerted on the cosmonaut increased to 8 to 9 g's (compared with the 5 g's experienced during launch) while the outside temperature rose to 10,000°C. After the spacecraft passed through reentry, the entrance hatch was blown off at an altitude of 7 km. Two seconds later the cosmonaut's ejection seat was activated and the cosmonaut was hurled free of the descending capsule. The cosmonaut's parachute system was immediately deployed and at an altitude of 4 km his ejection seat fell away. Also at an altitude of 4 km the Vostok's parachute hatch was opened with the drogue and main parachutes deploying at a height of 2.5 km. The cosmonaut and capsule landed a few minutes later in the same vicinity.[20]

Chapter 2

VOSTOK PRECURSOR FLIGHTS

Before the Vostok spacecraft and launcher could be used to place a man in orbit they had to be thoroughly tested and "man-rated". This check-out consisted of suborbital flights of the basic hardware and five orbital flights of which four carried dogs as passengers. Figure 23 is a chart depicting these flights and their major achievements. The suborbital testing of powerful space rockets would begin using a landing area in the Pacific Ocean 1700 km SW of Hawaii. Two launchings, one on 20 January and one on 31 January, were finally conducted. This presented the first opportunity to evaluate the conditions encountered by an object reenter-ing the earth's atmosphere.[21]

Four months after the completion of the suborbital testing, the first unmanned Vostok spacecraft was rocketed into orbit. On 15 May 1960 Space-ship-Satellite 1 (also known as* Korabl Sputnik 1 or Sputnik 4) was placed into an earth orbit of 369 km by 312 km at an inclination of 65°. The 4540 kg spacecraft was equipped with all the necessary systems to support a human being. A dummy with a weight equivalent to that of a cosmonaut was carried to simulate as closely as possible a manned flight. Although an initial press release from Pravda indicated that recovery of the cap-sule was not envisioned, it appears that the cabin with dummy might have been intended to complete the entire program including a soft landing on Soviet territory. At 0252 hr+ on 19 May Moscow time with the spacecraft on its 64th revolution, the retro-engine was fired with the intention of bringing the reentry capsule back to earth. However, due to a malfunction in the attitude-control system the spacecraft was not properly oriented at the time of the retro-burn. As a result, instead of deorbiting, the

* *Korabl Sputnik means "spaceship satellite."*

+ *In this book time is given using the military method: The first two digits are hours on the 24-hr. system and the second two digits are minutes. All times are Moscow time unless otherwise indicated.*

Vostok capsule separated from the instrument module and went into a higher elliptical orbit of 690 km by 307 km. The life-support systems reportedly functioned for more than eight days. The capsule's orbit eventually decayed and on 15 October 1965 it was destroyed reeentering the atmosphere. Shortly after launch the first mention was made of solar cells being attached to the outside of the spacecraft for additional electrical power. These solar cells were connected to a solar sensing system which kept the cells constantly oriented on the sun. Later the arrangement of the solar cells was revealed to be on two half discs with a diameter of one meter. With the exception of the attitude-control system at the time of retro-fire and excessive noise in cosmonaut communication frequencies all systems were reported to have operated correctly.[22]

After examining the data returned from Spaceship-Satellite 1 for three months, Soviet scientists and engineers readied the second in the series of unmanned Vostok orbital test flights. On 19 August 1960 Spaceship-Satellite 2 entered an earth orbit of 339 km by 306 km at 64.95°. This time, however, two dogs named Strelka and Belka were placed in a special container attached to the ejection seat. (For ejection seat layout see

VOSTOK PRECURSOR FLIGHTS

Designator	Date Launched	Date Returned	Orbits	Weight(kg)	Results
Suborbital testing	20 Jan 1960	---	--	--	First test of reentry vehicles
Suborbital testing	31 Jan 1960	---	--	--	Second test of reentry vehicles
Spaceship-Satellite 1	15 May 1960	15 Oct 1965	?	4540	Attempted reentry on 64th orbit failed when craft entered higher orbit
Spaceship-Satellite 2	19 Aug 1960	20 Aug 1960	18	4600	First return of living animals from space. Dogs Belka and Strelka safely returned after one day
Spaceship-Satellite 3	1 Dec 1960	2 Dec 1960	18 (?)	4563	Spacecraft destroyed during reentry at too steep an angle. Dogs Pchelka and Mushka perished
Spaceship-Satellite 4	9 Mar 1961	9 Mar 1961	1	4700	Dress rehearsal for first manned flight. Dog Chernushks safely returned after one orbit
Spaceship-Satellite 5	25 Mar 1961	25 Mar 1961	1	4695	Dress rehearsal for first manned flight. Dog Zvezdochka safely returned after one orbit

Figure 23

28

Figure 24). The object of this flight was to successfully return the two dogs after spending a day in outer space. Within the capsule, both on the ejection seat and elsewhere, were a total of 40 mice, 2 rats, plants, insects, seeds, fungi, microbes, and other biological payloads. By examining these specimens after 24 hours' exposure to the radiation of space, Soviet scientists hoped to determine whether man could safely follow. In addition to the listed plants and animals, human tissue removed from scientists working in the Soviet space program was carried.[23]

During the flight of the 4600 kg spaceship particular attention was given to the reactions of the two dogs. Their movements were monitored by two television cameras, one on the ejection seat for a frontal view of Belka and the other on a cabin wall for a profile of Strelka. Instruments were also placed in the capsule to record the levels of radiation to which the biological specimens were exposed. On 20 August during the spacecraft's eighteenth revolution a command from earth activated the landing system. This time the Vostok was correctly oriented and after the retro-fire it followed the programmed trajectory. At a height of 7 to 8 km the ejection seat with Strelka and Belka and most of the other animals was catapulted from the cabin. A short while later the animals and the Vostok cabin landed with a velocity of 6-8 m/sec and 10m/sec, respectively, within 10 km of the predicted landing site. For the first time living organisms had endured the rigors of space and had successfully returned. Belka and Strelka suffered no apparent ill effects of their day in space, nor did the other animals and plants on board. The human tissue carried was grafted onto the original donors to observe the possible effects of space radiation on humans. Detailed analysis of the experiments conducted on this flight can be found in the references listed at the end of this section.[24]

Three and one-half months passed from the successful flight of Spaceship-Satellite 2 to the launch of Spaceship-Satellite 3. Spaceship-Satellite 3 appeared to be a repeat of the previous flight with two dogs,Pchelka and Mushka, and other assorted plants and animals tagging along. This time, though, the spacecraft, launched on 1 December 1960, traveled along an orbit of 265 km by 187 km at 65° which was much closer to the orbits used by the later manned Vostoks. Again emphasis was placed on the automatic functioning of spacecraft equipment and state of the biological specimens

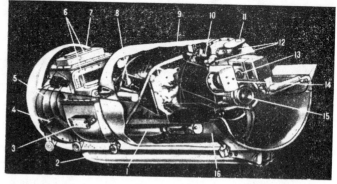

(1) Cylinder of air supply system; (2) ejection cartridge unit; (3) direction finder unit; (4) storage battery; (6) instrument compartment; (7) container body; (8) dog movement sensor; (9) air-tight cabin for animal; (10) microphone; (11) antenna of direction finder; (12) inhalation and exhalation valves; (13) TV camera; (14) mirror; (15) ventilation unit; (16) automatic device for combination feeding.

Figure 24   Layout of the Vostok ejection seat fitted to accommodate biological payloads during the 1960-1961 test flights

on board. Soviet sources revealed that new and improved systems were being tested. In particular new methods of transmitting physiological data back to earth were being evalutated. In addition, a new computer-operated spacecraft control system was being used for the first time on the 4563-kg Vostok.[25]

Unfortunately, the new control system still had a few kinks in it. When the command to begin deorbit was given after one day on 2 December the spacecraft reoriented itself and fired its retro-rocket. However, the attitude was slightly off and the spacecraft began its reentry at too steep an angle. The resulting aerodynamic heating was too much for the

capsule and the spacecraft was incinerated during the attempt, killing the
two dogs and other specimens on board. Thus, after three flights of unmanned Vostoks, two had suffered serious malfunctions during the return
phase of the flight--malfunctions so serious as to doom any cosmonauts had
they been on board. Interestingly, according to Gherman Titov who would
later pilot Vostok 2, the cosmonauts in training at that time were not
immediately told of the disaster. Soviet psychologists were apprehensive
of the effect the failure would have on the cosmonauts. Titov reported
that they were not told until several weeks after the accident when the
psychologists were present to observe their reactions. According to Titov
the cosmonauts were not unduly concerned.[26]

After the flight of Spaceship-Satellite 3 a reappraisal of the Soviet
manned space program probably took place. The overall design of Vostok
still appeared to be good. Only the reentry system was in question. Besides, a cosmonaut on board a Vostok capsule could insure that the attitude
of the spacecraft was correct before firing the retro-engine. However,
there seems to have been a decision at this time to attempt a less ambitious first manned flight. Reports had suggested that the initial manned
Vostok would remain in orbit for six to eighteen revolutions. Now the
decision was made to limit the first flight to a single orbit.

On 9 March 1961 Spaceship-Satellite 4 weighing 4700 kg was launched
into an earth orbit of 249 km by 183.5 km at 65°. For this flight only
one dog, Chernushka, was carried along with rats, guinea pigs, and other
biological specimens. Chernushka and the other specimens were housed in
the cabin proper and not on the ejection seat as had been done on the
second and third flights. A dummy dressed in an operational spacesuit
took the place of the cosmonaut. This was to be a full dress rehearsal
for a manned space flight. Spaceship-Satellite 4 was ordered down at the
end of the first orbit, and reentry proceeded without complications. At
the prescribed altitude of 7-8 km the ejection seat with dummy was shot
out of the capsule while Chernushka stayed within the cabin. Thus both
aspects of the landing system could be tested. The Soviets reported that
had a man been in the ejected seat or remained in the capsule he would
have landed safely.[27]

A final test of the completed Vostok spacecraft was ordered just 16 days after the flight of Spaceship-Satellite 4. On 25 March 1961 Spaceship-Satellite 5 was rocketed into a similar orbit of 247 km by 178 km at 65°. The spacecraft weighed 4695 kg--only 5 kg less than Spaceship-Satellite 4. Again a single dog, Zvezdochka, and a space-suited dummy were on board. After a successful flight of one orbit, the spacecraft landed safely. As with the previous flight, the dummy ejected and biological payload landed in the Vostok capsule. Twice in a little more than two weeks a Vostok spacecraft had been launched into space, had completed one orbit about the earth, and had been safely recovered at the predicted landing site. With the first American suborbital flight scheduled for May of that year, the Soviets had only one month left if the first man in space was to wear the hammer and sickle emblem.[28]

Chapter 3

VOSTOK OPERATIONAL FLIGHTS

VOSTOK 1

With the flawless flights of Spaceship-Satellites 4 and 5 behind them, Soviet authorities made the final decision to proceed with the world's first manned space flight. (See Figure 25 for a chart of Vostok flights.) Rumors were persistent since 1960 that a Soviet spaceship carrying one or two men was about to be launched. After the back-to-back flights of Space-ship-Satellites 4 and 5, which had been billed as predecessors to manned flights, these rumors reached fever pitch. On 10 April 1961 a correspond-ent for the London Communist newspaper *Daily Worker* stationed in Moscow wired a story to his home office that on 7 or 8 April a Soviet cosmonaut had orbited the earth once, but had returned deranged.[29] Although this story later was proven to be false and largely the product of the reporter's imagination, the newspaper printed the article on its front page with ban-ner headlines. While Soviet officials were frantically trying to deny the story, the final countdown of the real Vostok 1 was proceeding. (See Figures 26 to 29.)

At 0907 hr on 12 April 1961 Vostok 1 roared off the launching pad at Baikonur thrusting not only a man into space but the world into a new age. While the spacecraft was orbiting the earth the following announcement was made over Radio Moscow:

> On April 12, 1961, the world's first manned spaceship-sputnik Vos-tok (East) was launched in the Soviet Union into orbit around the earth.
> The pilot and astronaut of the orbital spaceship Vostok is Major Yuri Alexeyevich Gagarin of the Air Force, a citizen of the Union of Soviet Socialist Republics.
> The launching of the multi-stage rocket was successful. After attaining orbital velocity and separating from the last stage of the carrier rocket, the spaceship swung into free flight around the earth.

VOSTOK SUMMARY

Designator	Date Launched	Date Returned	Orbits	Weight(kg)	Results
Vostok 1	12 Apr 1961	12 Apr 1961	1	4725	Gagarin first man in space. Safely returned after one orbit.
Vostok 2	6 Aug 1961	7 Aug 1961	17	4713	Titov safely returned after one day in space. Operated manual orientation system. Experienced some dizziness and nausea.
Vostok 3	11 Aug 1962	15 Aug 1962	64	4722	Nikolayev safely returned after four days in space. First television broadcast from space. Group flight with Vostok 4.
Vostok 4	12 Aug 1962	15 Aug 1962	48	4728	Popovich safely returned after three days in space. Came within 6.5 km of Vostok 3.
Vostok 5	14 Jun 1963	19 Jun 1963	81	4720	Bykovsky safely returned after record five days. Group flight with Vostok 6.
Vostok 6	16 Jun 1963	19 Jun 1963	48	4713	Tereshkova first woman in space. Safely returned after three days. Came within 5 km of Vostok 5.

Figure 25

According to preliminary estimates, its orbital period is 89.1 minutes. The orbit's perigee is 175 km, the apogee 302 km; the orbital plane is inclined at 65°4' to the equatorial plane.

The spaceship together with the astronaut weighs a total of 4725 kg, exclusive of the weight of the carrier rocket's final stage.

Two-way radio communication has been established and is being maintained with Comrade Gagarin, the astronaut. The ship-borne short-wave transmitters operate on 9.019 and 20.006 mc/sec and in the ultra-shortwave range on 143.625 mc/sec. Radiotelemetry and TV observation of the state of the astronaut in flight are being conducted.

Comrade Gagarin, the astronaut, withstood satisfactorily the takeoff and injection into orbit and is now feeling well. The life-supporting systems in the cabin of the spaceship are functioning normally.

The spaceship Vostok, carrying the astronaut Comrade Gagarin, continues in orbit.

The actual parameters of Gagarin's orbit were later corrected to 327 km by 181 km at 64.95°. Since Vostok 1 was flying a rather northeasterly route, the spacecraft soon entered the shadow of the earth and darkness. At 0951 hr just before emerging into the light of the sun again, the automatic orientation system was activated. Gagarin was now passing over Cape Horn. By 1015 hr the Vostok 1 attitude-control system began the task of

Figure 26   Yuri Gagarin before his flight on Vostok 1

Figure 27   Suited up, Gagarin goes through a final check-out before
going to the launch pad

Figure 28   Yuri Gagarin waving good-bye before ascending to the
cabin of Vostok 1

Figure 29   Ground control monitors permit visual observation
of the first cosmonaut

orienting the spacecraft for the burn of the retro-engine as the ship approached the African continent. Ten minutes later with Gagarin merely observing, the engine ignited and the long descent to earth began. This of course was the point at which two of the five unmanned precursor Vostoks had failed. The instrument module separated and the spherical cabin containing Gagarin entered the atmosphere. The deceleration forces quickly pinned the cosmonaut to his seat. As the capsule first encountered the denser air at 1035 hr and the temperature on the outside of the spacecraft rapidly rose, the spaceship began to rotate, momentarily frightening Gagarin. However, these oscillations were quickly damped by the aerodynamic design of Vostok. By 1055 hr Gagarin and the capsule had safely landed southwest of the town of Engels near the village of Smelovka in the Saratov region.[30]

The actual method of landing employed by Gagarin is the subject of much debate. The two options available to the cosmonaut have already been described; the cosmonaut could remain in his cabin the entire time or eject at an altitude of 7 km and land as a conventional parachutist. Most Soviet officials imply that Gagarin selected the former alternative.[31] On the other hand, the preponderance of the evidence suggests that Gagarin ejected from the capsule. Many publications both Soviet and Western either state or imply that Gagarin did not land inside Vostok.[32] Of the three unmanned Vostok flights which successfully returned to earth and of the five manned Vostok missions which followed, all employed ejection of the cosmonaut seat. Finally when Voskhod 1 landed, much attention was given to the crew as the first to land in their ship. It appears that Vostok was never intended to land with the passenger inside, although the dogs which did remain in the capsule on Spaceship-Satellites 4 and 5 did survive. This would seem the basis of the Soviet claim that returning cosmonauts did have an alternative means of landing. One of the best rationales for this apparent deception was put forth in an article appearing in *Space World* magazine in January of 1975. In this article the author suggests that Soviet officials were motivated by the possibility that the Gagarin flight would not qualify under international standards for a manned space flight if the cosmonaut did not remain in the spacecraft for the entire flight.[33]

Finally, a detailed analysis conducted by Anthony Kenden further suggests that Gagarin ejected from his capsule before landing. By reviewing the retro-fire, cosmonaut ejection, capsule landing, and cosmonaut landing times for Vostok's 1 through 6 from a variety of Soviet sources Kenden has shown that cosmonaut ejection occurred approximately 16 minutes after retro-fire with cosmonaut and spaceship landing occurring some 25-29 minutes and 20-21 minutes after retro-fire, respectively. Since the announced landing time was 30 minutes after the Vostok 1 retro-fire, one can infer that Gagarin ejected from his spaceship.

Gagarin's flight was concerned primarily with the mechanics and physiological effects of placing a man in orbit and safely returning him to earth. During the flight of Vostok 1 the capsule's atmospheric conditions were maintained at: temperature, 19-22°C; pressure, 750-770 mm Hg; relative humidity, 62-71%. Gagarin entered the Vostok cabin approximately ninety minutes before launch, and thirty minutes prior to lift-off his heart beat was measured at 66 beats per minute. Gagarin's heart beat climbed to 97 bpm just three minutes before launch and soared to 158 bpm during the first few moments following lift-off. At one point in the flight there appeared to be trouble on board the spacecraft. When Vostok 1 was out of range of voice communications, Gagarin was instructed to send a brief code via telegraph every few minutes indicating the status of the flight. As Sergi Korolev, the designer of the Vostok ship, later recalled, the code suddenly switched from one of "fine" to one indicating a malfunction in one of the systems. Fortunately, the correct code quickly resumed and the error was traced to a communications problem. "It's seconds like that which shorten a designer's life," Korolev remarked.[34]

Very few new scientific experiments were performed during the 108-minute mission. Gagarin did not attempt to use the manual controls even though Soviet officials stressed their availability. No photographic apparatus either attached to the spacecraft or held by Gagarin was carried, although two television cameras allowed ground personnel to monitor the cosmonaut. Hence no photographs of space or the earth were returned. During the flight, Gagarin ate a meal in the form of pastes from tubes, drank liquids, recorded entries in his log book, and made detailed accounts of his observations and reactions for the on-board tape recorder.

Also carried on board were drosophila (fruit flies), dry seeds, and lysogenic bacteria for continued experiments in radiation effects of outer space. Gagarin did surprise many scientists by the detail which he reported could be seen at such high altitudes.[35]

Yuri Gagarin proved that man could safely venture into space. However, many reports, particularly from Western authors who were skeptical of or dismayed by the USSR's apparent preeminence in space flight, began to emerge referring to secret flights made by the Soviets in which a cosmonaut or cosmonauts perished.[36] Names have even been given to these deceased cosmonauts to add a sense of validity to the stories. Almost all of these fatal flights have been discounted whereas none of the remaining are substantiated by any firm evidence. Four fatalities have been acknowledged by the Soviets: Komarov during reentry aboard Soyuz 1 and Dobrovolskiy, Volkov, and Patseyev during reentry aboard Soyuz 11. Since all Soviet manned space flights have been announced early in the flight one must assume that all the purported deaths have occurred during launch or immediately thereafter. Sheldon has succinctly summarized the stand of those supporting these fictitious deaths in the following:

> With all this care and its known pattern of success, we are asked by those who believe many Russians have died in orbit in effect to accept the existence of a second Soviet manned flight program run with reckless abandon which always kills the flight crews. These purported failure flights, often detailed irresponsibly in the press with names and dates to make the unproven data look convincing, apparently would be conducted without advance warning, without tracking ships, without television, and [with] use [of] different models of larger, untried ships which always kill their crews or leave them stranded in orbit. Yet the "flights" cannot be detected by the same US tracking systems that usually find even chance pieces of space debris at the altitudes manned flights occur. This is hardly credible.[37]

Finally, it is impossible to do full justice to the flight of Vostok 1 or any other manned flight without violating the comprehensive yet concise nature of this book. The interested reader is urged to follow up with the references provided for each flight. In addition, several good biographical studies of the cosmonauts have been published along with some books written by cosmonauts themselves.[38]

VOSTOK 2

It has often been said that the progress of the Soviet space program has been in part a function of the political atmosphere at that time. Whether the selection of "convenient" launch dates for space missions is more prevalent in the USSR than in the United States is a matter for debate. However, as one will notice throughout this book, the Soviets are certainly aware of the advantages of carefully selecting mission times. Yuri Gagarin had flown his historic flight in Vostok 1 just three weeks before Alan Shepard piloted the United States' much publicized first manned suborbital flight in a Mercury spacecraft. Later, world acclaim and respect for the Soviet Union's impressive second flight of the Vostok space vehicle was still high when East Germany under the direction of the USSR closed the border between East and West Berlin and erected the infamous Berlin Wall.

Vostok 2 roared into space at 0900 hr Moscow time on 6 August 1961 with Gherman Titov at the controls. (See Figures 30-32.) After entering an orbit of 244 km by 183 km at an inclination of 64.9°, Titov settled down and prepared for a long stay in space. Weighing 4713 kg, Vostok 2 had undergone only minor changes as a result of Gagarin's flight in April. The objectives of the flight were given by Tass simply as follows:

1. Effect investigation on human organism of prolonged orbiting and subsequent descent to earth.

2. Efficiency investigation of a man during a long period in conditions of weightlessness.

In short, Titov was to complete 17 orbits around the earth and remain in space for just over 24 hours. Gagarin had withstood the rigors of weightlessness well during his 108 minute flight, but the effect of prolonged weightlessness was still an unknown. During the flight Titov was scheduled:

o To observe the performance of equipment aboard

o To test twice manual control of the spaceship

o To conduct visual observations through the cabin's portholes

o Besides the direct radio-communications with the earth, to carry out during the flight above the USSR territory short-wave communications twice during an hour

o To carry out physical exercises, etc.[39]

Figure 30   Gherman Titov during the bus ride to his
             awaiting Vostok 2 spacecraft

Titov was kept busy during his flight by a full schedule of experiments. At 1000 hr while still on his first orbit, he activated the manual
attitude system controls. Although he could not alter his orbital parameters, Titov was able to vary the ship's orientation with respect to the
earth by means of compressed gas jets. The cosmonaut reported that the
Vostok spacecraft handled quite well. This system was again tested on
the seventh orbit. On Vostok 2's third orbit Titov was instructed to eat
his first meal. Unenthusiastically, he ate the "joyless" soup-paste and
meat- and liver- paste from tubes. Photography was scheduled for the second, third, thirteenth, and fourteenth orbits. A new device named Zritel
(viewer) gave Titov magnifications of three or five while using one of the
portholes (Figure 33).[40]

Beginning on the fifth orbit, Titov experienced some nausea and orientation problems. Soviet scientists later attributed this to the effects
of weightlessness on Titov's vestibular system. The cosmonaut experienced

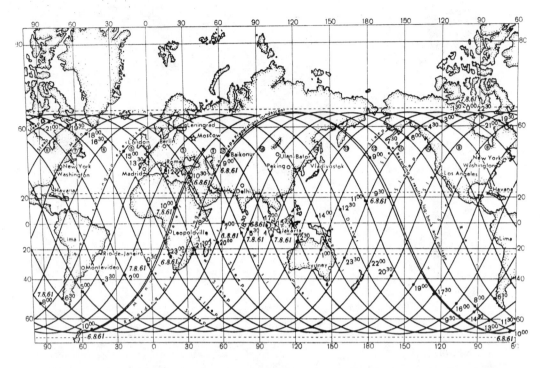

Figure 31   Ground trace of the orbital path of Titov during his one-day flight

Figure 32   Soviet mission control during the flight of Gherman Titov

Figure 33   Photograph of the earth taken by Gherman Titov from the
            porthole of his Vostok 2 spaceship

the most difficulties when turning his head sharply or following the motion of other objects. By the seventh orbit Titov was instructed to rest
and try to sleep. Ground control was hopeful that the problem of dizziness
would disappear when he awoke (which in part did happen). The seriousness
with which the Soviets regarded this phenomenon was reflected in the

altered cosmonaut training program following this flight. It has been reported that Titov continued to experience inner ear problems even after the completion of the flight.[41]

Of the two television cameras aimed at Titov on board Vostok 2, one was an improved model. The older system used on the Spaceship-Satellites and Vostok 1 had a resolution of 100 lines. The new camera had a resolution of 400 lines, although both systems returned ten pictures per second. Besides visual monitoring, Titov also had sensors attached to his body to provide electro-cardiographic, pneumographic, and kinetocardiographic information. A particular item of concern was the effect of radiation on the cosmonaut from solar activity. Two weeks before the flight of Vostok 2 a solar storm had erupted. However, continuous monitoring of the sun by observatories around the world permitted Soviet scientists to predict minimal activity for the day-long flight of Titov. As did Gagarin, Titov carried with him drosophila (fruit flies), dry seeds, and lysogenic bacteria for research concerning radiation effects.[42]

Titov slept during the seventh through the twelfth orbits and awoke at 0237 hr on 7 August, approximately thirty minutes late. He ate breakfast, performed the scheduled physical exercises, and carried out a photographic session of the earth. At the beginning of his seventeenth and final orbit, Titov readied the capsule for the return to earth. The automatic descent system took over, swung the spacecraft around, and at precisely the calculated moment ignited the retro-rockets. The deceleration forces of 8-9 g's slammed Titov into his couch after twenty-five hours of weightlessness. As the capsule descended to approximately 7 km, Titov activated the ejection landing system. The cosmonaut relived those few moments in his book *I am Eagle*.[43]

> Vostok 2 fell like a stone through the air, stabilized in an arrow-like drop toward the earth. I activated several switches and controls, gripped the contour seat carefully, and glued my eyes on the chronometer. The sweep hand came around, moving steadily closer to the moment when explosive charges would go off, and I would be hurled with the seat away from the falling spaceship. Ten - then only three more seconds to go. A red light flashed on the indicator panel....
> Thunder crashed into my ears at the same time I felt a tremendous force beneath me. The ejection shell exploded exactly on schedule, and in a blur I saw daylight flash before my eyes as the entire seat burst away from the spaceship. For the first time in

44

more than twenty-five hours, like a prisoner released from a cell, the entire sky presented itself in one swift glance to me. The horizon tilted sharply, clouds came into my line of sight, and then the earth rolled cleanly before me again.

At 1018 hr on 7 August after 25 hr 18 min in space and after traveling 700,143 km Cosmonaut Gherman Titov landed safely in the same region in which Gagarin had descended. The Soviet Union's second manned space flight was considered a stunning success around the world. Only four months after Gagarin's flight, Titov had set a record which the United States would not match for almost two years. Except for concern about Titov's inner ear problem, Soviet scientists were eager to press ahead in their manned exploration of outer space

VOSTOK 3, VOSTOK 4

A year passed since the flight of Vostok 2 without the return of a Soviet cosmonaut to the folds of space. Although many rumors circulated predicting multi-man spacecraft and circumlunar flights, the tight secrecy of the Soviet space program kept the world in the dark as to the true progress and goals of the USSR. By the first anniversary of Titov's flight in Vostok 2 reports began to filter out that a new mission was imminent. At 1130 hr on 11 August 1962 Vostok 3, piloted by Andriyan Grigoryevich Nikolayev, was launched from the Baikonur Cosmodrone into an earth orbit of 235 km by 181 km at an inclination of 64.98°. The initial announcement of the flight listed the objectives only as the further examination of the effects of weightlessness and the perfecting of spacecraft systems.[44]

As regular reports were issued by Tass on the progress of Vostok 3, Western observers became convinced that Nikolayev would try to surpass the 17 orbits of Titov and perhaps remain in space for several days. Pravda reported that on the fifth orbit the cosmonaut had unstrapped himself from his couch and floated free within the Vostok capsule. Nikolayev reported none of the disorientation or nausea which had plagued Titov. During the seventh orbit at 2040 hr Moscow time the Soviet Central television station broadcast the first live pictures of a cosmonaut in orbit. Nikolayev went to sleep at 2200 hr and was awakened at 0500 hr on 12 August. Although he himself would be a passive element, one of his space flight's major objectives would be attempted that morning.[45]

Late in the morning of the 12th of August the world was astounded to learn of the launch of a second manned spaceship. Vostok 4, carrying Pavel Romanovich Popovich, lifted off at 1102 hr and entered an orbit of 237 km by 180 km--very close to that of Vostok 3. The mere launching of two spacecraft within one day of each other was considered a tremendous technological feat. The timing of the launch of Vostok 4 and the accuracy with which it was placed in orbit were no less amazing. Initially Western observers assumed the Soviets had two separate launch facilities. However, later spokesmen revealed that both craft had used the same launch pad--an impossible task by Western standards. All this was possible due to the Soviet technique of horizontal assembly of the spacecraft and the launcher with transport to the launch pad only shortly before lift-off.[46]

The objectives of the flights were later revealed as:

o Checking and operating spaceships 'Vostok' in conditions of pro-longed flight

o Operating complex for the orbital insertion of the second space-ship in immediate vicinity of the earlier orbiting first ship

o Practical checking of the possible establishment of direct radio-communication between the two spaceships during the flight at dif-ferent distances from each other

o Working out complex for the ground control of several spaceships in near-by orbits.[47]

Due to the slightly different orbital parameters of the two spacecraft they quickly began to drift apart. Since Vostok was not capable of orbital maneuvers, rendezvous or docking was not possible. The closest approach of 6.5 km came soon after the launch of Vostok 4 and deviated only 1.5 km from the planned 5 km separation. Nikolayev was reported to have seen the Vostok 4 capsule through the portholes of his own cabin. In turn, Popovich described the Vostok 3 capsule as a small moon. Direct communi-cations between Nikolayev and Popovich were maintained.[48]

Having demonstrated some of the major components needed for future docking missions, the two cosmonauts concentrated on the second aspect of their flights--performance under extended weightless conditions. Niko-layev and Popovich followed simultaneous schedules. They worked, dined, and slept at the same hours. Orbit after orbit Vostok 3 and 4 continued their journey around the globe. Regularly the two cosmonauts appeared on television screens throughout the Soviet Union and Europe. The new vidicon televison cameras tested on Vostok 2 provided frontal and profile views of the pilots. For the first time, viewers could watch pencils and logbooks floating in a weightless environment (Figure 34). By 0600 hr on 15 August, Nikolayev had completed more than 61 orbits while Popovich had circled the earth over 45 times.[49]

As the joint flight of Vostok 3 and 4 neared the three-day mark, both men made preparations for the return to earth. At 0924 hr on 15 August after almost ninety-four hours in space Nikolayev felt the thrust of his retro-rockets. Six minutes later Popovich followed suit. Following the fiery reentry Nikolayev ejected from the descending capsule at an altitude of 7 km at 0939 hr 59 sec. By 0952 hr he had landed at 48°02'N, 75°45'E, south of Karaganda. Seven minutes later Popovich touched down in a similar manner at 48°10'N, 71°51'E within 200 km of Nikolayev. The Vostok 3 capsule had landed at 0944 hr 09 sec. Nikolayev had completed 64 orbits and traveled 2,639,600 km in the 4722-kg Vostok 3. Popovich had completed 48 orbits and traveled 1,981,050 km in the 4728-kg Vostok 4. They had flown together for seventy-one hours. From an initial 6.5 km separation the spacecraft drifted apart to almost 3000 km just prior to landing. Figure 35 is a chart indicating the orbital parameters of Vostok 3 and 4 at different times during the flight.[50]

Voluminous medical data were obtained during the flights. Emphasis of course was placed on the cosmonauts' vestibular systems following the difficulties of Titov. In addition to the physiological data returned

Figure 34   Cosmonaut Pavel Popovich demonstrating the effects of weightlessness on his pen

VOSTOK 3/VOSTOK 4 ORBITAL PARAMETERS

	Apogee (km)	Perigee (km)	Period (min)
11 August			
Vostok 3	234.6	180.7	88.330
12 August			
Vostok 3	229.9	178.0	88.260
Vostok 4	236.7	179.8	88.390
13 August			
Vostok 3	224.4	175.2	88.180
Vostok 4	231.7	177.4	88.310
14 August			
Vostok 3	217.7	172.0	88.084
Vostok 4	226.1	174.4	88.224
15 August			
Vostok 3	210.3	168.1	87.972
Vostok 4	220.4	171.4	88.133

Figure 35

with Vostok 1 and 2, the cosmonauts on Vostok 3 and 4 had sensors which transmitted electroencephalogram, electrooculogram, and skin galvanic re-action information. These latter three items were concerned with the nervous and vestibular systems. Both spacecraft carried the same biological payloads as did Vostok 1 and Vostok 2. Also carried were human cancer cells in Vostok 4 and microspores in both spaceships.[51]

Many other experiments were performed by the cosmonauts. In a further test of the human orientation system, Nikolayev and Popovich spent a total of 3.5 hours and 3 hours, respectively, floating freely within the Vostok cabin. Extensive visual and photographic observations of the earth and moon were carried out using binoculars and still and movie cameras. Popovich analyzed the effects of fluid and bubble motion under weightless conditions. Both cosmonauts also tested the manual control systems of their spacecraft.[52]

The Soviet Union had demonstrated that man could perform productively in a space environment for up to four days. The Vostok spacecraft had proven itself as a reliable vehicle. The next step appeared to be flights of even longer duration to evaluate the human organism (eight days was considered the minimum time needed for any future lunar landing mission) or the implementation of a new multi-man, more sophisticated spacecraft. However, almost another year elapsed before Soviets took to space again in what appeared to be an uncharacteristic repeat performance of the Vostok 3 and Vostok 4 flights.

VOSTOK 5, VOSTOK 6

Exactly one month after the United States had completed its manned Mercury program, the Soviet Union launched what would be the final flights of their Vostok spacecraft in its original configuration. On 14 June 1963 at 1500 hr Moscow time Vostok 5, piloted by Valery Fedorovich Bykovsky, was launched into an earth orbit of 221.1 km by 174.7 km at 64.96°. At the time Western observers believed this to be the beginning of a mission which would seek to double the four-day flight time of Nikolayev aboard Vostok 3. However, a possible booster malfunction may have curtailed this ambitious mission. Initial Soviet reports had quoted the orbital parameters of the 4720-kg spacecraft at 235 km by 181 km. The actual orbit was thus lower than anticipated. In addition, one Western source indicated that the final booster stage was still burning at the time of the spacecraft separation and that this booster stage had entered the orbit initially attributed to Vostok 5. Apparently Bykovsky was able to turn his spacecraft around immediately upon booster separation to observe the final stage of the launch vehicle. This source went on to point out that due to Vostok 5's actual orbit, the spacecraft would decay naturally within eight days instead of the usual ten-day natural decay orbits flown by previous Vostok spacecraft. To remain in space for the entire eight days, therefore, would place Bykovsky in jeopardy since reentry might take place outside the Soviet Union with only short notice.[53]

For the remainder of the day Bykovsky followed a flight program which was fast becoming routine for Soviet cosmonauts. He had to monitor and report his tolerance of g-forces, weightlessness, noise, and spacecraft vibrations. The cosmonaut made frequent radio transmissions to ground personnel concerning the Vostok environment including readings of oxygen and carbon dioxide concentrations, pressure, temperature, humidity, and dosimetric levels. Emphasis continued to be placed on the cosmonaut's

physiological condition and on his observations of earth and space. Bykovsky periodically was required to report his own pulse, respiration, and
general state of health. Although a solar flare had occurred just two days
prior to the launch of Vostok 5, no further flares or solar radiation in-
creases were predicted for the duration of Bykovsky's flight. No longer
did cosmonauts have to rely on the tasteless paste foods which Gagarin and
Titov ate. Simple solid foods were now available, and during his first
meal in space Bykovsky selected roast beef and boned chicken as well as a
variety of drinks. Bykovsky slept from 0005 to 0700 hr on 15 June. After
breakfast the cosmonaut continued his duties and tested the craft's attitude control system.[54]

As Vostok 5 neared the completion of its first day in space, speculation arose concerning the possibility of the launch of a second Vostok.
Due to the secrecy which surrounded the Soviet space program, outsiders
could only guess at the capabilities of the USSR spaceships. It was firmly
believed by many that a second Vostok would attempt a rendezvous and docking with Vostok 5. This was in retrospect far beyond the capacity of the
Vostok spacecraft. When Vostok 5 had completed 18 orbits with no appearance of a Vostok 6 Western observers began to doubt their own predictions.[55]

However, the Soviet Union, master of the unexpected, again took the
world by surprise when at 1230 hr on 16 June while Bykovsky was completing
his second full day in space Valentina Vladimirovna Tereshkova became the
first (and thus far only) woman to fly in space. Her 4713-kg Vostok 6
spacecraft was inserted into an earth orbit of 231.1 km by 180.9 km at a
64.95° inclination. However, Vostok 6 was not launched at the most opportune time, giving birth to stories that her rocket was launched a day
later than originally planned. Whereas Vostok 4 had been launched when
Vostok 3 was almost directly overhead, Vostok 6 entered an orbital plane
which was approximately thirty degrees away. Thus, while Vostok 3 and 4
were in close proximity during an entire orbit, Vostok 6 approached Vostok
5 only twice for a few minutes every revolution. In addition, the apogees
and perigees of Vostok 5 and 6 were not so close as those of the previous
group flight. On the day of Tereshkova's launch the orbital parameters
of Vostok 5 and Vostok 6 were 208.3 km by 168.4 km and 231 km by 181 km,
respectively.[56]

Prior to sending Tereshkova into orbit extensive testing was conducted to ensure as accurately as possible that a woman could endure the rigors of space as well as a man. Two simulated space flights were conducted by women in earth-bound mock-ups of Vostok. Lasting 12 and six days, respectively, these experiments concluded that the life support systems of Vostok were capable of accommodating cosmonauts of either sex for at least twelve days.

The motivation behind the Soviet Union's decision to send a woman into space has been widely debated. Probably the two major reasons were biological investigations and propaganda. The effects of spending prolonged periods in space were still largely unkown at the time. Thus, by comparing the reactions of a woman with those of a man, a better overall understanding of the hazards of space could be obtained. Since eventually women will have to be included in long planetary voyages or permanent stations, their ability to withstand the stresses of space flight is very important.[57]

The propaganda reaped from the flight of Vostok 6 was tremendous. Not so coincidentally, an international women's conference was scheduled to meet in Moscow less than a week after her return from space. Tereshkova attended several sessions and was the obvious darling of the conference. Neither did the Soviets fail to point out that Tereshkova had spent more time in space than the combined hours accumulated by all the American astronauts during the Mercury program. In addition, Tereshkova was billed as a "common" Soviet factory worker. Although she had had experience in parachuting before entering the cosmonaut corps, she was not a pilot. This fact has been pointed out by both advocates and detractors of the Soviet space program when debating the essentially automatic nature of the Vostok spacecraft with very little manual assistance required except in emergencies.[58]

A potentially more sinister third reason has also been suggested for the flight of Tereshkova. She and Cosmonaut Nikolayev, the pilot of Vostok 3, were very close friends prior to the flight of Vostok 6 and were subsequently married on 3 November 1963, less than five months after her return from space. Whether the marriage was planned prior to Vostok 6 and whether this fact may have had an influence on Tereshkova's selection is uncertain. However, the event did present Soviet scientists with a unique opportunity to examine what effects, if any, cosmic radiation would have on the reproductive systems and offspring of parents who had both spent several days in outer space. On 7 June 1964 just nine days before the first anniversary of Tereshkova's flight through space, the "cosmonette" presented Nikolayev with a healthy six pound thirteen ounce daughter, Yelena. Although Tereshkova soon retired from the cosmonaut corps, Nikolayev remained on the active list of cosmonauts and flew again in 1970 on the 18-day flight of Soyuz 9. Even today all three members of the first "space family" continue to be of interest to Soviet space doctors.

Bykovsky and Tereshkova continued to orbit the earth until 19 June. During this time Bykovsky surpassed the more than ninety-four hour flight time of Nikolayev by remaining aloft for 119 hours and 6 minutes and demonstrated his ability to work in a weightless environment while floating free of his harness during the 18th, 34th, 50th, and 66th orbits. Bykovsky paid particular attention to the time required to complete a maneuver and to the time before an additional correction was needed. Both Bykovsky and Tereshkova operated the manual orientation system of their spacecraft and took photographs, both still and moving, of the earth, moon, and stars. Again, biological payloads similar to those on board Vostok 1-4 were carried along with the cosmonauts. The two spacecraft made their closest approach immediately after launch of Vostok 6, when the minimum distance between the spaceships was calculated as approximately 5 km. Communications between Bykovsky and Tereshkova were maintained during portions of their joint flight.[59]

The medical objectives of the flight were given as follows:

1. Further study of prolonged effect of space factors on the human organism

2. Study of psycho-physiological possibilities and efficiency of a human being in conditions of prolonged weightlessness combined with other flight factors

3. Investigations of female organism reactions to effect of space-flight conditions

4. Further study of daily periodicity of the physiological processes of a man in space flight

5. Effectivity study of selection methods and special preparation of cosmonauts

6. Performance study of system for medico-biological checking of the state of the cosmonauts and microclimate of the space cabin

7. Efficiency study in performance of life-support system and safety means in space flight.[60]

Originally Tereshkova's flight was scheduled to last for only one day, but Soviet officials reported that she was allowed to remain aloft for three days since she was coping well with the environment. This is in contradiction to reports that Tereshkova was ill part or all of the flight, although she looked well when seen occasionally on Soviet television broadcasts. As Vostok 6 started its forty-eighth orbit, the spacecraft was oriented for the return to earth. The braking rocket was activated at 1054 hr and 48 sec and the reentry proceeded uneventfully until at an altitude of 6.5 km at 1110 hr and 40 sec Tereshkova ejected from her capsule. By 1120 hr on 19 June the "cosmonette" had landed at 53°16'18" N, 80°27'34" E, some 620 km NE of Karaganda after spending 70 hours 40 minutes and 48 seconds on her space mission.[61]

On the orbit following the descent of Vostok 6, Vostok 5 also returned to earth. Bykovsky landed at 1406 hr on 19 June 540 km NW of Karaganda at 53°23'45" N, 67°36'41" E. He had set a new space endurance record of 118 hours 56 minutes and 41 seconds and had traveled 3,325,957 km. With the landing of Bykovsky and Vostok 5 the Vostok program came to an end. The five men and one woman had logged a total of 382 hours and 21 minutes in space.[62]

A summary of various experiments completed during the Vostok program is given in Figure 36.*

The United States had completed its one-man spacecraft program the month before and had already announced its intention to launch the first of the two-man Gemini spacecraft in late 1964 or early 1965. The Soviet Union was also working on a multi-man spacecraft with much greater capabilities. However, this new spaceship was not expected to be ready to fly before Gemini. If the Soviet Union wished to maintain her preeminence in space, a drastic solution was needed.

---

* *Unfortunately we have been unable to identify our source for this excellent summary. But we wish to give credit to the original compiler of this table. Some information in the table has been updated.*

SUMMARY OF RUSSIAN FLIGHT EXPERIMENTS ASSEMBLED FROM VARIOUS SOURCES

Name	Vostok I	Vostok II	Vostok III
Launched	12 Apr 1961	6 Aug 1961	11 Aug 1962
Payload Weight	4725 kg	4725 kg	4722 kg
Orbit Time	89.1 min	88.6 min	88.3 min
Number of Orbits	1	17	64
Lifetime	Successful recovery 12 Apr 1961	Successful recovery 7 Aug 1961	Successful recovery 15 Aug 1962
Test Subjects	Man (Gagarin)	Man (Titov) and other biological objects	Man (Nikolayev) and drosophila, seeds, cancer cells
Aims	1.Orbit first manned satellite	1.Study effects on human during prolonged space flight & return to earth 2.Study man's ability to work during prolonged space flight	1.Study effects on man during prolonged flight 2.Study man's ability to work during space flight 3.Study effect of radiation on reproduction of Drosophila
Food and Water	Ate only mashed food from tube.	Ate only mashed food from tubes	Ate food similar to regular meal. Had supplies sufficient for moon trip.
Radiation Instruments	1.Dosimeters 2.Thermoluminescent glasses	1.Dosimeters 2.Thermoluminescent glasses	1.Dosimeters 2.Nuclear photoemulsions 3.Scintillators
Radiation Dosage	Average external dosage: 0.4-0.6 mrad/orbit	Average external dosage: 8.4 mrad/day inside dosage: 0.5mrad/day	Total dosage: 62± 5 tissue mrad (corrected from reading of 55 mrad)
Physiological methods used for tests	1.Electrocardiography 2.Pneumography 3.Kinetocardiography	1.Electrocardiography 2.Pneumography 3.Kinetocardiography	1.Electrocardiography 2.Pneumography 3.Electrooculography 4.Electroencephalography 5.Cutaneous-galvanic response 6.Kinetocardiography
Cabin Conditions	Pressure:750-770 mmHg Humidity:62-71% Temp 19-22°C	Pressure:740-760 mmHg Humidity:30-70% Temp: 10-25°C	Pressure:755-775 mm Hg Humidity:65-75% Temp: 13-26°C
Radiation Protection	1.Carried antiradiation medicine. 2.Had protective shield	1.Carried antiradiation medicine. 2.Had protective shield.	1.Carried antiradiation medicine. 2.Had protective radiation shielding.
Exercise			Put head and feet on stationary object and flexed muscles.
Other Experiments or Results	1.No effect of specific factors endangering cellular structures and functions	1.Suspensions of E.Coli 2.Lysogenic bacteria exposed to radiation	1.Drosophila reproduction experiments 2.With Vostok 4, coordinated space flight 3.Nikolayev made medical observations.
	1.Freed 1 hr in weight-state; ate,wrote,steered spacecraft, retained working capacity 2.Some unusual sensations from weightlessness	1.Retained working capacity and pulse and respiration rates remained normal during weightlessness.	1.During weightlessness had good orientation retained health and capacity to work 2.Drosophila reproduction occurred in weightless state. 3.Freed from restraining straps for about 1 hr
Respiration	16-26 cycles/min	4-28 cycles/min	10-18 cycles/min
Pulse	Awake 90-180 beat/min	Awake 80-156 beats/min Asleep 53-67 beats/min	Awake 60-120 beat/min Asleep 60-65 beats/min

Figure 36

Name	Vostok IV	Vostok V	Vostok VI
Launched	12 Aug 1962	14 Jun 1963	16 Jun 1963
Payload Weight	4728 kg	4720 kg	4713 kg
Orbit Time	88.4 min	88.4 min	88.4 min
Number of Orbits	48	81	48
Lifetime	Successful recovery 15 Aug 1962	Successful recovery 19 Jun 1963	Successful recovery 19 Jun 1963
Test Subjects	Man (Popovich) and drosophila,seeds,cancer cells	Man (Bykovsky) and flies	Woman (Tereshkova) and flies
Aims	1.Study effects on men during space flight	1.Study effects on man during space flight	1.Compare effects of space flight on men and women
	2.Study man's ability to work during space flight	2.Further biological investigations in sustained flight	2.Continued study of effect of flight factors on human
	3.Reproduction experiments on drosophila	3.Improve piloted spaceship systems	3.New medico-biological research
	4.Study possibility of space rendezvous		4.Improve systems of piloted spacecraft under conditions of simultaneous flight.
Food and Water	Ate food similar to regular meal. Had supplies sufficient for moon trip.	Ate individually prepared meals similar to regular meal. 1½ liter of water per day	Each day had 4 individually earthlike meals and 1½ liters of water.
Radiation Instruments	1.Dosimeters 2.Nuclear Photoemulsions 3.Scintillators		
Radiation Dosage	Total dosage: 46± 5 tissue mrad (corrected from actual reading of 41 mrad)	Total dosage: 35.40 mrad	Total dosage: 25 mrad
Physiological methods used for tests	1.Electrocardiography 2.Pneumography 3.Electrooculography 4.Electroencephalography 5.Cutaneous-galvanic responses 6.Kinetocardiography	1.Electrocardiography 2.Pneumography 3.Electrooculography 4.Seismography 5.Electroencephalography 6.Skin galvanic responses 7.Kinetocardiography	1.Electrocardiography 2.Pneumography 3.Electrooculography 4.Seismography 5.Electroencephalography 6.Skin galvanic responses
Cabin Conditons	Pressure:755-775 mmHg Humidity:65-75% Temp: 12-26°C % O_2 in air: 21%	Pressure:775-780 mmHg Humidity:40-65% Temp: 12-20°C % O_2 in air: 21%	Pressure:754-77 mmHg. Humidity:34% Temp: 18-23.6°C % O_2 in air: 20%
Radiation Protection	1.Carried antiradiation medicine 2.Had protective radiation shielding	1.Carried antiradiation medicine 2.Had protective shield	1.Carried antiradiation medicine 2.Had protective shield.
Exercise	Put head and feet on stationary object and flexed muscles	1.Exercised to prepare for landing 2.Exercised with rubber stretcher 3.Controlled ship	1.Exercised to prepare for stress of landing.
Other Experiments or Results	1.With Vostok 3, coordinated space flight 2.Popovich made medical observations 3.Drosophila reproduction experiments	1.Observations of sun, earth,moon constellation 2.Free from restraining straps for 1½ hr/day	1.Reproductive system not damaged 2.Experiments on nervous system and cardiovascular system
	1.Freed in weightless state for about 1 hr 2.Drosophila reproduction occurred in weightless state. 3.Retained health, working capacity during weightlessness.	1.Performed complex tasks while weightless. 2.Slept 1½ hr while free from restraining straps. 3.Study of human during prolonged weightlessness	1.Study of effect of weightlessness on women 2.Comparison of weightlessness on men and women 3.Slept well while free in weightless state.
Respiration	10-20 cycles/min	15-24 cycles/min	16-22 cycles/min
Pulse	Awake 60-130 beats/min Asleep 60-beats/min	Awake 60-106 beats/min Asleep 45-56 beats/min	Awake 64-82 beats/min Asleep 52-60 beats/min

Figure 36 (Continued)

REFERENCES AND NOTES - SECTION I

1. Wukelic, G.E., *Handbook of Soviet Space-Science Research*, pp.15-19; Caiden, Martin, *Red Star in Space*, pp. 253-258.

2. Wukelic, G.E., *op. cit.*, pp. 19-23; Blagonravov, A.A., et al.; *USSR Achievements in Space Research*, pp. 383-385; Smolders, P., *Soviets in Space*, pp. 60, 95-99; Riabchikov, E., *Russians in Space*, pp. 140-142, *Soviet Space Programs, 1971-1975*, p. 173. See Petrovich, G.V., *The Soviet Enclyclopedia of Space Flight*, pp. 384-386 and Gatland, K., *Missiles and Rockets*, pp. 18-22 and 185-187 for details of launch vehicles. See also the appendix of this book and Baker, David, *The Rocket*.

3. Blagonravov, A.A., et al., *op. cit.*, pp. 558-559; Petrovich, G.V., *op. cit.*, pp. 111-112; Wukelic, G.E., *op. cit.*, p. 28.

4. Skuridin, G.A., *Mastery of Outer Space in the USSR, 1957-1967*, pp. 34-84; *Ten Years of Space Exploration*, pp. 4-5; *Space Laboratories*, p. 38; Smolders, P., *op. cit.*, pp. 99-100; Blagonravov, A.A., et.al., *op. cit.*, pp. 558-561; *Soviet Space Programs, 1971-1975*, p. 174.

5. See Gatland's *Spacecraft and Boosters*, pp. 115-124 for sample of misconceptions held at that time.

6. *Space World*, Oct.1972, p. 29.

7. *Space World*, Aug.1971, pp. 26-27.
The following publications all have good descriptions of Vostok: *Legendary Vostok, Meet Aerospace Vehicles, Soviet Encyclopedia of Space Flight, The Sons of the Blue Planet, Soviet Satellites and Space Ships, From Spaceships to Orbiting Stations, USSR Achievements in Space Research, Soviets in Space, Manned Spacecraft, Mastery of Outer Space in the USSR, 1957-1967.*
Flight International, 6 May 1965, pp. 718-720 and 22 July 1965, pp. 127-129.

8. Zhemchuzhin, N., et al., *Meet Aerospace Vehicles*, pp. 456-461; *Legendary Vostok*, p. 14; Blagonravov, A.A., et. al., p. 587; *The Sons of the Blue Planet*, pp. 26-27; Sisakyan, N.M., *Second Group Flight and Certain Results of Flights of Soviet Cosmonauts on the Vostok Ships*, p. 83.

9. Vladimirov, L., *The Russian Space Bluff*, pp. 82-91; *Soviet Space Programs, 1966-1970*, p. 226; Borisenko, I.G., *Space Launches and Finishes*, p. 17.

10. *The Sons of the Blue Planet,* p. 27; *Legendary Vostok,* p. 11; Smolders, P., *op. cit.,* p. 114.

11. Skuridin, G.A., *op. cit.,* pp. 686-688; *The First Man in Space,* p. 68; *Legendary Vostok,* pp. 10-11; Caidin, Martin, *Rendezvous in Space,* p. 180.

12. *The Sons of the Blue Planet,* p. 27; *Legendary Vostok,* pp. 11-14.

13. Petrovich, G.V., *op. cit.,* pp. 223-224; Blagonravov, A.A., et al., *op. cit.,* pp. 396-398; Skuridin, G.A., *op. cit.,* pp. 682-683; *Legendary Vostok,* pp. 15, 23; Umanskiy, U.P., *Man in Space Orbit,* pp. 41-42; *The Sons of the Blue Planet,* p. 28.

14. Shelton, W., *Soviet Space Exploration: The First Decade,* pp. 258-259; Blagonravov, A.A., et al., *op. cit.,* pp. 396-397; *Legendary Vostok,* pp. 21-22; Petrovich, G.V., *op. cit.,* pp. 252-253; Skuridin, G.A., *op. cit.,* pp. 600-603.

15. Ponomarev, A.N., *The Years of the Space Era,* p. 201; *Legendary Vostok,* pp. 20-21; Skuridin, G.A., *op. cit.,* pp. 684-685; Romanov, A., *Spacecraft Designer,* p. 43; *Space World,* Aug. 1971, p. 26; Shelton, W., *op. cit.,* p. 129.

16. *The Sons of the Blue Planet,* p. 29; Umanskiy, U.P., *op.cit.,* pp. 72, 75; Sisakyan, N.M., *op. cit.,* pp. 11-12.

17. Ponomarev, A.N., *op. cit.,* pp. 200-201.

18. Wilding-White, T.M., *Jane's Pocket Book of Space Exploration,* p. 11; Smolders, P., *op. cit.,* p. 112; Vladimirov, L., *op. cit.,* p. 122; Aleksandrov, S.G. and Federov, R.Ye., *Soviet Satellites and Space Ships,* pp. 227-229.

19. Blagonravov, A.A., et al., *op. cit.,* pp. 583-585; *The Sons of the Blue Planet,* pp. 30-31; Zhemchuzhin, N., *op. cit.,* pp. 456-458; *Aviation Week and Space Technology,* 12 June 1967, p. 117 and 5 Feb. 1968, p. 58.

20. *Aviation Week and Space Technology,* 24 Apr. 1961; *Legendary Vostok,* pp. 24-25.

21. *Aviation Week and Space Technology,* 18 Jan. 1960, 1 Feb. 1960, 8 Feb 1960, and 15 Feb. 1960; *Ten Years of Space Exploration,* p. 13; *Spaceflight,* Sep. 1965, pp. 173-175; Gatland, Kenneth, *Astronautics in the Sixties,* pp. 265-267.

22. Skuridin, G.A., *op. cit.,* pp. 542-546, 554; Titov, G., *I am Eagle,* p. 92; Blagonravov, A.A., et al., *op. cit.,* pp. 495, 581; Petrovich, G.V., *op. cit.,* pp. 516-517; Wukelic, G.E., *op.cit.,* p. 33; Aleksandrov, S.G. and Fedrov, R.Ye., *op. cit.,* pp. 179-182, 185.

23. Petrovich, G.V., *op. cit.*, pp. 518-519; Wukelic, G.E., *op. cit.*, p. 33; Skuridin, G.A., *op. cit.*, pp. 546-547, 585; Aleksandrov, S.G. and Fedrov, R.Ye., *op. cit.*, pp. 184, 198-199.

24. Aleksandrov, S.G. and Fedrov, R.Ye., *op. cit.*, pp. 183-221; Skuridin, G.A., *op. cit.*, pp. 548-610; Blagonravov, A.A., et al., *op. cit.*, p. 582; Gatland, K., *Manned Spacecraft*, p. 109.

25. Titov, G., *op. cit.*, p. 93; Skuridin, G.A., *op. cit.*, pp. 610-613.

26. Titov, G., *op. cit.*, pp. 94-95; Shelton, W., *op. cit.*, pp. 78-79; Skuridin, G.A., *op. cit.*, p. 613; Aleksandrov, S.G. and Fedrov, R.Ye., *op. cit.*, pp. 221-222.

27. *First Man in Space* pp. 62, 65; Wukelic, G.E., *op. cit.*, p. 34; Blagonravov, A.A. et al., *op. cit.*, p. 582; Aleksandrov, S.G. and Fedrov, R.Ye., *op. cit.*, pp. 222-223; Riabchikov, E., *op. cit.*, pp. 155-156; Skuridin, G.A., *op. cit.*, pp. 613-614.

28. *Ten Years of Space Exploration*, p. 13; *First Man in Space*, pp. 62,65; Wukelic, G.E., *op. cit.*, p. 34; Blagonravov, A.A., et al., *op. cit.*, p. 582; Skuridin, G.A., *op. cit.*, pp. 615-616, 681-682; Aleksandrov, S.G. and Fedrov, R.Ye., *op. cit.*, pp. 223-224.

29. *Space World*, Jan. 1975, p. 11; Daniloff, N., *The Kremlin and the Cosmos*, p. 197; Vladimirov, L., *op. cit.*, pp. 98-102.

30. Petrovich, G.V., *op. cit.*, pp. 518-519; Gagarin, Yu., *Road to the Stars*, pp. 154-155, 159-161; Aleksandrov, S.G. and Fedrov, R.Ye., *op. cit.*, pp. 243-246.

31. Gatland, K., *op. cit.*, pp. 113, 253; Shelton, W., *op. cit.*, p. 122; Blagonravov, A.A., et al., *op. cit.*, p. 588; *The Sons of the Blue Planet*, p. 35; *Soviet Space Programs, 1971-1975*, p. 176; *First Man in Space*, p. 52; Skuridin, G.A., *op. cit.*, p. 703.

32. *Ten Years of Space Exploration*, p. 13; Aleksandrov, S.G., and Fedrov, R.Ye., *op. cit.*, p. 222; Lewis, R.S., *From Vineland to Mars*, p. 148; *Legendary Vostok*, p. 24; *Space World*, Dec. 1971, p. 44; Vladimirov, L., *op. cit.*, p. 105; Turnill, R., *The Observer's Book of Manned Spaceflight*, p. 168; Borisenko, I.G., *op. cit.*, p. 10; Riabchikov, E., *op. cit.*, p. 36.

33. *Space World*, Jan. 1975, p. 12; See also Borisenko, I.G., *Space Launches and Finishes*, pp. 2-6.

34. Skuridin, G.A., *op. cit.*, pp. 720-721; Gagarin, Yu., *op. cit.*, pp. 148-149; Romanov, A., *op. cit.*, p. 64.

35. *First Man in Space*, pp. 52, 67; Caidin, M., *Red Star in Space*, pp. 221-228; Gagarin, Yu., *op. cit.*, pp. 149-161; Skuridin, G.A., *op. cit.*, pp. 700-704; Wukelic, G.E., *op. cit.*, p. 54.

36. For further details of the various cosmonaut death stories see: *Space World*, Jan. 1975; *Penkovskiy Papers*, p. 342; *Russian Space Bluff*, pp. 88-90; *Soviet Space Technology*, p. 123; *Russian Space Hoax*, pp. 54-55; *Spaceflight*, Dec. 1975 and Jan. 1976; *True*, June 1961; *U.S. News and World Report*, 12 Mar 1962.

37. Sheldon, C.S., *United States and Soviet Progress in Space: Summary Data Through 1975 and a Forward Look*, pp. 30-31.

38. See *The Sons of the Blue Planet* and *Soviet Space Programs, 1971-1975* (thru Soyuz 19) for biographies of all cosmonauts from Vostok 1. Also *Spaceflight*, a publication of the British Interplanetary Society, runs periodic articles on all aspects of cosmonaut background and training. *Astronauts and Cosmonauts Biographical and Statistical Data*, July 1977.

39. Skuridin, G.A., *op. cit.*, pp. 722-723, 766, 772; Titov, G., *op. cit.*, pp. 146, 164; Wukelic, G.E., *op. cit.*, p. 54.

40. *Gherman Titov, the First Man to Spend a Day in Space*, pp. 96, 100; Titov, G., *I am Eagle*, pp. 149, 153, 172, 179-180, 184-185; Titov, G., *700,000 km Through Space*, pp. 105, 112-113; Skuridin, G.A, *op. cit.*, pp. 726-737, 748-755, 789-790.

41. Titov, G., *700,000 km Through Space*, pp. 115-116; Titov, G., *I am Eagle*, pp. 190-191; Shelton, W., *op. cit.*, pp. 121, 138; Wukelic, G.E., *op. cit.*, p. 327; Smolders, P., *op. cit.*, pp. 117-118; *Gherman Titov, the First Man to Spend a Day in Space*, p. 99; Turnill, R., *op. cit.*, p. 169; *The Sons of the Blue Planet*, p. 76.

42. Skuridin, G.A., *op. cit.*, p. 761, 786; *Ten Years of Space Exploration*, p. 14-15; Titov, G., *I am Eagle*, pp. 151-152; Wukelic, G.E., *op. cit.*, p. 54; Blagonravov, A.A., et al., *op. cit.*, pp. 394-395.

43. Skuridin, G.A., *op. cit.*, pp. 735-737; Titov, G., *op. cit.*, pp. 193-200.

44. *Legendary Vostok*, pp. 22-23; Petrovich, G.V., *op. cit.*, pp. 522-523; Blagonravov, A.A., et al., *op. cit.*, p. 395; Skuridin, G.A., *op. cit.*, pp. 794, 800.

45. Ponomarev, A.N., *op. cit.*, p. 210; Skuridin, G.A., *op. cit.*, pp. 798-805.

46. Petrovich, G.V., *op. cit.*, pp. 495-496, 522-523; Blagonravov, A.A., et al., *op. cit.*, p. 395; Skuridin, G.A., *op. cit.*, pp. 805-809, 888.

47. Skuridin, G.A., *op. cit.*, pp. 887, 889-891.

48. *Legendary Vostok*, p. 23; *Ten Years of Space Exploration*, p. 15; Petrovich, G.V., *op. cit.*, pp. 277, 496; Blagonravov, A.A., et al., pp. 589-590; Skuridin, G.A., *op. cit.*, pp. 809-810, 881, 896, 927.

49. Skuridin, G.A., *op. cit.*, pp. 810-828, 839, 902-903.

50. *The Sons of the Blue Planet*, p. 77; Turnill, R., *op. cit.*, p. 170; Gurney, G. and C., *Cosmonauts in Orbit*, p. 84; Blagonravov, A.A., et al., *op. cit.*, p. 589-590; Skuridin, G.A., *op. cit.*, pp. 828, 841-847, 900, 927, 930; *Flight International*, 1 Nov. 1962, p. 719.

51. Gatland, K., *op. cit.*, pp. 118-119; Wukelic, G.E., *op. cit.*, p. 54; Blagonravov, A.A., et al., *op. cit.*, p. 395; Skuridin, G.A., *op. cit.*, pp. 852-864, 894, 908-926.

52. Skuridin, G.A., *op. cit.*, pp. 889-890, 929-930; Further details of the flight can be found in: Skuridin, G.A., *op. cit.*, pp. 794-933; Borisenko, I.G., *op. cit.*, pp. 16-18; *The Sons of the Blue Planet*, pp. 75-79.

53. Petrovich, G.V., *op. cit.*, pp. 526-527; *Aviation Week and Space Technology*, 24 June 1963, pp. 33-35; Blagonravov, A.A., et al., *op. cit.*, p. 395; Skuridin, G.A., *op. cit.*, pp. 934-935, 939; Siskayan, N.M., *op. cit.*, p. 92.

54. Borisenko, I.G., *op. cit.*, p. 19; Skuridin, G.A., *op. cit.*, pp. 938-942; Siskayan, N.M., *op. cit.*, pp. 5-6.

55. *Aviation Week and Space Technology*, 24 June 1963, pp. 33-35.

56. *Soviet Space Programs, 1971-1975*, pp. 176-177; *Aviation Week and Space Technology*, 24 June 1963, pp. 33-35; Skuridin, G.A., *op. cit.*, pp. 944-953.

57. Smolders, P., *op. cit.*, pp. 123-125; Shelton, W., *op. cit.*, pp. 135-136, 147; *The Sons of the Blue Planet*, pp. 95-96, 102-103; Gatland, K., *op. cit.*, p. 129.

58. Shelton, W., *op. cit.*, p. 158; *The Sons of the Blue Planet*, pp. 95-98.

59. *The Sons of the Blue Planet*, pp. 102-104; Skuridin, G.A., *op. cit.*, pp. 954-1008.

60. Skuridin, G.A., *op. cit.*, pp. 991-992.

61. Vladimirov, L., *op. cit.*, pp. 114-115; Sharpe, M.R., *Living in Space*, p. 32; Wukelic, G.E., *op. cit.*, p. 55; Turnill, R., *op. cit.*, pp. 170-171; Borisenko, I.G., *op. cit.*, pp. 18-20; Riabchikov, E., *op. cit.*, p. 204; Blagonravov, A.A., et al., *op. cit.*, p. 591; *The Sons of the Blue Planet*, p. 103; Skuridin, G.A., *op. cit.*, p. 994; Sisakyan, N.M., *op. cit.*, pp. 91-94; *Flight International*, 17 Oct. 1963, p. 670.

62. Borisenko, I.G., *op. cit.*, pp. 19-20; Blagonravov, A.A., et al., *op. cit.*, p. 590; *Soviet Space Programs, 1971-1975*, p. 230; *Flight International*, 17 Oct. 1963, p. 670.

Section II

VOSKHOD

INTRODUCTION TO VOSKHOD

The single-man Vostok spacecraft put into orbit by the Vostok (A-1) launcher weighed in the neighborhood of 4725 kg. A multi-man spacecraft would necessarily weigh much more, requiring a launch vehicle of higher lifting capacity. The original Vostok rocket had been fitted with an elongated second stage and an additional smaller escape stage (A-2-e) for unmanned planetary probes as early as October 1960. Five months after the flights of Vostok 5 and 6 the augmented Vostok launcher sans escape stage (A-2) made its maiden flight in earth orbit carrying Kosmos 22. After four more flights during the following year the launch vehicle, capable of placing 7500 kg in low earth orbit, was declared man-rated.[1]

By the end of the Vostok program the advanced 6500-kg Soyuz spacecraft was already on the drawing boards. The versatile Soyuz was designed to be the workhorse of the Soviet Union's manned space program for at least the next ten years. Although the launch vehicle would be ready, the Soyuz spacecraft itself would not be available before 1966 or even later. Thus, Soviet leaders were faced with a difficult decision. Should the Soviets retreat from manned space flight until Soyuz was ready which would certainly be after a large portion of the US Gemini program had been completed or could Soviet scientists devise a less ambitious multi-man spacecraft during the interim between Vostok and Soyuz? Given the political climate of the time the first alternative was unthinkable. However, the feasibility of the second option was highly doubted.

Reportedly Khrushchev himself ordered spacecraft designer Korolev to beat the United States into space with a multi-man spaceship. To this day very few details of the 5300-5700 kg Voskhod spacecraft which flew in October 1964 and March 1965 have been released by the USSR. Until very recently only partial sketches or photographs of the interior or of the

shroud-covered craft had been released by Soviet officials. It is now
clear that Voskhod was only a slightly modified version of the single-seat
Vostok: a fact of which the USSR was not especially proud. The four
flights and a possible fifth flight of the short Voskhod*program are outlined in Figure 1. Regardless of the merits of the Voskhod program two
signficant achievements were realized: (1) For the first time a man exited
his spaceship in flight for a "walk" in space and (2) the Soviet Union
maintained her image as master of space exploration.[2]

VOSKHOD SUMMARY

Designator	Date Launched	Date Returned	Orbits	Weight(kg)	Results
Kosmos 47	6 Oct 1964	7 Oct 1964	16	?	Unmanned precursor of Voskhod 1
Voskhod 1	12 Oct 1964	13 Oct 1964	16	5320	First multi-man space flight in single ship; Komarov, Feoktistov, and Yegorov safely recovered after one day
Kosmos 57	22 Feb 1965	---	--	?	Unmanned precursor of Voskhod 2; exploded in space on second orbit
Voskhod 2	18 Mar 1965	19 Mar 1965	17	5682	First space walk lasting twelve minutes performed by Leonov; Belyayev and Leonov forced to use manual reentry when the automatic guidance system malfunc-tioned; safely recovered after one day
Kosmos 110	22 Feb 1966	16 Mar 1966	330	?	Twenty-two day biological flight with dogs Veterok and Ugolek; possible pre-cursor of a later cancelled long duration manned Voskhod.

Figure 1

Voskhod means "sunrise" in Russian.

Chapter 4

VOSKHOD SPACECRAFT DESIGN

As previously mentioned, the Soviet Union has been reluctant to divulge anything other than a very general description of the Voskhod spacecraft. The reason for this became apparent in the years following the flights of Voskhod 1 and 2. At the time of these flights the spaceship was billed as a new "considerably different" spacecraft. In retrospect the claims made for Voskhod (e.g. no need of spacesuits, water landing capability, high-altitude missions) could have been performed by Vostok. The fact that Voskhod 1 carried three cosmonauts and that Voskhod 2 was equipped with an airlock indicated that Voskhod was indeed much more advanced than Vostok. However, the reader must remember that no one outside of the Soviet Union had ever seen the Vostok spacecraft until after the flight of Voskhod 2. Thus, it was not suspected at that time that Voskhod might be a modified Vostok.

In late 1963 when the decision to orbit a spaceship with more than one man and to attempt a spacewalk (those objectives of the US Gemini program which the USSR had a chance of completing with a modified Vostok) was made, spacecraft designer Sergi Korolev found himself with a Herculean task. Vostok had been designed with a size and weight at the limited capability of the Vostok launcher. Although the improved second stage of the launch vehicle would permit a heavier payload to be orbited, the size of Vostok could not be significantly altered in the short time allowed. In addition, the Vostok capsule was already stripped to the barest essentials. Even though Vostok weighed approximately 2.5 times more than the US Mercury spacecraft, Vostok actually had less instrumentation and versatility due to the much heavier construction materials used on Vostok.

The problem then became one of fitting three men into a sphere of 2.3 meters in diameter previously used by one cosmonaut with little room to spare. The resultant design of Voskhod was one of give and take. The large ejection seat was the first item to go. It would be impossible for three cosmonauts to eject from the capsule simultaneously, let alone find room for three cumbersome ejection seats. Therefore, there was no choice-- the crew would have to land in their capsule. This, though, had been rejected for the the Vostok program due to the high impact velocity of the spacecraft. Furthermore, it has been reported that a drop-test of a prototype Voskhod capsule ended in failure when the three monkeys on board were found dead. Korolev solved this problem by enlarging the main parachutes and installing a solid fuel rocket system which was activated a few meters above the ground to further decelerate the spacecraft. The latter system has become standard on the later generation Soyuz spacecraft and conventional Soviet air-drops of large military payloads.[3]

Reentry as well as landing presented new problems. Vostok spacecraft flew in orbits which would naturally decay within ten days in the event of a retro-engine malfunction and carried food and water reserves for one cosmonaut for that time. It appears that the Soviets felt uneasy about using this same procedure with two or three men on board, not to mention the difficulty of finding room for the air and food supplies for up to twenty-one man-days. To alleviate this problem a second set of retrorockets was installed. If the main system (liquid fuel) failed, a separate back-up system (solid fuel) would then be available. This also permitted Voskhod to fly at higher altitudes than had Vostok.[4] Figure 2 is a sketch comparing Vostok with Voskhod 1 and the later Voskhod 2.

In the case of Voskhod 1 the mission was merely to orbit three cosmonauts for a period of one day. After taking out the single ejection seat and rearranging the interior instrument panels, three seats were installed side by side with the center seat slightly raised, forming a shallow triangular arrangement. Thus, three men could now squeeze into the capsule. However, they did so without space suits. Whether or not this was because there was no room to wear them in the capsule is unclear. Some Western observers indicate that pressure suits were stored on board, implying the suits could be donned if needed. One finds it difficult to imagine, though, how three men could put on such cumbersome garments in the highly restricted space available. During the Voskhod 2 flight which carried only two men

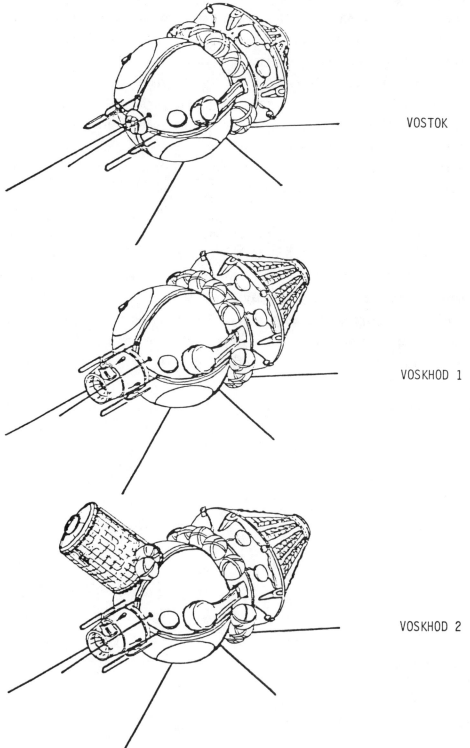

VOSTOK

VOSKHOD 1

VOSKHOD 2

Figure 2   Comparison of the Vostok, Voskhod 1, and Voskhod 2
           spacecraft   (drawings by R.F. Gibbons)

the third seat was removed, allowing the two cosmonauts room to wear their special space suits. Even in this case the suits were worn for the entire flight and not put on in orbit.[5]

Other changes could be found on the Voskhod spacecraft. An external television camera was added to give ground personnel and the crew the opportunity to observe the exterior of the spaceship. In addition a new television system with a 625-line, 25-frames-per-second scan-rate capability was used. This was especially important during Leonov's walk in space on Voskhod 2. Electrostatic ion engines were first tested on Voskhod 1 as a part of the attitude-control system.

Since no ejection seats were used and the spacecraft did not have an escape rocket while attached to the launch vehicle, there was no means of escape in the event of a launch malfunction. This is considered to have been exceptionally risky and may be an indication of the haste with which the Voskhod program was assembled. Although reports stated that Voskhod could remain in orbit for as long as one month and could make orbital maneuvers, no evidence to support these claims has ever been furnished.[6]

Chapter 5

VOSKHOD PRECURSOR FLIGHTS

Since, from all the evidence, Voskhod appears to have been only a modified Vostok spacecraft, extensive unmanned tests were not needed. Vostok itself had proven its reliability on six separate manned missions. The augmented launch vehicle was man-rated after five successful launches in the year between November 1963 and October 1964. Only two unmanned precursor flights are known to have been flown using the Voskhod spaceship. Both of these flights were last-minute dress rehearsals of Voskhod 1 and Voskhod 2, respectively.

On 6 October 1964, just two days after the seventh anniversary of Sputnik 1, Kosmos 47 was launched into a 413 km by 177 km earth orbit at a 64.77° inclination. After almost exactly twenty-four hours in space Kosmos 47 was brought down via an automatic reentry and is presumed to have been recovered on Soviet territory. Five days later on 12-13 October Komarov, Feoktiskov, and Yegorov flew Voskhod 1 on a twenty-four hour mission with orbital elements of 408 km by 177.5 km at 64.82°.[7]

The second precursor flight came on 22 February 1965 with the launch of Kosmos 57 into an orbit of 512 km by 175 km at 64.77°. However, before the second revolution had been completed, Kosmos 57 exploded in orbit leaving behind at least 182 pieces. No further details pertaining to a possible cause of the explosion have been released, although one report indicated that the spacecraft had been tumbling from the outset. Presumably the Soviets were either aware of the troubles at the time or soon determined the reason for the accident, since Voskhod 2 with Leonov and Belyayev aboard was orbited three and one-half weeks later in a very similar orbit without further orbital testing.[8]

A third unmanned Voskhod was perhaps launched nearly a year after the triumphant flight of Voskhod 2. Exactly one year after the launch of

Kosmos 57, Kosmos 110 was inserted into an earth orbit of 904 km by 187 km at 51.9°. This new inclination would be used in the later Soyuz flights and perhaps indicated the use of a heavier Voskhod vehicle. If two or three cosmonauts were to follow Kosmos 110 on a long-duration mission, the weight of the life-support supplies would be considerable. Two dogs, Veterok and Ugolek, accompanied the spacecraft for the highest (actually within the inner Van Allen radiation belt) and the longest biological flight to that time. Although the announced purpose of this flight was to obtain further valuable information concerning the effects of prolonged weightlessness and radiation exposure, it has been speculated that Kosmos 110 was a test flight for a future manned mission lasting up to thirty days. Veterok and Ugolek remained aloft for 22 days, completing 330 revolutions of the earth, before returning on 16 March 1966.

Each dog was placed in a special compartment within the spacecraft (Figure 3). Sensors were attached to and within the dogs' bodies in order to obtain a wide range of measurements during the flight. Included in these measurements were readings of pulse, respiration, arterial pressure, biocurrents of the heart, and certain nerve responses. Dosimeters recorded the higher radiation levels encountered as a result of the orbit's high apogee.

A second pair of dogs in a Soviet laboratory were being used as control subjects. Both sets of animals underwent the same routines as closely as possible in order to evaluate properly the effects of weightlessness and radiation on Veterok and Ugolek. All four animals were fed through surgically implanted tubes running directly into their stomachs. This permitted precise measurement of food intake and simplified the task of feeding the dogs for three weeks in a weightless environment.

Transparent plates at the forward end of the individual compartments allowed continuous observation of the animals via television cameras in a fashion similar to that employed on the satellite-spaceships of 1960 and 1961. Ugolek assumed the role of control specimen while Veterok was subjected to different medications designed to counter radiational effects. These drugs were introduced directly into the aorta through another implanted plastic tube.

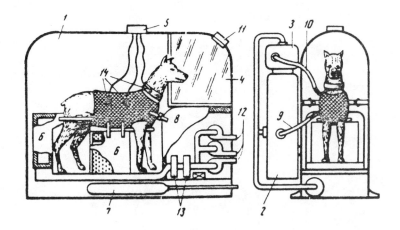

(1) Pressured capsule; (2) food container; (3) pharmacological container; (4) transparent hood; (5) physiological transducers; (6) waste collectors; (7) pneumatic system with tanks of compressed air; (8) compartment with instruments of life-support system; (9) food line; (10) hose for feeding biomedical preparations; (11) air intake; (12) fans; (13) filters for purifying air; (14) physiological transducers.

Figure 3   Diagram of cabin with animal on "Kosmos-110" satellite

Although both dogs were recovered in "good condition" the Soviets were reported dismayed at the medical degradation which had taken place, particularly concerning the absorption of bone calcium by the blood and urine. In addition, both dogs' movements were significantly impaired for up to 8-10 days following their return to earth. For reasons which have still not been disclosed (although budgetary, political, and manpower requirements of the ongoing Soyuz program have been mentioned) no further manned flights of Voskhod were ever flown.[9]

Chapter 6

VOSKHOD OPERATIONAL FLIGHTS

VOSKHOD 1

Both the US Mercury and Soviet Vostok single-man spacecraft series had ended in the summer of 1963. By the fall of 1964 the US Gemini program was fast nearing its initial launch scheduled for the spring of 1965. Since the return of Vostok 5 and 6 in June 1963 the Soviets as usual were silent concerning specific plans for continued manned spaceflight. As the seventh anniversary of Sputnik 1 approached, rumors of a new multi-man spacecraft surfaced. The 24-hour flight of Kosmos 47 at an inclination used by manned flights signaled the probable imminent launch of cosmonauts. Finally on 12 October 1964 at 1030 hr Moscow time Voskhod 1 became the first mutli-man spacecraft to be rocketed into earth orbit. The crew consisted of Vladimir Mikhailovich Komarov, commander; Konstantin Petrovich Feoktistov, scientist; and Boris Borisovich Yegorov, doctor. Not only was the size of the crew a surprise (three cosmonauts instead of two), but also the inclusion of a scientist and a doctor was unexpected.

The goals of the flight were announced as follows:

o Tests of the multi-seat piloted spaceship

o Efficiency and interaction investigation in flight of a group of spacemen, made up of specialists in different spheres of science and technology

o Scientific physio-technical investigations in conditions of space flight

o Continued study of the effect of various space-flight factors on the human organism

o Extended medico-biological investigations in conditions of a long flight.[10]

Only the last objective seems out of place. Voskhod 1 appears to have been planned from the start as a one-day flight. At this point in manned space exploration, 24 hours in orbit was still considered significant, especially since a new spaceship was being tested. (The first manned Gemini spacecraft would be in orbit for less than five hours.) Therefore the reference to a "long flight" seems misleading and later along with other events became one source for charges that Voskhod 1 was brought down early.

The 5320-kg spacecraft was placed into an orbit of 408 km by 177.5 km at 64.82°. The resemblance to Vostok, including the instruments and portholes was striking. The triangular arrangement of the cosmonaut seats was oriented 90 degrees with respect to the older Vostok ejection seat. Hence, the main instrument panel and Vzor porthole instead of being directly in front of the cosmonauts was positioned to the side of the spaceship commander, Komarov. The spacecraft atmosphere was generally maintained at 1.1 atmospheres pressure with a temperature of 18-21°C and relative humidity of 45-60%.[11]

The orientation of Voskhod was tested on the sixth and seventh revolutions using an attitude-control system similar to that employed by Vostok and using the experimental electrostatic ion engine system. The latter system worked on the principle of accelerating alkali metal ions by means of an electrostatic field and using this high-velocity ion flux to turn the spacecraft. As mentioned earlier a new television camera was attached to the exterior of the instrument module to allow the crew and ground control an additional view. Feoktistov, in particular, made detailed observations of the earth's horizon as an aid to use the earth for navigational purposes. He also made photographs of luminescent particles, polar aurora, and stellar positions.[12]

Although the bio-medical aspects of the flight were relatively minor when compared with the longer-duration flights of Vostok 3-6, these experiments were given quite a lot of publicity due to the presence on board of Yegorov, a physician. Emphasis was placed on Yegorov's ability to observe *in situ* the other two cosmonauts while giving a more detailed account of his own feelings. Some of the measurements made by Yegorov included "cerebral biocurrents, electric potentials, arising with voluntary and involuntary movements of eyes, parameters, characterizing coordination of movements in figure-drawing and writing, and also the curve of muscular efficiency in the rhythmic movements of the wrist." There is little evidence to confirm or deny rumors following the flight that Feoktistov experienced a severe reaction to weightlessness. These types of rumors are difficult to pin down and are believed to be occasionally started by the Soviets themselves to conceal other problems.[13]

The flight proceeded without complications for 16 orbits. As a rule one member of the crew would rest while the other two carried out the mission objectives. At the beginning of the sixteenth orbit preparations were made to return to earth. A rather cryptic exchange between Voskhod 1 and the ground controllers fanned speculation about an early return. While requesting an extension to their flight, the crew was reminded of the following famous partial quote: "There are more things in Heaven and earth, Horatio," by spacecraft designer Korolev. One interpretation of this message was to attribute it to the rapidly changing political situation in the Soviet Union. Whereas Premier Khrushchev had seen the three cosmonauts off into space, within a day of their landing Khrushechev had been ousted by Brezhnev and Kosygin and it was these two who greeted the cosmonauts when they returned to Moscow a few days later.[14]

Reentry followed the prescribed sequence with spacecraft orientation begun at 0955 hr 39 sec. After retro-fire at 1018 hr 58 sec the return capsule separated from the instrument module and began its fiery descent. At an altitude of 5 km and a velocity of 220 m/sec the parachute system was deployed. Finally, within a few meters of the ground the new solid-fuel propellant landing system was activated reducing the spacecraft's descent to a gentle landing. Touchdown took place at 1047 hr 04 sec on 13 October, 13 km NE of Kustanai at 54°02'00"N, 68°08'00"E. All crew members were reported in very good health.[15] The USSR had once again demonstrated her prowess in space. Yet an even more daring feat was in the planning stages.

VOSKHOD 2

If man was ever going to spend extended periods in space or explore the moon, two major operations had yet to be tested by the beginning of 1965: docking two spacecraft and exiting a spacecraft. The former evolution would have to wait until the Soyuz spacecraft was built and tested,

but the latter experiment could be attempted with modifications of existing hardware. The importance of a man being able to leave an orbiting
spacecraft to effect repairs or to transfer to another craft cannot be
over-stressed. Although from a technological standpoint "walking" in
space does not appear to be very difficult, a great deal of concern was
directed toward the cosmonaut's psychological reactions. Once in space
the cosmonaut would have no reference points as he flew at almost 8 km/sec
over the earth. Aleksei Leonov, who was to become the first man ever to
exit his spacecraft in orbit, underwent extensive psychological testing
and spent a great many hours in isolation under observation.[16]

At 1000 hr on 18 March 1965 five days before the planned launch of
the first manned US Gemini spacecraft, the 5682-kg Voskhod 2 roared off
a launching pad at the Baikonur Cosmodrome and entered an earth orbit of
497.7 km by 173.5 km at 64.79°. Almost immediately the two cosmonauts
on board, Pavel Ivanovich Belyayev and Aleksey Arkhipovich Leonov, began
preparations for man's first extra-vehicular activity (EVA). If for some
reason the space walk could not be performed, contingency plans called for
Voskhod 2 to remain aloft for two to three days.[17]

Voskhod 2 represented a third variation of the basic Vostok vehicle.
As with Voskhod 1, the Voskhod 2 passenger module started out as a completely stripped spherical cabin. The two cosmonaut couches were set side
by side slightly off center with Leonov's seat to the right of the airlock
chamber hatch. Only two cosmonauts could be accommodated due to the requirement that the cosmonauts had to wear bulky space suits during the EVA
experiment. The airlock arrangement was chosen in part because the equipment within Voskhod was not designed to operate under the rigorous conditions of the vacuum of space. All the electronic equipment was built to
operate under normal atmospheric temperatures and pressures. Therefore,
it would have been impossible to depressurize the entire cabin and open
the main entrance hatch to perform the EVA. Additionally, some reports
indicate that there was not enough reserved oxygen and nitrogen on board
to completely repressurize the spacecraft in the event of a complete loss
of atmosphere.[18]

The airlock itself was an accordion-type of tunnel almost two meters
long and one meter in diameter attached to the hull of the spacecraft.
During launch the airlock was kept in a compressed configuration, protruding

only slightly from the spaceship. Once Voskhod 2 reached orbit, the air-lock was extended and pressurized. One cosmonaut could then enter the chamber, shut the interior hatch, depressurize the chamber, and then open the exterior hatch to leave the vehicle (Figure 4). Figure 5 illustrates the sequence of events for exiting and entering the spacecraft. After the cosmonaut had returned to his seat, the airlock would be jettisoned before reentry.[19] Figure 6 presents a diagram of Voskhod 2 spacewalk systems.

One major obstacle had to be overcome to use this type of airlock system. To prevent the cosmonaut's space suit from ballooning into a rigid and unmanageable shape, the space suit pressure had to be reduced. When breathing a pure oxygen atmosphere (as did early US astronauts), reductions in pressure are not dangerous. However, similar pressure drops in an oxygen/nitrogen environment can initiate the bends. To avoid this painful and potentially fatal occurrence, the cosmonaut could breathe a pure oxygen atmosphere at standard pressure for a short period to purge his blood of the nitrogen. However, the Soviets sought to circumvent this problem by installing two pressure settings on Leonov's suit: one at about 0.4 atm (6 psia) and the other at 0.27 atm (4 psia) Figure 7). Operation at either of these two pressures for a short period of time was not believed to be harmful. This would also allow the cosmonaut more mobility during the exit/entrance phase when he must do considerable maneuvering.[20]

. Since it was decided to use an airlock system, life support could not easily be supplied to Leonov through an umbilical cord. Hence the cosmonaut wore a backpack which contained oxygen and other vital needs. The daring spaceman did carry a 5.35 meter long tether to insure that he did not float away from his spacecraft. Communications were also fed through this tether. Leonov did not possess any type of propulsion system such as a hand held compressed gas gun or similar device to aid him in his walk.[21]

The interior of the cabin contained much the same equipment as did Voskhod 1. An additional instrument control panel was installed inside the cabin proper for remote operation of the airlock by the cosmonaut commander. Inside the airlock was a duplicate panel which could be used by the transferring cosmonaut. An internal television receiver gave Belyayev a view of Leonov as the latter floated around outside the ship. Belyayev

Figure 4a Mating of the Voskhod 2 spacecraft and protective
shroud with the upper stage of the launch vehicle

was to remain within the spacecraft and maintain its attitude while Leonov
conducted EVA. In the event of an emergency Soviet scientists reported
that Belyayev could put the spacecraft on automatic and go to Leonov's aid
outside the ship. The actual feasibility of this procedure leaves some
doubt.[22]

While Voskhod 2 was still completing its first revolution about the
earth, Leonov began preparations to take the walk for which he had been
practicing since 1963. The airlock was extended and pressurized while
Belyayev helped Leonov don the space suit backpack which contained the
life-support systems. After ensuring the integrity of the airlock system,
the inner hatch was opened inward and Leonov floated inside, closing the
hatch behind him. Less than an hour and a half after launch the airlock
chamber was depressurized. Approximately five minutes later at 1132 hr
54 sec Leonov opened the outer hatch of the chamber and became the first
man to foresake the security of his spaceship. During this process a camera at the far end of the airlock recorded Leonov's movements. One of the

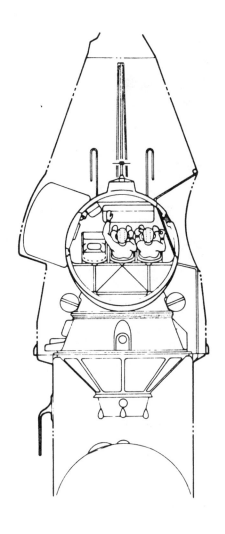

first duties for Leonov was to place a S-97 movie camera onto a mounting on the exterior of Voskhod 2 to record his EVA.[23]

At 1134 hr 51 sec Leonov emerged from the airlock and began his walk in space (Figure 8). Immediately Leonov was temporarily overwhelmed by the glare of the sun and earth. The solar filter on his helmet protected the cosmonaut from the brillant sun, yet allowed him to perform the tasks set forth. With relative ease Leonov removed the camera lens and installed the camera on its mounting. While Leonov indicated that he could move with little effort, Belyayev reported that Voskhod 2 rolled and responded whenever Leonov hit or pushed off from the spacecraft. Leonov could freely move about Voskhod 2 even though movement within the space suit was more restricted. Leonov was captivated by the immense beauty of the earth and space.[24]

Figure 4b   NASA rendering of the Voskhod 2 spacecraft atop its launch vehicle

After a few minutes in space Belyayev notified Leonov that he was to return to the airlock and terminate the EVA. Thus began the most dangerous portion of the space walk. Leonov reported difficulties in retrieving the exterior movie camera. Once the device was removed Leonov attempted to reenter the chamber feet first. However, to Leonov's surprise he at first found himself unable to enter the airlock. Two explanations have been purposed for this situation. The first deals with the ballooning of the cosmonaut's space suit, making it slightly bigger than the airlock opening. The second explanation suggests that the camera became wedged between Leonov and the hatch, preventing further movement. After much physical exertion and a reduction in pressure

1. Airlock pressurization
2. Leonov prepares to enter the airlock by doning the backpack.
3. Leonov enters the airlock.
4. Main hatch is closed and airlock pressure is released.
5. Leonov exits the airlock for spacewalk.
6. Leonov floats beside Voskhod 2.
7. Leonov reenters the airlock.
8. Airlock is repressurized.
9. Main hatch is opened and Leonov reenters Voskhod 2 cabin.
10. Airlock is depressurized and later released.

Figure 5   Diagram of Leonov's egress and ingress through the
            Voskhod 2 airlock chamber

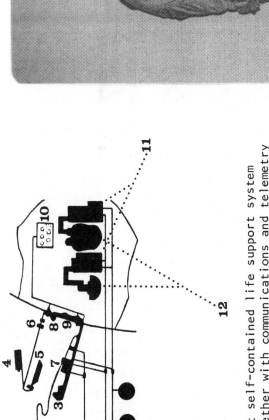

1. Cosmonaut self-contained life support system
2. Safety tether with communications and telemetry wires
3. Light
4. Movie camera
5. Airlock exit hatch
6. Airlock pressure relief valve
7. Duplicate airlock control panel
8. Movie camera
9. Interior airlock hatch (main hatch)
10. Exit system control panel
11. Shipboard life-support units for cosmonauts in spacesuits
12. Cosmonaut couches
13. Independent airlock pressurization system
14. Spacesuit and cockpit pressurization system

Figure 6   Voskhod 2 spacewalk systems

Figure 7   Display of Voskhod 2 extra-vehicular activity (EVA) spacesuit (photograph courtesy of R.F. Gibbons)

Figure 8   Photograph of Leonov during his historic spacewalk

of his space suit, a tired Leonov managed to squeeze into the chamber and to close the hatch behind him. The time was 1148 hr 40 sec. In all Leonov was exposed to space for 23 minutes and 41 seconds. Of that time 12 minutes and 09 seconds were spent outside the airlock.[25]

Following Leonov's return to the spacecraft, the two cosmonauts settled down and proceeded to follow the remainder of the flight plan. One of Leonov's first duties was to begin a detailed written description of his experience in space. During the day Belyayev and Leonov conducted motion and still photography. Tests were run to determine if weightlessness has any effect on color perception. Belyayev experienced a 26.1 per cent reduction in his ability to view certain colors while Leonov noted a loss of 25 per cent. The two triumphant cosmonauts concluded their day in space without further excitement and retired to a well-deserved rest.[26]

On the morning of 19 March as Leonov and Belyayev were making their sixteenth revolution, the two Soviets began preparations for the return to earth. Retro-fire was planned to take place at the end of the sixteenth orbit. Just as the moment approached, a signal indicated that the automatic

guidance system had malfunctioned and the spacecraft was not properly
oriented for the return to earth. Quickly Belyayev was ordered to continue
for one more orbit while the situation could be analyzed. A short time
later the crew commander was given permission to attempt a manual reentry
at the end of the seventeenth orbit. This would be the first time a Soviet spaceship had landed by manual control. At 1119 hr Belyayev oriented
Voskhod 2 and by 1136 hr 27 sec he had fired the main retro-rocket. The
spacecraft then began a normal reentry sequence with the command module
separating from the instrument module. At an altitude of 5 km and a velocity of 220 m/sec the parachute system was activated. Approximately six
minutes later at 1202 hr 17 sec the spacecraft landed 180 km NE of Perm at
59°34'03"N, 55°28'00"E.[27]

Unfortunately, since Voskhod 2 had completed an extra orbit of the
earth and the descent was done manually, the final landing site was not
in the normally designated area. As a matter of fact Leonov and Belyayev
came down in a heavily wooded area in deep snow. Search helicopters soon
located the site but could not land. A makeshift helicopter landing pad
was made several kilometers away and the rescue party had to ski to the
cosmonaut's touchdown area. One report stated the two cosmonauts were even
unable to open the hatch of the spacecraft and had to be assisted by the
rescue party. Most reports agree that the cosmonauts were forced to spend
the night near Voskhod 2. The next morning the entire party including the
cosmonauts skied back to the clearing, where Leonov and Belyayev were
picked up and flown to Baikonur.[28]

The excitement surrounding the extraordinary flight of Voskhod 2 did
not end with their return to earth. During Leonov's famous space walk
blurry pictures of him floating were seen on televisions across the Soviet
Union. Soon after the recovery of Voskhod 2 the much awaited movie films
were released. Unfortunately, without comment, the Soviets had spliced
in some footage taken during Leonov's training sessions on earth which appeared to the uncritical eye to be taken in space. Some Western observers
who were skeptical that the USSR had indeed performed an EVA pounced on
these fake photographs and called the entire flight a hoax. It now appears
that, although some of the films released were shot on earth, the rest of
the footage and all other evidence supports the fact that Leonov was actually the first man to float in space.[29]

Thus ended the highly successful Vostok/Voskhod program amid Western speculation of a long-duration Voskhod 3 flight. Soon after the return of Leonov and Belyayev a noted US aerospace periodical suggested that Voskhod 2 had been scheduled to rendezvous with a Voskhod 3 and exchange crews. Some unforeseen circumstance supposedly had prevented this. However, the article did go on to predict a flight of one week with three cosmonauts for the summer of 1965.[30]

In retrospect, a true rendezvous of two Voskhod was beyond the capability of the spacecraft, much less a docking and/or crew exchange. Part of the basis for such predictions was the Soviet insistence (maintained to this day) that Voskhod was maneuverable and capable of sustaining two cosmonauts for a period in excess of one month. No firm evidence exists to support either claim. The three-week flight of Kosmos 110 a year later utilizing what was probably a Voskhod spacecraft strengthened the belief that a manned flight was soon to follow. But for reasons known only to the Soviets, Voskhod 3 never materialized. Perhaps the mission was too little and too late in light of the successes the US Gemini program was experiencing. Or, more probably, the manned part of Voskhod had been dropped in 1965 to concentrate on development of a second generation spacecraft.[31]

The new spacecraft, Soyuz, was then under construction and would be capable of executing the orbital maneuvers required of a true spacecraft. Two years would pass from the completion of Voskhod 2 to the maiden flight of Soyuz during which time the US began and completed its ten-flight Gemini program with astounding success. From March 1965 to April 1967 the world wondered what had become of those daring young cosmonauts. Sadly, their questions were answered by the tragic flight of Soyuz 1.

The illustrious career of the Vostok/Voskhod spacecraft did not end with the flight of Voskhod 2 or Kosmos 110. Although an average of thirty Vostok-derivative photo reconnaissance satellites are launched yearly by the Soviet Union, the spacecraft also still serves more scientific purposes. In 1973 and 1974, Vostok spacecraft were used to carry two biological payloads (Kosmos 605 and Kosmos 690) for investigations into the effects of long periods of weightlessness on living organisms. Following the successful Apollo-Soyuz Test Project in 1975, a multi-national effort

resulted in the orbiting of Kosmos 782 on a 20-day biological mission.
A replica of Kosmos 782 on display in Moscow clearly indicates the strong
resemblance to the original Vostok spacecraft orbited 15 years earlier.
(Figure 9).

Figure 9   Replica of the Kosmos 782 international biological space-
            craft. Note the forward instrument package and the enlarged
            propulsion module.   (Courtesy of R.F. Gibbons)

REFERENCES AND NOTES - SECTION II

1. *Soviet Space Programs, 1971-1975,* pp. 49-51, 554-559.

2. Vladimirov, L., *The Russian Space Bluff,* pp. 120-127; *Space World,*
   Oct. 1972, pp. 29-30 and May 1974, p. 21; Turnill, R., *The Observer's
   Book of Manned Spaceflight,* pp. 161-162; Gatland, K., *Manned Space-
   craft,* p. 132; Smolders, P., *Soviets in Space,* pp. 35, 133; Wilding-
   White, T.M., *Jane's Pocket Book of Space Exploration,* pp.12-13;
   Spaceflight, Apr. 1974, pp. 145-149 and Nov. 1974, pp. 404-409.

3. *The Sons of the Blue Planet,* pp. 128-131; Skuridin, G.A., *Mastery of
   Outer Space in the USSR, 1957-1967,* p. 1052; Gatland, K., *op. cit.,*
   p. 258; Turnill, R., *op. cit.,* p. 162; Wilding-White, T.M., *op.
   cit.,* p. 13; Vladimirov, L., *op. cit.,* pp. 129-130.

4. Skuridin, G.A., *op. cit.,* pp. 1039-1042, 1052; Blagonravov, A.A.,
   et al., *USSR Achievements in Space Research,* p. 408; Turnill, R.,
   op. cit., p. 163; Gatland, K., *op. cit.,* p. 258; *Spaceflight,* Nov.
   1974, pp. 404-409 and May 1978, p. 200 and Aug. 1978, pp. 317-318.

5. Vladimirov, L., *op. cit.,* p. 128; Smolders, P., *op. cit.,* pp. 127,
   133; *Soviet Space Programs, 1971-1975,* p. 177; *Space World,* May 1974,
   p. 21; Turnill, R., *op. cit.,* p. 163.

6. Skuridin, G.A., *op. cit.,* p. 1052-1053; Blagonravov, A.A., et al.,
   op. cit., p. 592; Petrovich, G.V., *The Soviet Encyclopedia of Space
   Flight,* p. 493; Vladimirov, L., *op. cit.,* pp. 129-133; Wukelic, G.E.,
   Handbook of Soviet Space-Science Research, p. 59; *The Sons of the Blue
   Planet,* pp. 128-131; Borisenko, I.G., *In Outer Space,* pp. 83-84;
   Soviet Space Programs, 1971-1975, p. 498; *Space World,* May 1974,
   p. 21; Gatland, K., *op. cit.,* p. 258; Wilding-White, T.M., *op. cit.,*
   p. 13.

7. Petrovich, G.V., *op. cit.,* pp. 534-535; Smolders, P., *op. cit.,* p. 83;
   Soviet Space Programs, 1971-1975, p. 177.

8. *Aviation Week and Space Technology,* 12 Apr. 1965; Petrovich, G.V.,
   op. cit., pp. 536-537.

9. Shelton, W., *Soviet Space Exploration: The First Decade,* pp. 209-210;
   Blagonravov, A.A., et al, *op. cit.,* pp. 386-387; Petrovich, G.V.,
   op. cit., pp. 546-547; Smolders, P., *op. cit.,* pp. 106-107; *Space
   World,* Apr. 1975, p. 21; Wilding-White, T.M., *op. cit.,* p. 13;
   Gatland, K., *op. cit.,* pp. 137-138; *Soviet Space Programs, 1971-1975,*
   p. 221; *Spaceflight,* July 1966, pp. 236-237 and Sep. 1966, p. 317.

10. Skuridin, G.A., *op. cit.*, p. 1009.

11. Petrovich, G.V., *op. cit.*, pp. 534-535, 493; Skuridin, G.A., *op. cit.*, pp. 1009-1013; Blagonravov, A.A., et al., *op. cit.*, p. 591.

12. *The Sons of the Blue Planet*, pp. 107, 132-134; Wukelic, G.E., *op. cit.*, p. 59; Shelton, W., *op. cit.*, p. 172; Petrovich, G.V., *op. cit.*, pp. pp. 124-125; Skuridin, G.A., *op. cit.*, pp.1019, 1020, 1022, 1052-1056; Rebrov, M. and Khozin, G., *The Moon and Man*, pp. 69-76.

13. Smolders, P., *op. cit.*, p. 131; Shelton, W., *op. cit.*, pp. 167-171; Skuridin, G.A., *op. cit.*, pp. 1058-1064; *The Sons of the Blue Planet*, p. 134.

14. Daniloff, N., *The Kremlin and the Cosmos*, p. 161; Skuridin, G.A., *op. cit.*, p. 1048; Shelton, W., *op. cit.*, p. 169.

15. Blagonravov, A.A., et al, *op. cit.*, p. 591; Borisenko, I.G., *Space Launches and Finishes*, p. 24; Petrovich, G.V., *op. cit.*,p. 493; Skuridin, G.A., *op. cit.*, pp. 1023, 1058.

16. Smolders, P., *op. cit.*, p. 140.

17. Borisenko, I.G., *In Outer Space*, p. 38; Petrovich, G.V., pp. 538-539.

18. *Spaceflight*, May 1976, pp. 169-170.

19. Borisenko, I.G., *In Outer Space*, p. 97; Gatland, K., *op. cit.*, p. 259; *Spaceview*, Apr. 1976, p. 27 / 63.

20. *Spaceflight*,May 1976, p. 170; Smolders, P., *op. cit.*, p. 141; Lebedev, V. and Gagarin, Yu., *Survival in Space*, p. 27; *From Spaceships to Orbiting Stations*, p. 18; Gatland, K., *op. cit.*, pp. 134-135; *Spaceflight*, Jan. 1965, p. 18.

21. Borisenko, I.G., *In Outer Space*, p. 62.

22. Borisenko, I.G., *In Outer Space*, pp. 41, 96; Shelton, W., *op. cit.*, pp. 181-182; Gatland, K., *op. cit.*, pp. 259-260.

23. Borisenko, I.G., *In Outer Space*, p. 14; Borisenko, I.G., *Space Launches and Finishes*, p. 26; Skuridin, G.A., *op. cit.*, pp. 1096-1097; *The Sons of the Blue Planet*, pp. 146-148; Leonov, Aleksei, *My First Steps in Space*.

24. *From Spaceships to Orbiting Stations*, p. 19; Borisenko, I.G., *Space Launches and Finishes*, pp. 26-28; Borisenko, I.G., *In Outer Space*, p. 62-68; Skuridin, G.A., *op. cit.*,pp. 1093, 1097-1100; *The Sons of the Blue Planet*, pp. 148-150.

25. Riabchikov, E., *Russians in Space,* pp. 223-224; Lebedev, V. and Gagarin, Yu., *op. cit.,* p. 28; Skuridin, G.A., *op. cit.,* p. 1100; Borisenko, I.G., *In Outer Space,* pp. 68, 93; *From Spaceships to Orbiting Stations,* pp. 19-20; Turnill, R., *op. cit.,* p. 165; *Space World,* June 1975, p. 19 and Feb. 1976, p. 10; *The Sons of the Blue Planet,* p. 150; Smolders, P., *op. cit.,* pp. 142-143.

26. Sharpe, M.R., *Living in Space,* pp. 34-35; Borisenko, I.G., *In Outer Space,* pp. 58-59.

27. Ponomarev, A.N., *The Years of the Space Era,* p. 224; Blagonravov, A.A., et al., *op. cit.,* p. 592; Borisenko, I.G., *In Outer Space,* pp. 75, 95; Smolders, P. *op. cit.,* pp. 143-145.

28. *Aviation Week and Space Technology,* 5 Apr. 1965; Shelton, W., *op. cit.,* p. 186; Smolders, P., *op. cit.,* p. 145; Borisenko, I.G., *In Outer Space,* pp. 75, 82; *Space World,* June 1975, pp. 10-11.

29. Sheldon, C.S., *United States and Soviet Progress in Space: Summary Data through 1975 and a Forward Look,* pp. 31-32; *Space World,* June 1975, p. 22; See Lloyd Mallan's *Russia's Space Hoax* for typical analysis of photographs.

30. See Kosmos 110 and *Aviation Week and Space Technology,* 29 Mar. 1965. Also see United Press International releases for 10 and 16 Mar. 1966.

31. *Spaceflight,* Nov. 1974, pp. 408-409.

Section III

SOYUZ

INTRODUCTION TO SOYUZ

Advanced earth orbital and deep-space manned missions require space-craft with capabilities far in excess of those of either Vostok or Voskhod. Fundamental to the building of an earth-orbital space station or the assembly in orbit of a lunar or planetary spaceship are the techniques of rendezvous and docking. In the Vostok program the USSR had demonstrated its remarkable accuracy in placing two spacecraft in nearly identical orbits during the Vostok 3-4 mission. But neither Cosmonaut Nikolayev nor Cosmonaut Popovich could maneuver their spaceships to bring about a true rendezvous, and hence they slowly drifted apart.

Spacecraft designer Korolev, who had almost single-handedly commanded the Vostok and Voskhod projects, was deep in the design and construction of the second generation manned spacecraft, Soyuz, at the time of his sudden death in January 1966. It is believed by many that Soyuz was intended to serve as the heart of a Soviet manned lunar landing program in much the same way as the Apollo spacecraft assumed a similar role for the United States. Only later when the Soviet lunar effort was indefinitely postponed in the 1969-1970 time period was Soyuz converted to fulfill earth orbital/space missions.

Soyuz*represented the USSR's first true manned spaceship. In Vostok and Voskhod the cosmonauts were merely passengers in virtually automatic craft. Not only could Soyuz cosmonauts perform critical orbital maneuvers to complete a rendezvous and docking mission, but they could also carry out sophisticated earth and space science programs for periods up to thirty days. Since 1967 no less than 34 manned Soyuz missions have been flown (Soyuz 2, 20, and 34 were flown unmanned); and although there is some reason to believe that the USSR is currently developing a new reusable manned

---

* Soyuz means "union" in Russian.

spacecraft, Soyuz will probably remain the workhorse of the Soviet space program for several years to come.

This section will trace the initial (pre-Salyut) deployment of Soyuz from 1967-1970 and will also examine those later Soyuz missions which were not directly related to the Salyut space station. The Soyuz/Salyut program is covered in the following two sections.

Chapter 7

SOYUZ SPACECRAFT DESIGN

When Soviet space scientists first began to consider design requirements for the multi-man Soyuz, they were forced to restrict the weight and size of the spaceship to within the launch capabilities of the original Vostok booster equipment with an improved upperstage.[1] Although subsequent lunar mission Soyuz could be launched by the much larger Proton booster (at this time also still under development), the initial earth orbital Soyuz flights were planned before the Proton booster could be man-rated. As will be seen, this programmed evolution of launch vehicles was partially responsible for the final appearance of Soyuz.

In 1971 a book entitled *From Spaceships to Orbiting Stations* was published in the Soviet Union revealing for the first time many details of the manned Soyuz spacecraft. In the introduction to the design of Soyuz the following tasks were set forth as the prime objectives of this new generation spacecraft:[2]

o Extensive maneuvering in group flights in earth orbit and docking with other spacecraft

o Completion of prolonged space flights to study the effects of space factors on the human organism

o Implementation of an extensive program of scientific investigations in near space

o Investigations of the earth for practical purposes (weather forecasting, determination of water resources and the state of agricultural lands, observation of forest fires and the ice situation, solution of a number of problems of geodesy, geology, etc.)

o Development of new navigation and spacecraft control systems.

Just as the second generation US Gemini spacecraft relied upon experience gained with the single-seater Mercury capsule, so too was Soyuz a logical progression from Vostok/Voskhod. The idea of modulizing spacecraft for specific functions to minimize weight and space requirements was extended with the implementation of Soyuz. The roughly spherical command module of Vostok became a more spacious orbital workshop within which cosmonauts could rest, perform experiments, or transfer to other orbiting spacecraft. Also retained was a propulsion module to carry major life-support and propulsion equipment. Finally, inserted between these two modules was a third compartment, the Soyuz command module, in which the cosmonauts remained during launch, reentry, and orbital maneuvers.

The overall spacecraft weighs (depending upon the mission) approximately 6650 kg and is nearly 7.5 meters in length. In orbit the striking Soyuz resembles a majestic bird soaring effortlessly in flight (see Figures 1 and 2). This appearance is derived from the spacecraft body's roughly cylindrical shape with a maximum diameter of 2.7 m and wing-like solar panels stretching almost 8.4 m from tip to tip. Inside, the total habitable volume of the spacecraft is close to 9 m,^{3} almost twice that of Vostok.^{3}

Often described as resembling an automobile headlight,[4] the 2800 kg command module[5] is 2.2 m tall with a base diameter of 2.2 m and furnishes a habitable work space of approximately 4 m^3 (Figure 3 and 4). The change from the spherical reentry module of Vostok to the more aerodynamic bell

Figure 1   The Soyuz spacecraft in orbit as seen from the US
            spacecraft during the Apollo-Soyuz Test Project in
            1975   (Courtesy of NASA)

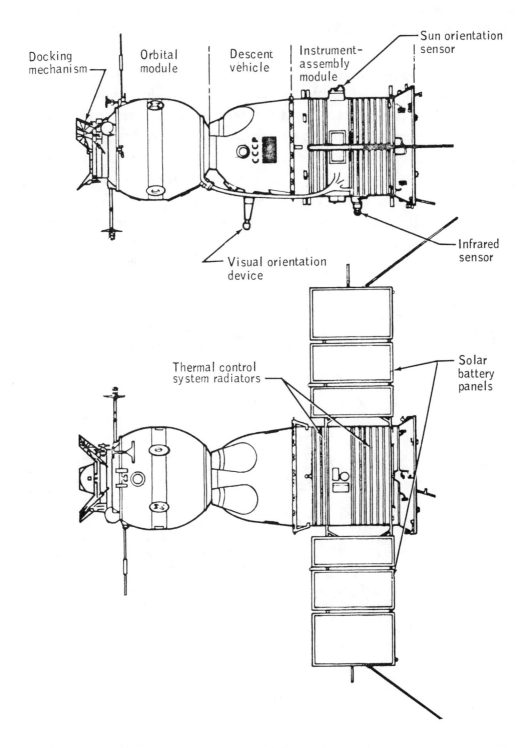

Figure 2   General design of the Soyuz spacecraft illustrating the modules of the Soviet spaceship. This is the Soyuz variant used for the Apollo-Soyuz Test Project.

shape of the Soyuz command module was necessitated by two considerations. First, the average 8- to 9-g load endured by cosmonauts returning from the Vostok flights was considered excessive for long-duration Soyuz earth orbital missions which would some day carry less conditioned space scientists as well as pilot-cosmonauts. These deceleration forces were minimized by the lifting properties of the Soyuz command module such that the reentry path was no longer truly ballistic, resulting also in a more accurate landing. Secondly, if Soyuz's design was intended to serve as well with a Soviet manned lunar mission*, then a controlled reentry at lunar return velocities was absolutely essential. In operation, g loads of only three to four are actually felt by returning cosmonauts on board Soyuz.[6]

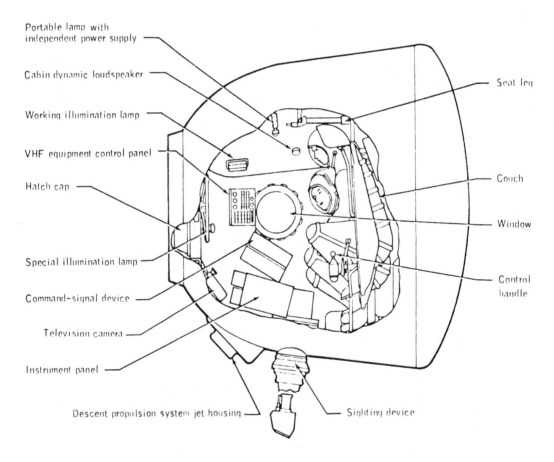

Figure 3   Layout of the Soyuz command (descent) module. This is the two-man version of Soyuz adopted after the fatal accident of Soyuz 11 in 1971

* See Volume 47, Science and Technology, Zond section.

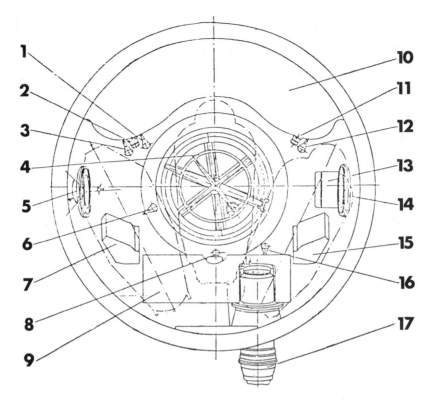

1. TV light
2. Light
3. TV light
4. Command module/Orbital module
   hatch wheel
5. Porthole
6. TV light
7. Sequencer control panel
8. TV camera
9. Main control panel
10. Parachute compartment
11. Light
12. TV light
13. Main radio control panel
14. Porthole
15. Sequencer control panel
16. TV light
17. Periscope for manual orientation

Figure 4   Top view of the Soyuz command module

Soyuz has been flown in one-man, two-man, and three-man variations. For safety reasons all Soyuz spacecraft since 1971 have only carried two men. Soyuz 1 and 3 carried only one cosmonaut on the first test flight in 1967 and 1968 (Soyuz 2 was unmanned). Although Soyuz 4 contained only one cosmonaut during launch, two of the three cosmonauts who had been launched on Soyuz 5 transferred in space to Soyuz 4 for the return to earth. Thus both Soyuz 4 and 5 were equipped for three cosmonauts. Only Soyuz 7, 10, and 11 flew again with three cosmonauts. During the reentry of Soyuz 11 in June of 1971 an accidental depressurization of the command module resulted in the death of all three cosmoanuts. In order to fit three men into the cramped compartment, space suits had been eliminated. Had the Soyuz 11 crew been wearing space suits, they would most probably not have perished as a result of the depressurization of the cabin. Hence all Soyuz flights since that time have been manned by two men with space suit capabilities while the third chair has been replaced by the space suit environmental control equipment. However, recent reports have indicated that a further redesign of Soyuz will soon allow three man crews to fly again.[7]

With the commander seated in the center couch the flight engineer is located on his right, and the space-suit support equipment (former research engineer's couch) is at his left. In front of him is the main Soyuz instrument panel as illustrated in Figures 5-7. Consisting mainly of only system readouts and visual displays this instrument reflects the basic lack of interaction between the cosmonaut and the spacecraft.[8] In general, Soyuz is an automatic space ferry which can be controlled by the crew when necessary, but most operations are preprogrammed into the ship's computers and are controlled by ground personnel. Among the more prominent instruments are a revolving earth globe similar to that used on Vostok to indicate spacecraft position, a television screen to allow visual observation of rendezvous and docking maneuvers, an automatic checklist readout to permit cosmonaut check of the programmed sequencer, and a large bank of system indication lights.[9]

Above this panel is a television camera (625 lines per frame with 25 frames/sec) which enables ground personnel to observe the crew members. There are usually three other cameras on board: one in the orbital module and two located on the outside hull for external viewing of the spacecraft systems and for use during rendezvous and docking.

Just below the right side of the main control panel is a circular window upon which is etched a grid and which is part of a periscopic system protruding from the command module. This optical viewer is used for orientation purposes and is similar to the Vzor device employed by the Vostok spacecraft. However, the use of a periscope for attitude control greatly restricts the versatility of the spacecraft by requiring a specific orientation with respect to the earth during navigation and maneuvering operations (Figure 8).

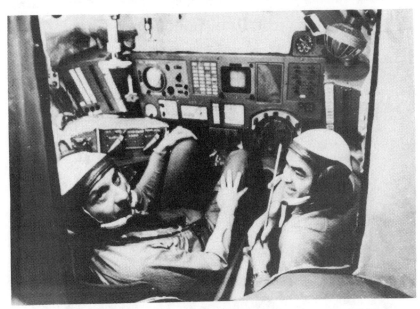

Figure 5   Interior view of Soyuz command module indicating control panel layout. Seated in this Soyuz trainer are US astronaut Thomas Stafford (left) and USSR cosmonaut Andriyan Nikolayev during training for the Apollo-Soyuz Test Project. The pointer in Nikolayev's hand is used to activate systems on the control panels in the cramped Soyuz compartment. (Courtesy of NASA)

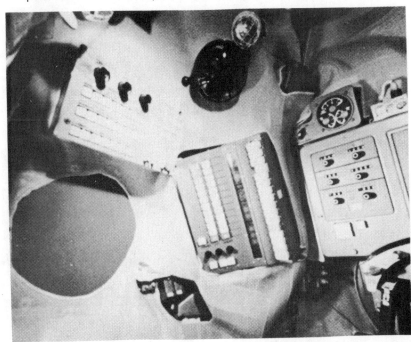

Figure 6   Flight engineer's side of main control panel and the Flight engineer's sequencer control panel. (Courtesy of NASA/USSR Academy of Sciences)

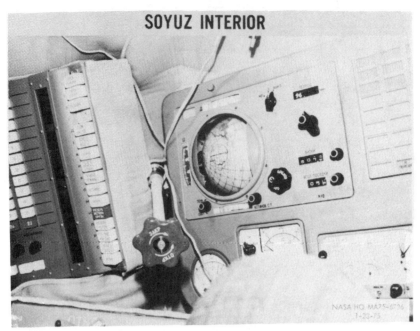

Figure 7   Command pilot's side of main control panel and command pilot's sequencer control panel. Note the globus instrument in the center of the picture used to indicate position of the spacecraft relative to the earth.   (Courtesy of NASA)

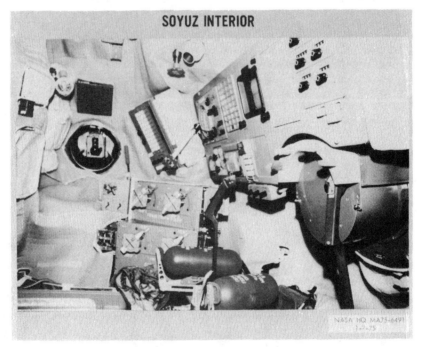

Figure 8   Closeup view of command module instrumentation. The two cylinders at the bottom of the picture are the attitude-control levers. (Courtesy of NASA)

To the left and right of the main control panel are the command system control panels used to switch on and off various primary and back-up systems and to monitor medical readouts. Below the commander's (left side) system control panel is the equipment for regulating the cosmonaut space suit environmental parameters. This system must protect the space-suited cosmonaut in the event of a loss of cabin atmosphere. Directly beneath the main instrument panel are two control levers resembling cylindrical bottles which activate the manual attitude and translational control systems (Figure 9). The attitude controller can provide rates of 0.5 deg/sec and 3.0 deg/sec in conjunction with spacecraft orientation or rendezvous with another spacecraft. The translation controller enables the commander to make fine adjustments in the speed of spacecraft during docking maneuvers.[10]

On either side of the cabin a single circular porthole permits cosmonaut inspection of companion spacecraft and celestial observations (Figure 10). By means of a sextant, cosmonauts can take a fix through these windows on stellar formations to determine Soyuz's exact position for navigational purposes. The remaining rear portion and sides of the command

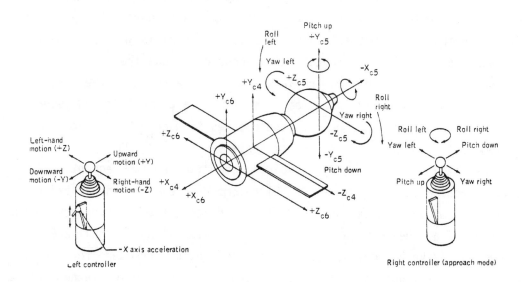

Figure 9   Soyuz spacecraft coordinate system for attitude-control system

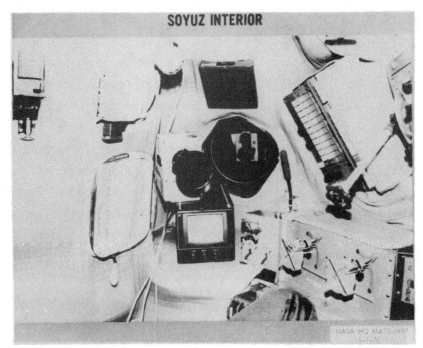

SOYUZ INTERIOR

Figure 10   Command pilot's side of Soyuz command module. Circu-
             lar object in center of the picture is the command
             pilot's porthole.   (Courtesy of NASA)

module are largely bare with only occasional lights, loudspeakers, or
storage bags attached to the fabric-covered walls (Figure 11). Near the
flight engineer's porthole (starboard side of cabin) is the radio communications control panel from which he can choose various frequencies for
communicating with ground controllers. Out of the reach of the cosmonauts
above the couch heads in a separate compartment are the main and reserve
parachutes while directly beneath the couches is much of the electronic
equipment for the spacecraft control systems.

     The bottom of the descent vehicle is comprised of two segments. The
outer circular shield is made of a high-temperature-resistant ablative
material similar to that used on Vostok to protect the crew members inside
the cabin from the searing heat of reentry. Also along the hull are positioned six 10-kg hydrogen peroxide reaction-control thrusters for use in
maintaining attitude and lift during reentry. After the module has passed
through this reentry stage and the parachutes have been deployed, the heat
shield of the command module drops away. Left exposed now are the nozzles

SOYUZ INTERIOR

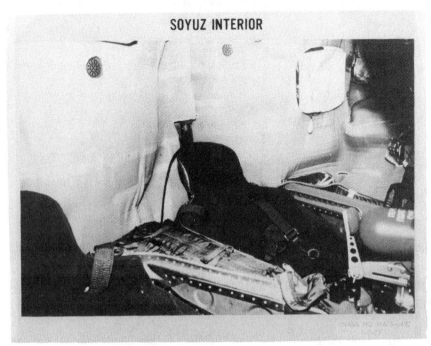

Figure 11   Fabric wall behind the cosmonaut couches hides the Soyuz
parachute system compartments. (Courtesy of NASA)

of the soft-landing system. These powerful solid fuel rockets are fired
when the command module is two meters above the ground, slowing the cabin
to a gentle landing.[11]

Directly above the cosmonauts as they recline in their couches during
lift-off is a large wheel which secures the hatch connecting the command
and orbital modules (Figure 12). The orbital module is basically spherical in shape (Figure 13) with a weight of 1200 kg and a diameter of 2.2 m.
The interior design of the orbital module is highly dependent upon the
mission of the Soyuz in question. For example, the orbital compartment
of Soyuz 6 was outfitted with an intricate welding device to test different welding techniques in the vacuum of space and the Soyuz 22 orbital
module was modified to carry and operate a multi-spectral East German
camera for a detailed earth-resources mission.

However, certain basic equipment is standard in most orbital module
variations (Figures 14 and 15). Food and water supplies and scientific
apparatus are stored here along with receptacles for waste collection.
A workbench equipped with the orbital module control panel provides space

Figure 12   The large wheel at the top of the Soyuz command module
activates the airtight hatch to the orbital module.
(Courtesy of NASA)

Figure 13   Soyuz orbital modules during fabrication. Note the
Soviet worker in the orbital module on the right.
(Courtesy of NASA)

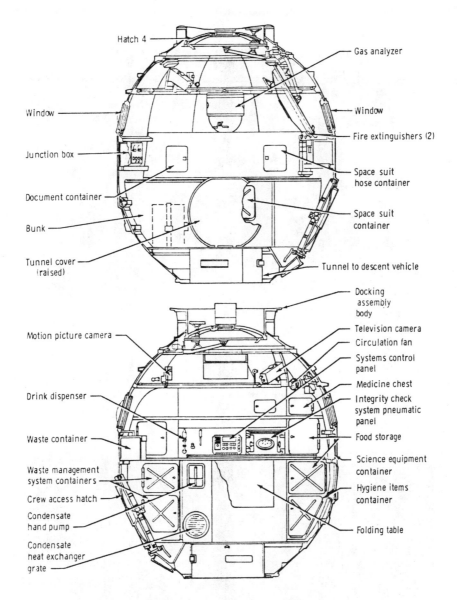

Figure 14 Interior layout of the Apollo-Soyuz Test
Project Soyuz orbital module

for conducting experiments and making notes. From this panel a cosmonaut
can control the module's lights, radio equipment, and the external Soyuz
television cameras. There is also at least one portable television camera
located within the orbital module to enable either ground controllers or
other crew members in the command module to observe experiments being performed. A rail runs around the cabin at the forward end to provide a
handhold for the weightless cosmonauts (Figure 16).

Figure 15   Cosmonauts Leonov and Kubasov at work in the Soyuz orbital
            module. The cosmonaut in the center is in the command module/
            orbital module hatch way.   (Courtesy of NASA)

Figure 16   Interior of orbital module. Note the porthole and handrails
            which ring the module.   (Courtesy of R.F. Gibbons)

The orbital module serves two additional functions. First, it is
used as recreation and sleeping quarters by Soviet crew members. This
roomier compartment is a welcome change from the rather cramped command
module. A couch and sleeping bags are provided to keep cosmonauts from
floating into the walls while asleep. Secondly, when specifically fitted
for the purpose, the orbital module acts as an airlock between the command
module and the vacuum of space or another spaceship.

During the Soyuz 4/5 mission in 1969 the spacecraft commanders of both
spaceships remained in their respective pressurized command modules while
the two other cosmonauts launched aboard Soyuz 5 entered and depressurized
the Soyuz 5 orbital module, exited the spacecraft through a hatch in the
lower portion of the module, floated to the orbital module of Soyuz 4, and
reversed the process, completing the first in-orbit crew transfer. Since
that time all crew transfers have taken place through a docking tunnel between two docked spacecraft without the need of depressurization and EVA.

Almost all Soyuz spacecraft have carried some type of docking mechanism at the extreme forward end of the orbital module for use when docking
with other Soyuz spacecraft or Salyut* space stations. The early versions
of Soyuz (through Soyuz 9) depended upon a simple probe-drogue technique
to ensure a rigid mechanical and electrical connection. Once docked there
was no method for removing the probe and drogue to allow internal transfer
of the crew. Since Soyuz 10, most Soyuz spacecraft have been equipped with
removable probes and drogues. A third type of docking mechanism was tested
during the Apollo-Soyuz Test Project (ASTP). All three docking systems
are described later in this book.

Taken together, the orbital and command modules form the habitable
compartments of the Soyuz spacecraft. This section of the spaceship is
approximately 5 m long and has a volume of 9 m^3. The exterior of these
modules is adorned with several operational systems and sensors. At the
forward end of the orbital module is the rendezvous and docking radar system. With the exception of the two ASTP-related missions (Soyuz 16 and
19) this system is characterized by a protruding cylindrical radome at a
90-degree angle from the large, girder-type rendezvous antenna. About
the midsection of the orbital module are circular antennae of the radio,
television, and telemetry systems. The most prominent feature of the command module is the cosmonaut periscope extending from beneath the interior

* Salyut means "salute."
                                    107

main control panel. Encompassing the aft end of the command module are almost 40 small T-shaped antennae of the telemetry system. An umbilical conduit runs from the aft end of the orbital module along the command module to the propulsion module, furnishing electrical and environmental connections.

The remaining compartment of the Soyuz spacecraft is the roughly 2.3-m long propulsion module. The propulsion module is a 2.2-m diameter cylinder with a flared base extending to 2.7 m for mating with the launch vehicle. Weighing close to 2650 kg, the propulsion module itself is partitioned into two sections. The forward section is pressurized and contains the major portion of the electronic gear for the electrical, environmental, attitude-control, communications and propulsions systems (Figures 17 and 18).

The power supply for Soyuz is derived from chemical batteries which are charged by the distinctive solar panel arrays extending from the sides of the propulsion module. Early versions of Soyuz employed two 4-segmented solar wings of approximately 3.6 m in length and 14 m^2 collecting area. Those used on Apollo/Soyuz were not quite three meters long and consisted of only three segments. These wings are folded up against the spacecraft body during launch to be extended once in orbit. Although the later 3-segmented solar panels are extended flat, Soyuz flown in the 1960s had slight bends at the segment joints, emphasizing their bird-like appearance. Long antennae of the communications and telemetry systems extend from the ends of these solar wings.

In order to maintain a full charge on the chemical batteries a solar sensing and attitude-control system keeps the active side of the solar panels trained toward the sun. Proper spacecraft orientation is usually accomplished by setting the Soyuz rotating about the Sun-Soyuz axis. The Soyuz 9 crew who remained in earth orbit in a Soyuz spacecraft longer than any other cosmonauts apparently experienced unpleasant sensations due to this spin stabilization.[12]

Although more complex as a result of an additional living compartment, the principle of operation of the basic life-support system for a Soyuz spacecraft is the same as that used on the Vostok and Voskhod spacecraft. Normal atmospheric conditions include temperature of 20° ± 3°C, cabin pressure of 710 to 850 mm Hg of which 140 to 200 mm Hg is due to oxygen content,

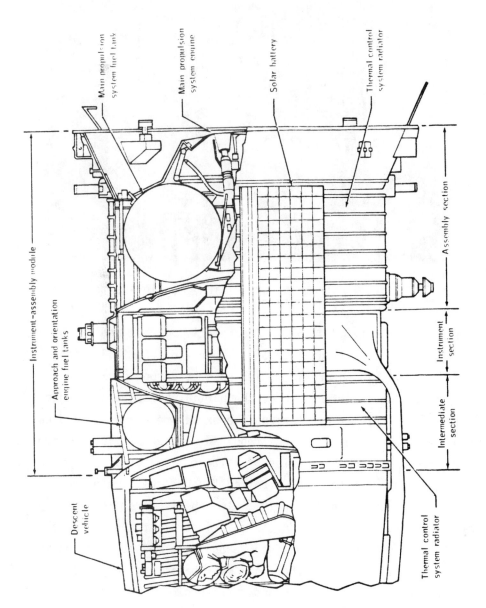

Figure 17 Soyuz instrument (propulsion) module - interior view

Main propulsion system fuel tank

Main propulsion system engine

Solar battery

Thermal control system radiator

Instrument-assembly module

Approach and orientation engine fuel tanks

Descent vehicle

Thermal control system radiator

Assembly section

Instrument section

Intermediate section

109

Figure 18   Soyuz instrument (propulsion) module - exterior view
             (Courtesy of R.F. Gibbons)

and relative humidity of 40-55%. The relative oxygen and carbon dioxide
content of the air is maintained by a superoxide chemical which liberates
oxygen and by lithium hydroxide which absorbs carbon dioxide. A special
sensing device constantly measures the partial pressure of oxygen, regulating the flow rate of air through the oxygen regeneration and carbon
dioxide absorbers to maintain the required atmospheric levels. Odors and
dust are removed through a series of filters. Spacecraft atmospheric
temperature and humidity are controlled through the single-loop series of
heat exchangers shown in Figure 19. Atmospheric parameters and system
operating status is provided on the main instrument control panel.[13]

The unpressurized aft end of the propulsion module contains the Soyuz
propulsion systems. In all there are four basic engine systems: (1) the
primary and back-up maneuvering and retro-engines, (2) the attitude-control
engines, (3) the vernier translation engines, and (4) the reentry attitude
engines of the command module. Located at the center rear of the propulsion module the 417-kg thrust hypergolic primary-propulsion engine burns

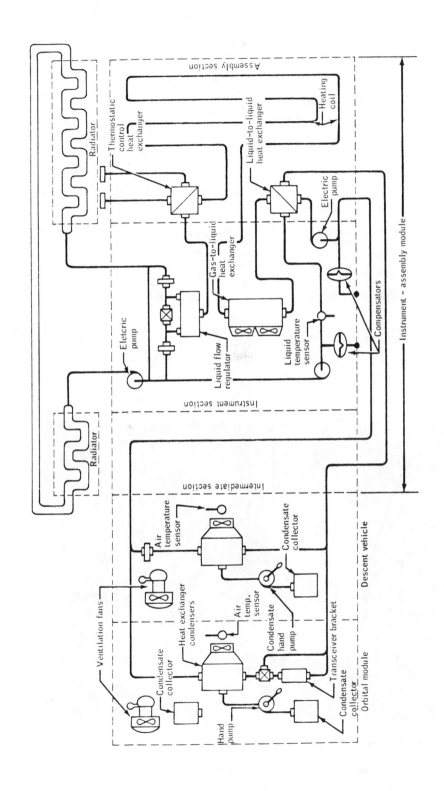

Figure 19   Partial Soyuz environmental control system schematic

111

turbine-fed nitric acid and unsymmetrical dimethylhdrazine.[14] An almost identical back-up engine utilizing two twin nozzles on either side of the main engine nozzle can achieve a thrust of 411 kg. In certain propulsion module configurations using either of these systems Soyuz can maneuver up to a 1300-km altitude and safely deorbit. Four spherical tanks hold the oxidizer and fuel supplies (Figure 20), although on earlier models of Soyuz (1-9) an additional torus tank was installed around the main engine exhausts (Figure 21).[15]

The reaction-control system includes a total of 18 (of which four are back-ups) 10-kg thrusters and 12 (of which four are back-ups) 1-kg thrusters. These hydrogen peroxide (H_2O_2) engines are used for translation and attitude control. The same hydrogen peroxide supply is also called upon to power the fuel and oxidizer turbines for the main propulsion system. Mention has already been made of the six additional 10-kg thrusters employed by the descent module during reentry.[16]

Attached to the aft exterior of the propulsion module is one of the two rendezvous antennae (Figure 22). It is identical to the one located at the forward end of the orbital module and permits rendezvous from

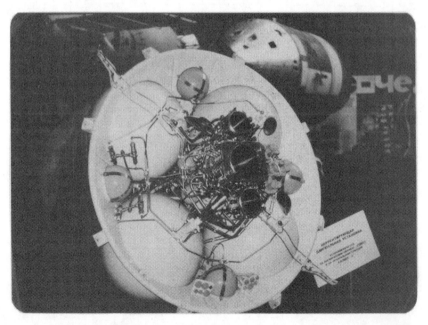

Figure 20   Soyuz propulsion system. The four large spherical tanks contain the primary and reserve propellants. This same system was used by the early Salyut space stations. (Courtesy of R.F. Gibbons)

Figure 21   Soyuz propulsion module with additional torus propellant
            tank, characteristic of pre-1971 Soyuz spacecraft.
            (Courtesy of R.F. Gibbons)

Figure 22   Rear view of Soyuz propulsion module indicating the
            location of the rendezvous antenna at the left
            (Courtesy of R.F. Gibbons)

either direction. Also positioned on the outer surface of the instrument module are the solar sensor of the solar array and the radiators of the environmental control system.

Figures 23 and 24 illustrate the final construction and check out of a typical Soyuz spacecraft. Each component must undergo vigorous temperature, vibration, and vacuum tests. When a spacecraft is completely assembled and has successfully passed all these preliminary tests, the next step calls for the horizontal mating of the spacecraft to the launch vehicle (Figure 25). Before this has been done, a protective shroud is placed over the spacecraft. The purpose of the shroud is two-fold. First, it protects the delicate Soyuz external fixtures (solar panels, etc.) from the severe atmospheric pressures and temperatures encountered during launch. Second, on top of the shroud is the emergency escape rocket system. In the event of a launch vehicle malfunction these powerful solid fuel escape rockets will lift the orbital and command modules away from the launch vehicle, and once clear of the rocket the command module will separate and parachute the crew to safety.[17]

Now the completed Soyuz and rocket assembly are transported by rail from the fabrication facility to the launch pad (Figures 26 and 27). Upon arrival at the pad, the entire launch vehicle is uprighted and enclosed by service gantries (Figures 28-29). Here the final system check-outs and fueling operations take place. This method of horizontal assembly and testing before transfer to the launching pad significantly reduces the turn-around time between launches at the same pad. Soviet officials have confirmed that a complete check and launch can be performed within 24 hours.

Finally, the spacecraft is ready for launch. About two hours before lift-off the crew enters the orbital module through the side-access hatch and then climbs down into the command module. At the moment of ignition the 20 main engine nozzles and 12 vernier steering engines on the 49.3 meter rocket come to life (Figure 30). After sufficient thrust has been built up (only slightly in excess of launch vehicle weight) the support clamps fall backward and the thundering vehicle inches upward, slowly at first and then much more rapidly. In a typical (Soyuz 19) launch the Soyuz spacecraft/launch vehicle combination reaches speeds of 500 m/sec,

Figure 23   Soyuz spacecraft undergoing final checkout before mating
            with its launch vehicle. Note thermal blankets covering
            the command and orbital modules. (Courtesy of NASA/USSR
            Academy of Sciences)

Figure 24   Soyuz checkout building at the Baikonur Cosmodrome. Note
            the Soyuz launch shrouds in a horizontal position at the
            side of each spacecraft.   (Courtesy of NASA)

Figure 25   Upper stages of the Soyuz launch vehicle before mating with
the lower stage. (Courtesy of NASA)

Figure 26   Exit of the assembled Soyuz spacecraft and launch vehicle
from the assembly building on its way to the launch pad.
Note the launch escape system at the top of the launch
shroud. (Courtesy of NASA/USSR Academy of Sciences)

Figure 27   Soyuz launch vehicle on the way to the launching pad
             (Courtesy of NASA/USSR Academy of Sciences)

Figure 28   Raising of the launch vehicle at the pad
             (Courtesy of NASA/USSR Academy of Sciences)

Figure 29   With the launch vehicle now in the vertical position the four
              gantries will be raised to support the vehicle and to provide
              access for ground support personnel and cosmonaut entry.
              (Courtesy of NASA/USSR Academy of Sciences)

Figure 30   Blast-off of a Soyuz rocket
              (Courtesy of NASA/USSR Academy of Sciences)

1.5 km/sec, and 6 km/sec after 70, 120, and 450 seconds, respectively.
As the rocket climbs and picks up speed, the vehicle begins to pitch over,
jettisoning the four strap-on stages when their fuel is exhausted. When
the spacecraft has passed the point of maximum aerodynamic strain, the
shroud separates and is carried away by the four released air brakes which
until this time had been folded against the shroud. Soon the central stage
drops away, followed by the ignition and subsequent separation of the second stage. Soyuz is now in orbit. Figure 31 shows the launch and landing
sequence of the Soyuz spacecraft.

Having entered orbit the Soyuz solar panels and antennae are deployed.
The cosmonaut crew busily checks all spacecraft systems and begins the
planned mission profile. The maximum length of stay in earth orbit by a
Soyuz alone is reported to be 30 days although the longest flight not associated with a Salyut space station was performed by the Soyuz 9 crew
for 18 days.

In order to maintain the proper attitude of the Soyuz vehicle with respect to the sun for the purpose of charging the batteries via the solar
panels, the Soviets employ a technique they call "solar warping". Using
the optical orientation system, one of the cosmonauts rolls the spacecraft
with the aid of the reaction-control system thrusters until the sun appears
in the cross-hairs of the periscope. A second maneuver now puts the Soyuz
into a rotation about the Sun-spaceship axis, resulting in direct illumination of the solar panels. The spacecraft remains in this attitude for
quite some time without additional use of the thrusters. If an orbital
maneuver is later desired, the spacecraft is rolled around until the earth
appears in the periscope, the gyroscopes are engaged, and the correction
is made. Upon completion of the maneuver, the spaceship is again placed
in the "solar warping" mode.[18]

When the mission has been completed or an emergency arises, Soyuz is
reoriented using automatic and visual systems to point the aft end in the
direction of flight. The main or back-up engines supply a retro-force for
approximately two and one-half minutes (depending upon altitude), then
shut down. As the spacecraft begins to drop out of orbit the orbital and
propulsion modules are jettisoned. Using the six thrusters and the natural
lift of the command module, the returning cosmonauts can guide their spacecraft through the intense heat of reentry. At an altitude of 10 km the

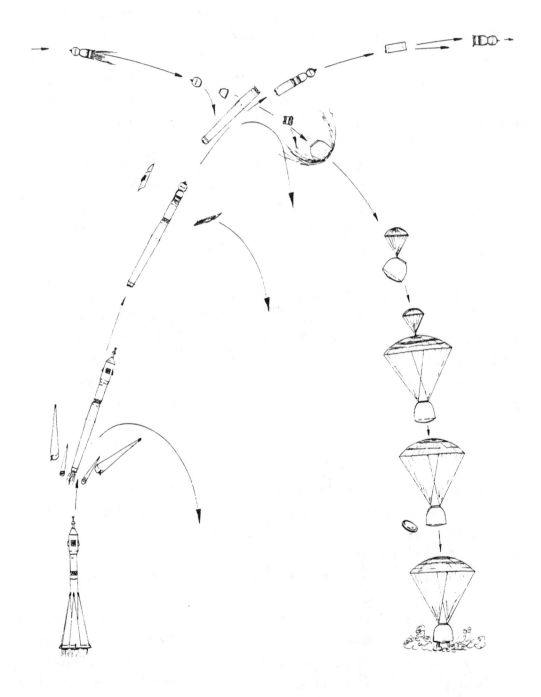

Figure 31   Launch and landing sequence of a Soyuz spacecraft
(Drawing by R.F. Gibbons)

120

parachute system is activated with the drogue chute deploying at 9 km and the single main chute deploying at 8 km. With the deployment of the main parachute the spent heat shield is jettisoned, exposing the solid fuel landing rockets which fire one meter above the ground. The descent capsule lands gently at less than 3 m/sec on Soviet territory.[19] (See Figures 32 and 33.)

The command module is equipped for either a land or water recovery. Although a land recovery is always planned, Soyuz 23 accidentally made the first Soviet manned water landing by coming down in a lake during a snow storm after an early return from an abortive flight to the Salyut 5 space station. In the event an emergency landing occurs in water or a desolate region, the Soyuz spacecraft carries portable emergency supplies. Included in these supplies are heat-insulating suits, a boat, gloves, foodstuffs of 4500 kilocalories, a medicine chest, radio equipment, a signal flare, a knife, and two sea life suits. The last item is essential to protect the cosmonauts if they are unlucky enough to land in chilly water (below 28°C).[20]

Figure 32   Descent of a returning Soyuz command module moments
             before landing. Note the rescue helicopter already
             at the scene. (Courtesy of NASA/USSR Academy of Sciences)

Figure 33   Touchdown of the Soyuz command module. The cloud of
             dust is formed by the last second firing of the solid
             fuel soft landing engines.
             (Courtesy of NASA/USSR Academy of Sciences)

Chapter 8

SOYUZ VARIATIONS

The Soyuz spacecraft has been the mainstay of the Soviet man-in-space program since 1967. As with any other product of high technology many improvements and alterations have been incorporated in Soyuz during the past twelve years. However, the procedure for classifying new Soyuz space-craft has been hampered by the varied missions undertaken by Soyuz. Ini-tially employed in earth orbit as a test and research vehicle (with an eye to lunar missions), Soyuz has also served as a space-station ferry and an earth-resources spaceship and in conjunction with the Apollo-Soyuz Test Project. Thus, there has been no simple evolution of Soyuz from 1967 to the present, and no convenient classification process has been accepted.

Since Soyuz is a modular spacecraft and it is these modules which are modified to fit a particular mission profile, a simple quick-identifying system for classification of Soyuz spacecraft can be formulated. A three-digit designator is attached to each Soyuz with each digit representing the configuration of the orbital, command, and propulsion modules, re-spectively.

Even though the orbital module interior is designed to meet each flight's needs, the compartment serves one of two general purposes: (1) an orbiting laboratory or (2) a crew transfer/supply module. In the case of the latter, four different arrangements are possible in the construction of the docking apparatus. Hence the type of <u>orbital module</u> is designated as follows:

0 - No orbital module present (all Zond spacecraft)

1 - No docking apparatus (research missions not primarily associ-ated with other spacecraft)

2 - Probe (active) docking collar with no internal crew transfer possible

3 - Drogue (passive) docking collar with no internal crew transfer possible

4 - Probe (active) docking collar with internal transfer hatch

5 - Androgynous* docking mechanism with internal transfer hatch.

Following the tragic accident of Soyuz 11, the Soyuz command module also underwent a major refabrication. As already noted the third cosmonaut couch was removed and replaced by a space suit life-support system for the remaining two cosmonauts. The command module classification below foresees the probable introduction of a new three-man command module in the near future:

0 - No command module

1 - Three-seat capacity with no space suits

2 - Two-seat capacity with space suits

3 - Three-seat capacity with space suits.

Finally the propulsion module, too, has undergone two significant modifications since the original design. After Soyuz 9 and the apparent abandonment of the Soviet manned lunar landing program, all propulsion modules on manned Soyuz flights have omitted the torus fuel tank. With the Soviet manned space program reoriented toward earth-orbital space stations (Salyut), the heavy solar wing now became a liability. Since the Soyuz spacecraft can operate for at least two days on chemical batteries alone, it was decided that ferry spacecraft intended to rendezvous and dock with Salyut stations could dispense with the solar panels. Once docked with Salyut, all Soyuz systems could be run off the Salyut electrical system which employed its own much larger solar wings. However, on recent solo missions (Soyuz 16, 19, and 22) Soyuz propulsion modules have retained the solar panels. Hence four types of propulsion modules can be classified (see also Figure 24):

1. Solar panels; toroidal fuel tank

2. No solar panels; toroidal fuel tank

3. Solar panels; no toroidal fuel tank

4. No solar panels; no toroidal fuel tank.

Therefore all recent Salyut ferries can be classified under this system as having used the 4/2/4 Soyuz spacecraft. During the Apollo-Soyuz

* A docking mechanism that permits docking with any other docking mechanism in the same system as opposed to a male/female type in which matching would be required.

Test Project, Leonov and Kubasov rode in a 5/2/3 Soyuz. One of the advantages of this classification system is the quick determination of primary mission profile by merely examining the Soyuz designator (see Figure 35). Figure 36 is a table of all Soyuz flights with the type of Soyuz spacecraft utilized.

In addition, Soyuz spacecraft used in different programs are easily identifiable. For instance, the Zond 4-8 circumlunar flights were all 0/1/3 Soyuz and are quickly distinguished by the absence of the orbital module. There is some thought that Kosmos 379, 398, and 434 were tests of a fully fueled propulsion module without either the orbital or command modules. If this is the case the spacecraft might be identified as a 0/0/1 Soyuz.

To remain a simple and workable classification system minor variations which do not significantly affect the performance of a module have been omitted. For instance, no distinction is made between the 3-segmented and the 4-segmented solar panels nor is the high-gain antenna on the Zond command modules specifically mentioned. Also, Soyuz 1-11 and

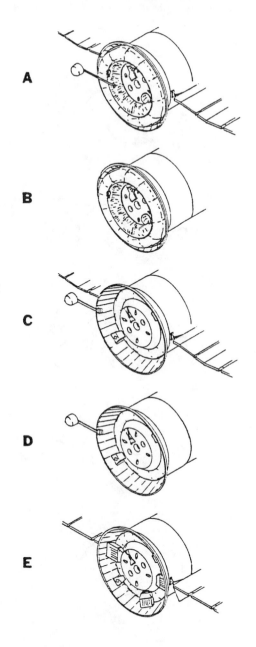

A. 1967: Soyuz 1
B. 1967: Kosmos 159 (Postulated)
C. 1971: Soyuz 10
D. 1973: Soyuz 12
E. 1974: Soyuz 16

Figure 34   Soyuz propulsion module variants (Drawings by R.F. Gibbons)

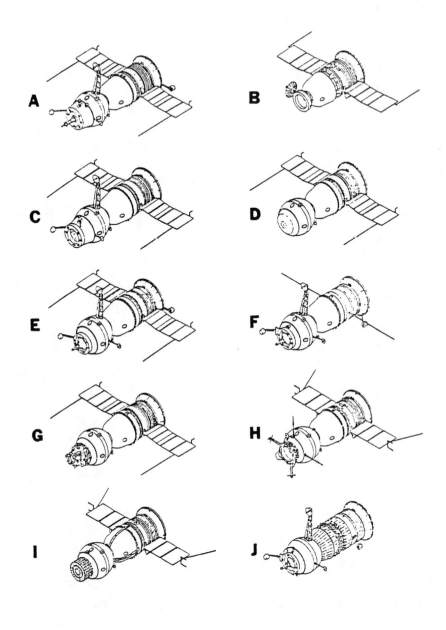

A. 1967: Soyuz 1 (Soyuz 2/1/1)
B. 1968: Circumlunar Zond
         (Soyuz 0/1/3)
C. 1968: Soyuz 2 (Soyuz 3/1/1)
D. 1969: Soyuz 6 (Soyuz 1/1/1)
E. 1971: Soyuz 10 (Soyuz 4/1/3)

F. 1973: Soyuz 12 (Soyuz 4/2/4)
G. 1973: Soyuz 13 (Soyuz 1/2/3)
H. 1974: Soyuz 16 (Soyuz 5/2/3)
I. 1976: Soyuz 22 (Soyuz 1/2/3)
J. 1978: Progress

Figure 35   Evolution of the Soyuz Spacecraft System
             (Drawings by R.F. Gibbons)

and Zond 4-8 are designated as utilizing the three-man capacity (no space suits) command module regardless of the actual number of cosmonauts on board.

SOYUZ PROGRAM VARIANTS

Soyuz	Type	Date Launched	Days in Orbit	Mission Performed
1	2/1/1	23 Apr 1967	1	First manned Soyuz test
2	3/1/1	25 Oct 1968	3	Unmanned target for Soyuz 3
3	2/1/1	26 Oct 1968	4	Rendezvous with Soyuz 3
4	2/1/1	14 Jan 1969	3	Rendezvous and docking with Soyuz 5
5	3/1/1	15 Jan 1969	3	Rendezvous and docking with Soyuz 4; EVA crew transfer
6	1/1/1	11 Oct 1969	5	Research and triple rendezvous with Soyuz 7 and 8
7	3/1/1[1]	12 Oct 1969	5	Triple rendezvous with Soyuz 6 and 8
8	2/1/1[1]	13 Oct 1969	5	Triple rendezvous with Soyuz 6 and 7
9	1/1/1	1 Jun 1970	18	Long-duration research
10	4/1/3	23 Apr 1971	2	Rendezvous and docking with Salyut 1; Crew transfer failed
11	4/1/3	6 Jun 1971	24	Rendezvous and docking with Salyut 1
12	4/2/4	27 Sep 1973	2	Test flight
13	1/2/3	18 Dec 1973	8	Research
14	4/2/4	3 Jul 1974	16	Rendezvous and docking with Salyut 3
15	4/2/4	26 Aug 1974	2	Failed to dock with Salyut 3
16	5/2/3	2 Dec 1974	6	ASTP test flight
17	4/2/4	10 Jan 1975	30	Rendezvous and docking with Salyut 4
18A	4/2/4	5 Apr 1975	0	Launch aborted
18B	4/2/4	24 May 1975	63	Rendezvous and docking with Salyut 4
19	5/2/3	15 Jul 1975	6	ASTP mission
20	4/2/4	17 Nov 1975	91	Rendezvous and docking with Salyut 4; unmanned long-duration test
21	4/2/4	6 Jul 1976	49	Rendezvous and docking with Salyut 5
22	1/2/3	15 Sep 1976	8	Research
23	4/2/4	14 Oct 1976	2	Failed to dock with Salyut 5
24	4/2/4	7 Feb 1977	18	Rendezvous and docking with Salyut 5
25	4/2/4	9 Oct 1977	2	Failed to dock with Salyut 6
26	4/2/4	10 Dec 1977	97[2]	Rendezvous and docking with Salyut 6
27	4/2/4	10 Jan 1978	5[2]	Rendezvous and docking with Salyut 6
28	4/2/4	2 Mar 1978	8	Rendezvous and docking with Salyut 6
29	4/2/4	15 Jun 1978	81	Rendezvous and docking with Salyut 6
30	4/2/4	27 Jun 1978	8	Rendezvous and docking with Salyut 6
31	4/2/4	26 Aug 1978	8	Rendezvous and docking with Salyut 6
32	4/2/4	25 Feb 1979	175[2]	Rendezvous and docking with Salyut 6
33	4/2/4	10 Apr 1979	2	Failed to dock with Salyut 6
34	4/2/4	6 Jun 1979	74	Unmanned Soyuz ferry to Salyut; used to return Soyuz 32 cosmonauts to earth

---

[1] *Soyuz 7 may have been a 2/1/1 Soyuz (active) while Soyuz 8 was a 3/1/1 Soyuz (passive)*

[2] *Represents length of mission, not duration of specific spacecraft. Soyuz 26 was aloft for 38 days, while the Soyuz 27 spacecraft was in orbit for 65 days and the Soyuz 32 spacecraft was in orbit for 108 days.*

Figure 36

Chapter 9

SOYUZ PRECURSOR FLIGHTS

Despite the death of Spacecraft Designer Korelov in January 1966, the construction of the first Soyuz vehicles continued. The lull of manned space flights between Voskhod 2 (March 1965) and Soyuz 1 (April 1967) was the longest in the fledgling Soviet manned-space program. As with Vostok and Voskhod before it, the Soyuz spacecraft had to undergo unmanned orbital tests before Soviet leaders would commit men to the new spaceship. In addition, when major spacecraft designs were later introduced, unmanned Soyuz were used to test the new systems. Figure 37 is a table of 24 known and suspected Soyuz-type vehicles which have flown under the Kosmos label.

The Soyuz era was inaugurated on 28 November 1966 when Kosmos 133 was launched into an earth orbit of 232 km by 181 km at an inclination of 51.8°. Although Vostok and Voskhod had all flown at 65° inclinations, the Kosmos 110 biological flight and other factors pointed to this as being the new inclination for manned flights. One reason for switching to a lower inclination was an increased payload capability while using the same launch vehicle which lifted Voskhod 1 and 2 into orbit. Even though some Soviet observation satellites also had used this orbital inclination in orbits which possessed apogees and perigees not significantly different from Kosmos 133 (Kosmos 120, 124, 127 for example), the Kosmos 133 flight was distinguished by two main features. The spacecraft was recovered after only two days and utilized communication frequencies reminiscent of Vostok and Voskhod.[21]

Slightly more than two months later on 7 February 1967, Kosmos 140 entered a 241 km by 170 km orbit at 51.7°. Again within two days the spacecraft was brought down and recovered. With two apparently successful tests of an as-yet-unknown new spacecraft, expectations of a resumption of manned

KOSMOS PROGRAM SOYUZ VARIANTS

Kosmos	Type	Date Launched	Days in Orbit	Mission Performed
133	2/1/1	28 Nov 1966	2	Test for manned flight
140	2/1/1	7 Feb 1967	2	Test for manned flight
146	0/1/3[1]	10 Mar 1967	8	"Lunar Zond" test flight
154	0/1/3[1]	8 Apr 1967	2	"Lunar Zond" test flight
159	0/0/2	16 May 1967	3032?	Propulsion Module test
186	2/1/1	27 Oct 1967	4	Automatic rendezvous and docking with Kosmos 188
188	3/1/1	30 Oct 1967	3	Automatic rendezvous and docking with Kosmos 186
212	2/1/1	14 Apr 1968	5	Automatic rendezvous and docking with Kosmos 213
213	3/1/1	15 Apr 1968	5	Automatic rendezvous and docking with Kosmos 212
238	2/1/1[2]	28 Aug 1968	4	Retest after Soyuz 1 accident
379	0/0/1[3]	24 Nov 1970		Possibly related to lunar propulsion systems test
398	0/0/1[3]	26 Feb 1971		Possibly related to lunar propulsion systems test
434	0/0/1[3]	12 Aug 1971		Possibly related to lunar propulsion systems test
496	4/2/3	26 Jun 1972	6	Retest after Soyuz 11 accident
573	4/2/4	15 Jun 1973	2	First test of 2-man CM and wingless ferry
613	4/2/4	30 Nov 1973	60	Long-duration test flight
638	5/2/3	3 Apr 1974	10	ASTP test flight
656	4/2/4 ?	27 May 1974	2	Possible test of automatic rendezvous and docking equipment
670	4/2/3 ?	6 Aug 1974	3	?
672	5/2/3	12 Aug 1974	6	ASTP test flight
772	4/2/3 ?	29 Sep 1975	3	? Similar to Kosmos 670
869	4/3/3 ?	29 Nov 1976	18	Possible test of 3-man command module and redesigned propulsion module
1001	4/3/3 ?	4 Apr 1978	11	Similar to Kosmos 869
1074	4/3/3 ?	31 Jan 1979	60	Similar to Kosmos 869

---

[1]*May have also carried toroidal fuel tank (0/1/) Soyuz).*

[2]*Kosmos 238 may have been a 3/1/1 Soyuz and the target for a Soyuz 2-3 type mission which was cancelled after Kosmos 238 was in orbit.*

[3]*Presence of solar panels in uncertain (possible 0/0/2 Soyuz).*

Figure 37

Soviet space flights rose.[22] Two months later, Cosmonaut Vladimir Komarov
rode Soyuz 1 into earth orbit in a flight that would have a tragically
different outcome.

Before Soyuz 1 was launched on 23 April 1967 two more Soyuz-type vehicles were placed in earth orbit. These were designated Kosmos 146 and
Kosmos 154. However, these flights are suspected of being more oriented
toward the Zond circumlunar program and are described in the companion
volume *(Volume 47, Science and Technology)* of this work.

After the crash of Soyuz 1 a moratorium was placed on further manned
and unmanned testing of Soyuz until a review of the accident could pinpoint
the cause or causes. The two-year hiatus between Voskhod 2 and Soyuz 1
had already set back the Soviet manned space program more than anticipated.
Another year or two-year delay might have proved disastrous to the program
and would almost certainly have forced concession of the moon race. However, by October 1967, the Soviets were confident enough of Soyuz to attempt
the world's first automatic rendezvous and docking. This procedure was subsequently carried out twice with Kosmos 186/188 and Kosmos 212/213. Due
to their importance, both of these group flights are discussed in detail
in the Operational Flights chapter of this section.

By August 1968 the Soviet Union had recovered from the death of Komarov
and had completed the necessary redesign of Soyuz. One unmanned flight
test of Soyuz was apparently deemed necessary before resuming the manned
programs. On 28 August 1968, Kosmos 238 was inserted into a nearly circular orbit of 219 km by 199 km at 51.7°. This time the spacecraft remained
aloft for four days before receiving the command for retro-fire. Although
little is known of the experiments conducted, Kosmos 238 must have fulfilled
its mission goals, for two months later on 25 and 26 October Soyuz 2 and
Soyuz 3 were launched to mark the new beginning of the second-generation
manned spacecraft.

An alternative explanation of the Kosmos 238 flight has been offered
which gives the spacecraft a more important purpose. It is possible that
Kosmos 238 in conjunction with a second manned Soyuz was the intended target for a rendezvous and docking mission of the Soyuz 2/3 type. If this
was indeed the case, one must assume that the manned Soyuz to follow was

Handbook of Soviet Lunar and Planetary Exploration, 1979

131

never launched due to a malfunction. Thus Kosmos 238 was brought down after four days when the manned Soyuz did not appear.

The years 1969 to 1970 saw the group flights of Soyuz 4/5 and Soyuz 6/7/8 and the long-duration flight of Soyuz 9. At this juncture, though, the USSR man-in-space program appears to have been redirected. All previous flights and press statements implicitly -- and at times explicitly -- seemed to point to a goal of landing men on the moon. But with the successes of Apollo and the failure of the Soviet "superbooster" (discussed elsewhere in this book) Soviet leaders opted, at least temporarily, for the development of short-term and long-term manned space stations. The first flights of the Soyuz-Salyut program occurred in the spring of 1971.

However, in the space of three months in late 1970 and 1971 two Kosmos satellites performed missions of unknown purposes which have been linked to the testing of propulsion systems for manned lunar explorations. These two spacecraft, Kosmos 379 and 398 along with Kosmos 434 launched in August 1971 are discussed with the Zond circumlunar missions in *Volume 47, Science and Technology*.*

Tragedy again struck the USSR on the second Salyut mission when the three returning cosmonauts of Soyuz 11 perished as their command module underwent an accidental depressurization. Since all command modules up to that time had not provided for the wearing of space suits during reentry, the three brave Soviets died. A second grounding of all manned space flights, until September 1973, ensued. During the 27-month interim two more unmanned Soyuz were tested under the guise of the Kosmos program to evaluate two modifications of the spacecraft.

On 26 June 1972 almost exactly one year after the Soyuz 11 accident, Kosmos 496 streaked into an orbit of 342 km by 195 km with all the earmarks of a test of the new command module capable of supporting two cosmonauts with full space suit gear.[23] The Soviets later confirmed the purpose of this mission during the Apollo-Soyuz Test Project preparations.[24] It is also possible that Kosmos 496 was designed to requalify Soyuz in conjunction with a new Soyuz-Salyut mission planned for July-August of that year. However, this is largely unconfirmed.[25] Kosmos 496 reentered the earth's atmosphere and was recovered after a flight of six days.

Handbook of Soviet Lunar and Planetary Exploration, 1979

One year later in a dress rehearsal for the Soyuz 12 flight scheduled for launch in three months a new wingless version of Soyuz was tested by Kosmos 573. Launched on 15 June 1973 into an orbit of 329 km by 196 km, Kosmos 573 employed the new two-man command module and a new propulsion module sans solar panels. This new variant of Soyuz was designed to serve solely as a Salyut ferry vehicle. Following a flight of two days (the estimated lifetime of a battery-powered Soyuz) Kosmos 573 returned to earth.

With a successful manned test of Soyuz by the Soyuz 12 crew in September of 1973, Soviet scientists again eyed the potentials of extended Salyut space missions. Kosmos 613, using a ferry version of Soyuz, flew an unprecedented 60-day mission between November 1973 and January 1974 in a powered-down simulated test of the reliability and survivability of a Soyuz vehicle attached to a Salyut space station. This then was a precursor to the Soyuz 18B/Salyut 4 flight flown a year and a half later. The initial orbital parameters were apogee of 295 km and perigee of 195 km, but these were altered six days later to 396 km by 255 km. On 29 January 1974, after reactivation a few days earlier, Kosmos 613 was successfully guided to a touchdown on Soviet territory.[26]

In April and August of 1974 two unmanned Soyuz spacecraft were flown to test new equipment on the scheduled Apollo-Soyuz Test Project for July 1975. Kosmos 638 and Kosmos 672 were placed in initial 325-km-by-195-km and 239-km-by-198-km orbits on 3 April and 12 August, respectively. Both spacecraft carried the new androgynous docking device to be used during ASTP. Both craft later maneuvered close to the established ASTP orbital parameters. Kosmos 638 was brought down after ten days in space, whereas Kosmos 672 remained aloft for only six days.[27]

Between the flights of Kosmos 638 and Kosmos 672 two other unmanned Soyuz spacecraft flew under the Kosmos label, but the purposes of these missions is less certain. On 27 May 1974, Kosmos 656 entered an earth orbit of 354 km by 194 km. Kosmos 656 utilized a wingless ferry version of Soyuz and remained in space for two days. Coming approximately one month before Soyuz 14 and three months before Soyuz 15 which were both connected with Salyut 3 space station, Kosmos 656 may have been testing new systems for these flights. Kenneth Gatland has suggested that the new automatic docking system which subsequently failed on Soyuz 15 may have been the object of this unmanned Soyuz.[28]

Kosmos 670 launched on 6 August 1974 less than a week before Kosmos
672 was even more enigmatic. Although initially believed to be a reconnaissance satellite, radar signature analysis clearly identified the spacecraft as a Soyuz vehicle. Not only were the solar panels present, but also
the orbital inclination of 50.6° was used for the very first time by the
Soyuz launch vehicle. Although at a loss to classify specifically the
Kosmos 670 mission, Smith has pointed out that this inclination was similar to the one which had been predicted for the Soviet "superbooster". If
there is indeed a connection, then this would imply that the large G-1
launcher is still under development--a fact which is not otherwise substantiated.[29]

The next unmanned Soyuz spacecraft did not fly until 29 September 1975
under the name of Kosmos 772. In an orbit of 320 km by 201 km at an inclination of 51.8° this mission exhibited characteristics similar to Kosmos
670. Although Kosmos 772 remained aloft for three days, the presence or
absence of solar panels has yet to be positively confirmed in the public
domain. Thus, Kosmos 772 may have been a repeat of the Kosmos 670 mission
or may have been used for testing a new three-day battery-powered Soyuz
ferry.[30]

The next suspected Soyuz in the Kosmos program came during 29 November
and 17 December 1976 with the 18-day flight of Kosmos 869. This spacecraft
equipped with solar panels maneuvered extensively from 293 km by 198 km to
390 km by 268 km to 309 km by 299 km. In addition, some Western experts
believe Kosmos 869 to be the forerunner of a return to the three-man Soyuz
spacecraft. Kosmos 869 was one of the longest-duration full Soyuz flown
in the Kosmos program, exceeded only by the 60-day flights of Kosmos 613
and Kosmos 1074. Although Soviet spokesman have definitely said a return
to three-man crews is forthcoming, whether Kosmos 869 is in fact the first
test of such a vehicle remains to be seen.[31]

In 1978 and 1979 the most recent unmanned Soyuz spacecraft in the
Kosmos program were flown. Both missions pursued flight profiles highly
reminiscent of Kosmos 869. The first, Kosmos 1001, was launched on 4 April
1978 into an orbit of 228 km by 199 km at 51.6°. Two days later the orbit
had been altered to 228 km by 196 km which in turn was followed by a third
maneuver which occurred before 11 April raising the spacecraft's apogee

and perigee to 318 km and 307 km, respectively. Four days later on 15 April Kosmos 1001 was deorbited and recovered on Soviet territory after a mission duration of 11 days.

Approximately ten months later on 31 January 1979, Kosmos 1074 was launched on a similar, but much longer space flight. With initial orbital parameters (238 km by 195 km) quite similar to those of Kosmos 1001, Kosmos 1074 was flying, within eight days, in an orbit of 383 km by 364 km after a brief stay in an intermediate orbit of 319 km by 310 km. Not until 1 April 1979 after a mission lasting 60 days was Kosmos 1074 brought back to earth and recovered.

Thus since 1974 there have been five unmanned Soyuz test flights which as yet cannot be assigned to specific Soyuz improvements. The uncharacteristically long test period may be related to developmental problems or to a connection with other new Salyut-associated systems which have not yet come on line. With the acknowledged Soviet desire to refit Soyuz spacecraft with a three-man capacity and the recent innovations in the Salyut propulsion system (a Soyuz derivative) a new model Soyuz for use during the coming decade can be expected to debut in 1980.*

---

* Publication Note. While this manuscript was being prepared for publication, the much heralded modified Soyuz finally appeared. Launched
on 16 December 1979 and designated Soyuz T-1 (transport) the unmanned
spacecraft rendezvoused and docked with the unoccupied Salyut 6 space
station for a mission lasting 100 days. Soviet officials also confirmed
the adoption of a new pressure-fed main propulsion system similar to
that of Salyut 6 along with the reintroduction of Soyuz solar panels
for Salyut missions. See also page 373.

Chapter 10

SOYUZ OPERATIONAL FLIGHTS

With the spectacular triumphs of Voskhod 1 and 2 the world was bewildered when month after month passed without further fantastic feats by what had been billed as the second-generation Soviet spaceship. In retrospect, of course, it is clear that Voskhod was not the long-awaited orbital ship the West had been led to expect. While the Americans planned and completed the ten-flight Gemini program, the Soviets had worked furiously to ready Soyuz, always with an eye on the moon.

To those few dedicated Soviet space watchers who studied such events the flights of Kosmos 133 and Kosmos 140 (and to an extent Kosmos 146 and 154) signaled the imminent resumption of cosmonauts in space. Although saddened by the deaths of their comrades of the stars, Grissom, White, and Chaffee, in the Apollo 1 fire in January 1967, Soviet space program managers must have been delighted to see an eighteen-to-twenty-four month delay in the ambitious Apollo program. This meant that the Soviet Union was the odds on favorite to win the moon race without yet even having flown a Soyuz manned spacecraft. Tragically, this elation was dashed in the span of the 27-hour flight of Soyuz 1.

Figure 38 is a table of the manned research Soyuz space flights not associated with the Salyut space station. Kosmos 186, 188, 212, and 213 have been included in this group by virtue of their great significance in the development of the Soyuz program.

SOYUZ 1

By April 1967 Moscow was swarming with rumors of impending space spectaculars. The majority of these rumors centered around a dual launch of spacecraft coupled with rendezvous, docking, and a crew exchange involving as many as six cosmonauts.[32] April 12th, the sixth anniversary

SOYUZ (NON-SALYUT) SUMMARY

Designator	Date Launched	Days in Orbit	Initial Orbit (km)	Crew
Soyuz 1	23 Apr 1967	1	224 by 201	Komarov
Kosmos 186	27 Oct 1967	4	235 by 209	Unmanned
Kosmos 188	30 Oct 1967	3	276 by 200	Unmanned
Kosmos 212	14 Apr 1968	5	239 by 210	Unmanned
Kosmos 213	15 Apr 1968	5	291 by 205	Unmanned
Soyuz 2	25 Oct 1968	3	224 by 185	Unmanned
Soyuz 3	26 Oct 1968	4	225 by 205	Beregovoi
Soyuz 4	14 Jan 1969	3	225 by 173	Shatalov (commander; returned with addition of Yeliseyev and Khrunov
Soyuz 5	15 Jan 1969	3	230 by 200	Volynov (commander) Khrunov (flight engineer) Yeliseyev (technical scientist)
Soyuz 6	11 Oct 1969	5	223 by 186	Shonin (commander) Kubasov (flight engineer)
Soyuz 7	12 Oct 1969	5	226 by 207	Filipchenko (commander) Volkov (flight engineer) Gorbatko (research engineer)
Soyuz 8	13 Oct 1969	5	223 by 205	Shatalov (commander) Yeliseyev (technical scientist)
Soyuz 9	1 Jun 1970	18	220 by 207	Nikolayev (commander) Sevast'yanov (flight engineer)
Soyuz 12	27 Sep 1973	2	249 by 194	Lazarev (commander) Makarov (flight engineer)
Soyuz 13	18 Dec 1973	8	246 by 188	Klimuk (commander) Lebedev (flight engineer)
Soyuz 16	2 Dec 1974	6	190 by 137 ?	Filipchenko (commander) Rukavishnikov (flight engineer)
Soyuz 19	15 Jul 1975	6	221 by 186	Leonov (commander) Kubasov (flight engineer)
Soyuz 22	15 Sep 1976	8	281 by 200	Bykovsky (commander) Aksenov (flight engineer)

Figure 38

of the world's first manned space flight by Cosmonaut Yuri Gagarin, came and went without a launch, but rumors of a new flight were reaching fever pitch. On that date an East Berlin radio broadcast stated, "New Soviet flights, after a two-year delay will accomplish all the elements attained by the 12 costly Gemini flights in a single step, and penetrate more deeply into space."[33]

Finally, on 23 April Soyuz 1 carrying Cosmonaut Vladimir Milchailovich Komarov, the first cosmonaut ever to fly twice in space, lifted off a launching pad at Baikonur at 0335 hr Moscow time. Resting on top of a modified rocket of the type used by Gagarin, the 6450-kg spacecraft swiftly climbed into the early morning sky. Komarov must have been excited as the launch shroud fell away, and he could once again admire the beauty and serenity of space. Soon the last stage of the launch vehicle shut down and fell away, leaving Soyuz 1 in an orbit of 224 km by 201 km at the predicted new orbital inclination of 51.7°.

Approximately one hour after Komarov had entered the weightless environment of space, the launching of Soyuz 1 was revealed to the rest of the world.[34] The objectives of the flight were listed as:

- o Testing of the new piloted spacecraft
- o Operation of systems and construction elements of space ship in conditions of space flight
- o Carrying out extended scientific and physio-technical experiments and investigations in conditions of space flight
- o Continuation of medico-biological investigations and study of the of various space flight factors on the human organism.[35]

The sparsity of details did not discourage those expecting the promised space spectacular. The initial announcements released during the Vostok 3 and Vostok 5 missions did not hint of the subsequent launchings of Vostok 4 and Vostok 6, respectively. In fact, several other observations pointed to the launch of the oft-mentioned Soyuz 2. Soyuz had been billed as a multi-man spacecraft, yet only one cosmonaut was now on board. Would it not seem logical that other cosmonauts from a second Soyuz might join him? The orbit of Soyuz 1 was the most circular of any Soviet manned flight to that date. Thus a rendezvous and docking procedure would be simplified. For the first time a new spacecraft series had been designated by the Soviets as "No. 1". Although Vostok 1 and Voskhod 1 are

standard terms in the Western world, they are referred to as simply
"Vostok" and "Voskhod" by the Soviets themselves. Since Komarov was flying Soyuz 1, could it not be possible that a Soyuz 2 was not far behind?[36]

Finally, the term Soyuz itself was interpreted as suggesting a rendezvous and docking effort. In Russian "Soyuz" means "union". Although many
have attributed the obvious connotation to a "union in space" between two
or more spacecraft, it has been suggested that "Soyuz" could also refer to
the Soviet Union in much the same way as "Vostok" could be translated "east"
and "Voskhod" could be translated "sunrise" (perhaps not a too disguised
reference to "east" since Voskhod was merely a Vostok variation).

The flight of Komarov and Soyuz 1 continued, but the sparse and irregu-
lar updates were uncharacteristic of the importance of a space mission
which had been two years in the making. In retrospect, two motives could
be attributed to this apparent lack of Soviet propaganda: The Soviets were
playing down the initial hours of the flight to contrast with the announcement of a second Soyuz and docking; or Soyuz 1 was already in trouble. After
the third and fifth revolutions, Komarov was said to be feeling well and
cheerful and to be successfully implementing the planned program. Between
1330 and 2230 hr Moscow time Soyuz 1 was out of direct radio contact with
Soviet territory. During this period Komarov is said to have rested as
was the practice of previous cosmonauts.[37]

At 2230 hr on 23 April Komarov once again came over the radio horizon.
Again a short report indicated that all was going well and gave no indication when the flight might end. As Soyuz 1 flew over the Baikonur cosmodrome shortly after midnight Moscow time reporters waited anxiously for
word of the launch of Soyuz 2. It never came. Komarov continued in orbit
completing his sixteenth and seventeenth revolutions. Then there was silence. Twelve hours later came the shocking news.

> As informed on the 23rd of April 1967 a new spaceship 'Soyuz-1' was
> placed into earth orbit in the Soviet Union for the purpose of the
> flight tests. The ship was piloted by the pilot cosmonaut of USSR,
> Hero of the Soviet Union, Col. Vladimir Mikhailovich Komarov.
>
> During the test flight, which continued more than twenty four hours,
> V.M. Komarov fully implemented the planned program of operating the
> new ship's systems, and also the planned scientific experiments.
>
> During the flight, Pilot Cosmonaut V.M. Komarov maneuvered the space-
> ship, tested its various systems in different conditions and was
> giving a qualified estimate of the new ship's technical data.

On the 24th of April, when the test program was completed, it was suggested that he could finish the flight and land.

After implementation of all the operations, corrected with transition to landing conditions, the spaceship safely passed the most difficult and responsible branch of braking in dense layers of the atmosphere and totally dissipated the orbital velocity.

However, during the opening of the main parachute canopy at altitude of 7 km, according to preliminary data, as a result of twisting of the top cord of the parachute, the spaceship descended at high velocity, which was the cause of death of V.M. Komarov.

The untimely death of the outstanding spaceman, test-engineer of spaceships, Vladimir Mikhailovich Komarov is a great loss for the whole Soviet people.

By his work in the sphere of testing spaceships Vladimir Mikhailovich Komarov has given a priceless contribution to development and perfecting of space technology.[38]

The Soyuz descent capsule has but a single large main parachute. With the parachute not being fully deployed the cabin fell to earth like a speeding projectile. Most estimates put the impact velocity at between 450 and 550 km/h with the landfall near Orenburg in the Urals.[39]

Death in space. Few talked openly about it, but both the US and USSR knew that specter would cast its unwelcome shadow some day. The deaths of the three American astronauts three months earlier was a shock, but had occurred during a ground test and thus was viewed differently. There was a double irony in the death of Komarov. When Grissom, White, and Chaffee had perished in the Apollo fire, the Soviets were sympathetic, but did not hesitate to place the blame of the accident on the haste of the US program. Soviet space scientists had been planning this flight for over two years, only to see it fail in the final minutes.[40]

Secondly, there was an erie coincidence in the fatalities in both the American and Soviet space programs on the inauguration of new-generation spacecraft which were intended to bring the dream of landing men on the moon nearer. Both manned programs would remain idle until October 1968, when they both resumed within two weeks of one another.

Surprisingly enough, the cause of Komarov's death is still hotly debated.[41] Almost immediately after the Soviet announcement of the fate of Soyuz 1 observers from around the world refused to accept the official story. Most would not believe the cause could be as simple as a tangled parachute line. The tight security of the Soviet space program which in the past had been credited with surprising "space spectaculars" was now responsible for the biggest wave of disbelief since the cosmonaut "death" stories of the early 'sixties.

The most prevalent version of the demise of Komarov appearing immediately after the accident centered around Komarov's inability to control the attitude of Soyuz 1 on the last three orbits. Such causes as a stuck thruster or break down in spacecraft stabilization equipment have been cited. In addition, the following theories have also appeared: An antenna failed to deploy, hindering communications with the ground; solar panels failed to deploy which resulted in an attempt to free them by centrifugal force during which time the spacecraft control was lost; one solar panel did not deploy, reducing power and interfering with attitude-thruster operation; design of the computer systems was inadequate to handle needed data for orientation systems. In general, most writers on the subject agree that Soyuz 1 was tumbling either prior to or immediately after retro-fire. This unstabilized configuration, therefore, caused the parachute lines to tangle, resulting in the fatal crash.[42]

One report proposes that reentry at the wrong angle partially welded the parachute compartment hatch shut until the spacecraft was at too low an altitude.[43] Even Komarov's previous heart condition was suggested to have been partly to blame for his death.[44]

In 1972 and 1975 two reports surfaced concerning "tapes" of the Soyuz 1 mission which purported to show that serious problems had arisen before reentry and that Komarov knew he was probably going to die.[45] The authenticity of these tapes, however, is highly suspect. In them Komarov is supposed to have had heart-rending conversations with his wife and Premier Kosygin before attempting the hopeless reentry.

In his book *Soviet Space Exploration: The First Decade,* William Shelton describes how many of the rumors pertaining to spacecraft troubles prior to reentry were a result of a "faulty connection and a misunderstanding" between Joe Zygielbaum and UPI*. Shelton had suggested UPI contact Zygielbaum after the latter had intercepted a Radio Moscow broadcast. Shelton states that by the time the story hit the wire services some of Zygielbaum's own opinions and speculations had been transformed into irrefutable facts.

---

* United Press International

To combat what the Soviets probably saw as a situation quickly getting out of hand, Yuri Gagarin himself came out to deny the charges of anything other than the unfortunate parachute accident originally announced by Tass.[46] Gagarin stated that he had been at the Baikonur cosmodrome during the flight of Soyuz 1 and had many times heard the communications between Komarov and ground controllers. Gagarin reiterated that no hint of malfunction arose until the spacecraft had already passed through reentry.

In the final analysis, all the circumstances and events surrounding the flight of Soyuz 1 are still not known. The persistent rumors concerning Komarov's death are probably more symptomatic of the distrust held for the Soviet Union than for their own validity. However, the Soviets have almost certainly been less than candid themselves. Instead of the usual landing after the 16th or 17th orbits Komarov had attempted to land on the 18th orbit - a highly unusual maneuver. A minimum two-day flight was expected, following the pattern set by Kosmos 133 and 140. Although Soviet bureaucracy may account for the 12-hour delay in the announcement of Komarov's fate, the refusal to release any details of the accident other than to say the parachute lines became tangled is certainly unsatisfactory.

KOSMOS 186 and 188

Following the Soyuz 1 tragedy the Soviet man-in-space program suffered an extensive and detailed review. During this period all manned flights were postponed while the design and safety of the Soyuz spacecraft could be reaffirmed. Apparently, however, Soviet space scientists and political leaders were confident that Soyuz would once again carry cosmonauts through space. In the meanwhile, all effort was shifted to the unmanned testing of the basic Soyuz hardware. Six years had passed since the historic flight of Gagarin aboard Vostok 1, and the USSR had not exhibited a manned spacecraft capable of orbital maneuvers, let alone practicing the vital procedure of rendezvous. If the Soviets still held plans to land men on the moon in the 1969-1970 time period, they were in the position of being knocked out of the race unless they could develop and test the necessary equipment while awaiting the report on Soyuz 1.

A scant six months after the death of Komarov, a Soyuz spacecraft under the guise of a Kosmos satellite was again in space. Named Kosmos

186, the spacecraft was launched on 27 October 1967 and entered an initial orbit of 235 km by 209 km at 51.7°. The orbital parameters and communication frequency of 20.008 Mhz immediately identified the craft as one related to the manned space program.

During the next three days Kosmos 186 continued to circle the earth approximately every 89 minutes. By 30 October the spacecraft's orbit had been altered to 260 km by 180 km. Shortly after 1000 hr Moscow time on 30 October Kosmos 188 roared off a launching pad at Baikonur to begin a chase which would culminate, more than half-way around the earth, in the world's first automatic rendezvous and docking.[47]

At the time of Kosmos 188's orbital insertion at 276 km by 200 km the two spacecraft were only 24 km apart with a relative velocity of 90 km/hr-- truly a remarkable accomplishment. Immediately Kosmos 186 assumed the "active" role in searching out and closing in on Kosmos 188. A search radar system on both spacecraft measured the relative distance between them and the rates of change of this distance. Up to a distance of 300 meters the main propulsion engine and the larger thrusters were utilized. During the remaining distance only the low-thrust engines were fired to ensure small changes in relative velocities and to prevent a hard collision.

Every time Kosmos 186 made an attitude maneuver Kosmos 188 would respond with a complimentary movement to align the craft as an aid to rendezvous. By 1220 hr with Kosmos 188 still on its first orbit the spacecraft inched closer together and finally docked. The relative velocity of the vehicles at contact was only 10-50 cm/sec. As the joined pair reentered Soviet communication regions the docked spacecraft were shown to the delighted Soviet ground controllers via the external television cameras (Figure 39).

For 3.5 hours the spacecraft remained docked. During this time mechanical and electrical connections between the two spacecraft were checked and rechecked. Then at 1550 hr while again over Soviet territory a command was given to separate the pair. With the aid of a camera on Kosmos 186, the Soviet television audience watched as the two spaceships gracefully and quickly drifted apart.

Almost a day later at 1120 hr on 31 October Kosmos 186 was safely guided through the reentry procedure to a soft landing in the Soviet Union after completing 65 revolutions about the earth. Two days later on 2 November Kosmos 188 followed suit. Kosmos 186 and 188 had not only demonstrated the feasibility of automatic rendezvous and docking, but also had successfully retested those systems which had plagued Komarov in Soyuz 1.

In the propaganda released following the achievement of Kosmos 186 and 188, Soviet emphasis was placed on the automatic versus manned aspect of the mission and on the potential uses of such a system in remotely constructing unmanned planetary probes in earth orbit and in fuel transfer operations between spacecraft.[49] This latter procedure is considered vital for resupply to larger permanent stations in earth orbit.[50] One report credits a Soviet space engineer with revealing that nitric acid and kerosene had actually been transferred between the two spacecraft in a simulated space refueling.[51] However, the accuracy of this story is doubtful due to the absence of Soviet confirmation of such an important feat and due to the vastly more complicated docking mechanism which would have been involved.[52]

1. Docking apparatus   3. Solar panels
2. Rendezvous antennae   4. Communications antennae

Figure 39   Automatic docking of Kosmos 186 and Kosmos 188

Another six months passed following the remarkable automatic rendez-vous and docking of Kosmos 186 and 188 without a sign of a return to manned space flight. In March a mysterious spacecraft called Zond 4 had been launched on an apparent lunar mission. Although the probe's fate is not known, most observers believed it to be related to a manned circumlunar test flight of a Soyuz-related spacecraft.[53]

Finally on 14 April 1968 at 1300 hr another Soyuz spacecraft designated Kosmos 212 left Baikonur and entered an orbit of 239 km by 210 km at 51.7°. At 1910 hr on 14 April an orbital correction was performed by Kosmos 212, but its mission was not long in doubt. Within twenty-four hours Kosmos 213 had been launched into an orbit of 291 km by 205 km with the intention of repeating the Kosmos 186 and 188 experiment. This time the vehicles were initially separated by only 5 km with a relative velocity of 108 km/hr.[54]

Again while both craft were out of range of Soviet communications, Kosmos 212 carefully sought out Kosmos 213 and completed a textbook docking at 1321 hr Moscow time just 47 minutes after the launch of Kosmos 213. The following is a description of the docking process furnished by Tass:

> After the entry of the second satellite into orbit, and mutual radio "capture", and after the turning of the satellite into the necessary position with respect to the sightline, the process of automatic rendezvous started.
>
> The computers received from the radio detection devices information about the distance between the satellite, rate of change of this distance, angular velocity of the sightline, and the angles between the sightline and the constructional axes of the satellite.
>
> On the basis of this information the maneuvering of the active satellite was calculated and carried out, while the passive satellite was put in the required position.
>
> The process of automatic rendezvous of the satellite continued till the distance between the satellite was 350 meters. The relative velocity of the satellite at this time was of the order of 2 meters per second. At this moment the process of automatic "mooring" of the satellite began. At the time of "mooring" the satellites were stabilized with respect to the sightline in such a way that their docking units faced each other while the mutual roll attitude remained within the particular limits.

The "mooring" ended with the mechanical coupling of the satellites.

When the satellites touched each other, the relative displacement of the axes of the docking units did not exceed 0.4 meter, while the relative velocity was of the order of 0.1-0.2 meter per second.

The docking units have shock absorbers which ensured a careful and shockproof mechanical coupling.

After alignment, the satellites were brought closer till the butt joints coincided. Meanwhile the plug joints were connected, and electric connection between the spacecraft was established.

The automatic functioning of the docking units at the time of docking and uncoupling was provided by special sensors, computers, and control instruments.

On receiving the signal for uncoupling, the mechanical coupling was unlocked and the satellites separated because of the reaction of the springs.

After uncoupling, the satellites continued in orbit according to the flight program.[55]

Kosmos 212 and 213 remained coupled for three hours and fifty minutes with undocking taking place at 1711 hr again under the watchful eyes of Soviet engineers via television cameras on the spacecraft. The two space-craft continued in space to test further the Soyuz propulsion and orientation systems. Kosmos 212 remained aloft for two more days, returning to earth on 19 April, while Kosmos 213 was not called down until 20 April.

Both spacecraft had completed flawless flights of five days each and had repeated the intricate rendezvous and docking procedures first tested by Kosmos 186 and 188. The orbits of the two "active" spacecraft, Kosmos 186 and 212 were noted to be remarkably similar to that flown by Komarov in Soyuz 1. Thus the Soyuz spacecraft indeed seemed to have been requalified as the USSR's next generation of manned spaceships. Emphasis was now placed on the potentials of such a rendezvous system for both manned and unmanned space exploration. A new manned flight was thought to be imminent.[56]

SOYUZ 2 AND 3

The summer of 1968 passed with very little indication from the Soviets of when Soyuz might be expected to fly again. On 28 August Kosmos 238 was placed into an orbit closely resembling that of Soyuz 1. Analysis of the satellite revealed that it was indeed a Soyuz vehicle. However, four days later Kosmos 238 returned to earth with no mention or clue as to its mission.

As discussed earlier Kosmos 238 is believed to have been a final recheck-out of Soyuz before a manned mission, or was intended to be the target vehicle for a manned Soyuz which was subsequently scrubbed. But the presence of Kosmos 238 was just one more piece of evidence to conclude that cosmonauts were getting ready to fly again.

On 26 October 1968 Moscow news agencies proudly announced that Soyuz 3, carrying Pilot-Cosmonaut Georgii Timefeevich Beregovoi, had been launched at 1134 hr that day and was now orbiting the earth between 225 km and 205 km. But what of Soyuz 2? Belatedly, it was learned that Soyuz 2 had been launched unannounced and unmanned on 25 October at 1200 hr into an orbit of 224 km by 185 km at 51.7°. If indeed Kosmos 238 had been planned for a similar mission, Soviet authorities were not going to commit themselves to naming Soyuz 2 until the 6575-kg Soyuz 3 was safely in orbit. This also marked the first time that an unmanned spacecraft had been given a manned program designator. All previous Soviet unmanned flights of manned vehicles were given Kosmos or Zond nomenclatures.[57]

Taking a page from the Kosmos 186/188 and Kosmos 212/213 flight plan, Beregovoi, using the automatic radar systems, quickly maneuvered Soyuz 3 to within approximately 200 meters of Soyuz 2 on the first orbit.

Here, an examination of rendezvous procedures should be made. During the US Gemini program the target (passive) vehicle was always launched first with the launch of the chase (active) vehicle coming as the target later flew over the launching area. However, the Kosmos 186/188 and Kosmos 212/213 flights followed the opposite tactic: The active spacecraft was put up first with the target following later. But during the Soyuz 2/3 space flight, the Soviets reversed themselves and followed the US lead. (In the next dual mission, Soyuz 4 and 5, the first launched was again the active vehicle). Although some theories have been presented to account for the Soviet versus US method,[58] no conclusive answer is available.

Following the word that Beregovoi had maneuvered Soyuz 3 to a close rendezvous with Soyuz, an announcement was expected to reveal that the two spacecraft had in fact docked. Surprisingly, that report never came. Soviet authorities only admitted that when Soyuz 2 and 3 came with 200 meters, Beregovoi took over the manual controls and brought the two ships "closer"--to within a few meters. After a period Beregovoi is said to have retreated 565 km in Soyuz 3 and then completed a second rendezvous close to Soyuz 2 the next day. During the second rendezvous, pictures of Soyuz 2 were taken along with other engineering data.[59]

Immediately, the question of a failure to dock was raised. Almost all evidence including statements from Soviet government agencies indicate that docking was a primary objective. Beregovoi and other Soviet spokesmen have been quoted as saying that one or both spacecraft carried docking equipment.[60] Whether docking was impossible due to a malfunction in either spacecraft's docking mechanism or whether the failure was caused by Beregovoi himself is not known.[61]

Television pictures from Soyuz 3 depicted both Beregovoi and a blurred Soyuz 2. Throughout the flight Beregovoi held several televised interviews, showing off his new spaceship. For the first time, a description of the Soyuz spacecraft was offered. Following the tragic flight of Soyuz 1 very few details of Komarov's spacecraft had been disclosed. Now, the modular design and basic construction of Soyuz were revealed (Figure 40).

1. Orbital module
2. Command module
3. Propulsion module
4. Solar panel
5. Interior working area of orbital module
6. Rest and recreation section of orbital module
7. Orbital module side entrance hatch

Figure 40   Cutaway of the Soyuz 3 spacecraft

During the fifth orbit, Beregovoi moved into the orbital module to sleep while the spacecraft was out of direct radio contact with the Soviet Union (1918 hr 26 October to 0516 hr, 27 October). The next morning the second rendezvous maneuver was carried out and the joint mission phase of the flight terminated. Upon completion of these maneuvers Soyuz 3 entered an orbit of 252 km by 1979 km and Soyuz 2 moved to an apogee of 231 km and a perigee of 181 km. At 1025 hr on 28 October Soyuz 2 was commanded to fire its retro-engine and return to earth. Twenty-six minutes later the unmanned spaceship entered the earth's atmosphere and headed toward a soft landing on Soviet territory.[62]

For the next two days Beregovoi remained in space performing experiments, conducting earth surveys, and testing the Soyuz systems. His duties included observation and photographing of the stars, the planets, and the earth. He detected weather patterns, cyclones, typhoons, and forest fires. His photographs were intended to aid in the construction of geophysical, geological, glaciological and agricultural maps for the purpose of predicting subsequent natural trends. Medical analysis also held a high priority. Over five years had passed since the Soviets had kept a manned spacecraft in orbit for over a day.[63]

Finally on 30 October, Beregovoi made preparations to return to earth. All loose equipment was properly stored, and Soyuz 3 was reoriented for the retro-burn. Following a 145-second burn of the main propulsion engine, Soyuz 3 began to fall out of orbit. A few minutes later the orbital and propulsion modules were discarded. Employing the lifting characteristics of the command module, Beregovoi made a guided descent to the designated landing area. Touchdown occurred with pinpoint accuracy in snow at 1025 hr Moscow time with rescuers looking in his window before Beregovoi could climb out.

After four days and 64 revolutions, Beregovoi had restored the confidence in Soyuz needed before more daring and spectacular missions could be undertaken. Despite denials to the contrary, the Soviet Union was still apparently deeply committed to a manned lunar landing program. Soyuz was a key element in that program, and with it now recertified, effort could be shifted to the other components under development.

In fact, some observers saw Soyuz 3 as a duration test for a one-man circumlunar flight before the end of 1968. When Beregovoi landed after only four days, these observers felt something had gone wrong. Unexpected solar activity was soon given as the explanation for the "early" return. Although some solar activity did take place during the mission, it is doubtful that this ended the flight prematurely.[64]

SOYUZ 4 AND 5

During the last months of 1968 the world watched in wonder as the race to put men around the moon heated up. The Soviets had successfully sent two probes looping around the moon using admittedly unmanned versions of a manned spacecraft (see Zond chapter*). Meanwhile the US was nearing its announced deadline to place three men in orbit around the moon in Apollo 8. For unknown reasons, the Soviet manned circumlunar mission never materialized, while the Christmas voyage of Apollo 8 was a stunning success.

Therefore it came as no small surprise when Moscow announced that Soyuz 4 had been launched at 1039 hr Moscow time on 14 January 1969. Not only had the Soviets apparently switched from their circumlunar plans back to earth orbital missions with amazing speed, but Soyuz 4 represented the very first winter launch of a Soviet manned spacecraft. Commanding Soyuz 4 in an orbit of 225 km by 173 km was again a sole cosmonaut, Vladimir Aleksandrovich Shatalov. Although Soyuz had been billed as a multi-man spaceship, after three manned flights no more than a single cosmonaut had been carried. The old stories of a rendezvous and crew transfer were re-vived.

On the first few orbits Shatalov performed routine tasks. He conducted televised broadcasts and checked out on-board systems in both the command and orbital modules. An orbital correction was made at 1635 hr on orbit 5, bringing the spacecraft to a more circular orbit of 237 km by 207 km. This, too, seemed to foreshadow another rendezvous attempt. From 1816 hr, 14 January, to 0412 hr, 15 January, Shatalov was outside Soviet territory and rested for the events of the day ahead.[65]

The announcement that Soyuz 5 had been launched at 1014 hr on 15 January had been half-expected. But for the first time Soyuz was manned by a full crew of three: Boris Valentinovich Volynov, Aleksey Stanislavovich

_____

* Volume 47, Science and Technology

Yeliseyev, and Evgenii Vasil'evich Khrunov. While completing his sixteenth revolution Shatalov had been able to watch as Soyuz 5 entered the planned orbit of 230 km by 200 km.[66]

A first orbit rendezvous and docking was obviously not intended. Neither spacecraft was attempting to close the gap. This, of course, differed markedly from the only three previous Soviet space rendezvous: Kosmos 186/188, Kosmos 212/213, and Soyuz 2/3. Perhaps the difficulties Beregovoi (and other Vostok and Voskhod cosmonauts) had suffered initially adjusting to weightlessness had convinced Soviet flight planners to postpone the rendezvous attempt until all had their "space legs".[67]

Soyuz 5 followed the same routine of Soyuz 4 during the beginning orbits. The spaceship systems were double-checked, the orientation of the spacecraft was aligned, and before completing the sixth revolution, the orbital parameters were altered to: apogee - 253 km, perigee 211 km. Medical, navigational, and observational tasks accounted for most of the time spent by the three-man crew. To maintain similar work schedules both crews rested between 2000 hr, 15 January and 0400 hr, 16 January.[68]

Early the next day the procedures to bring the two spacecraft together were implemented. Soyuz 4 took the active role and by 0900 hr had maneuvered into an orbit of 253 km by 201 km. Then manual control of both spacecraft reduced their separation to within a few kilometers. At 1037 hr the automatic search-and-rendezvous system was activated. Shatalov watched as his ship performed the necessary engine firings and when the spacecraft were within 100 meters of one another he took over the manual controls to finish the docking process. Slowly he edged the probe of his ship (Figure 41) into the receptacle of Soyuz 5 (Figure 42). Contact! A firm mechanical lock completed the docking (Figure 43), creating what the Soviets have ever since claimed to be the "first experimental space station in the world."[69]

The docking mechanisms of Soyuz 4 and Soyuz 5 were of the probe/drogue type. The head of the probe assembly attached to Soyuz 4 (Figure 44) was carefully guided by Shatalov into the concial portion (drogue) of Soyuz 5 (Figure 45). After the initial securing of the capture latches the purposes of the docking mechanisms were:

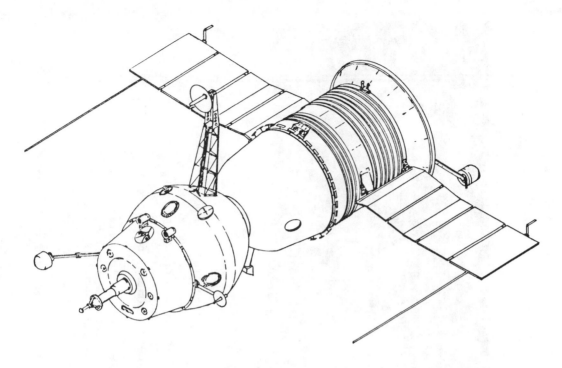

Figure 41   Soyuz 4 spacecraft with active (probe) docking apparatus.
(Drawing by R.F. Gibbons)

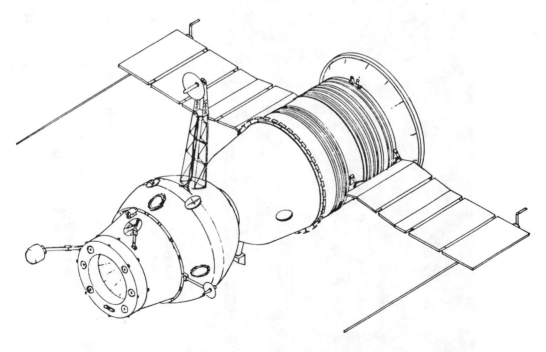

Figure 42   Soyuz spacecraft with passive (drogue) docking apparatus.
(Drawing by R.F. Gibbons)

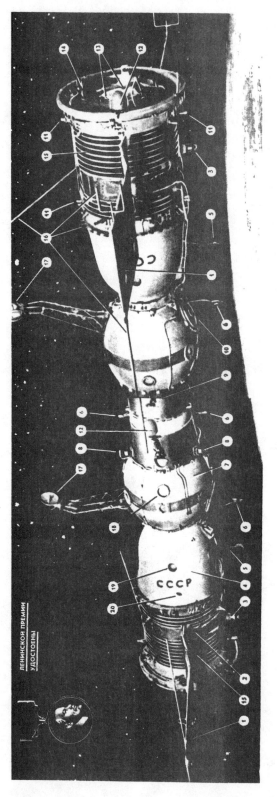

1. Solar panels
2. Propulsion module
3. Orientation sensor
4. Command module
5. Optical periscope
6. Part of the docking/transfer system
7. Orbital module
8. Television cameras
9. Docking collar
10. Orbital module side hatch
11. Attitude control engines
12. Rendezvous transponder
13. Main propulsion engine
14. Propellant tank
15. Thermal control radiators
16. Telemetry antennae
17. Rendezvous antennae
18. Orbital module porthole
19. Command module porthole
20. Command module orientation engine

Figure 43   Docked configuration of the Soyuz 4 and Soyuz 5 spacecraft

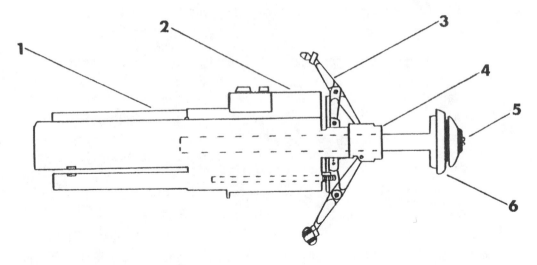

1. Main assembly housing
2. Electric drive
3. Linkage assembly
4. Electromechanical brake
5. Contact transducers
6. Capture hatch

Figure 44   Soyuz 4 docking assembly

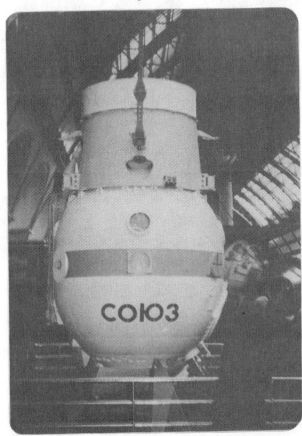

Figure 45   Orbital module with drogue docking assembly. Note stowed position of large girder rendezvous antenna at left side of orbital module. (Courtesy of R.F. Gibbons)

o Pulling the two spacecraft together and holding the docking
   rings in contact until coupling had been achieved

o Attenuation of the shocks occurring when the probe head impacted
   the drogue and attenuation of the relative motion of each spacecraft after coupling

o Capture of the probe head by the drogue socket

o Alignment of the two spacecraft in pitch, yaw and roll

o Transmission of the required signals to the spacecraft automatic
   instrument system, and transmission of data to the pilot's control channel and the telemetering system

o Undocking with the two spacecraft pushing off at a specified
   velocity.[70]

The rendezvous maneuvers had been closely watched by ground personnel
via television. In addition to TV the crews of Soyuz 4 and Soyuz 5 could
use either porthole in the command modules or the optical periscope. With
the mechanical link, came the joining of electrical and phone circuits
also. Immediately the cosmonauts tested the intercom system and exchanged
congratulations. Meanwhile, Volynov quickly tested the orientation system of the spacecraft combination while an even bolder experiment was in
the making.

Unlike the docking apparatus of the later Soyuz and Salyut spacecraft
and of the US Apollo/Lunar Module spacecraft there were no provisions for
internal transfer of cosmonauts between the coupled orbital modules. Instead the respective docking mechanisms were bolted on to the roughly
spherical orbital modules with no exit hatch at the forward end. Therefore, if a transfer of cosmonauts was to be undertaken, the spacemen would
have to attempt to leave the spacecraft via the orbital module side hatch
and conduct a "space walk" to the adjoining spaceship.

Docking had occurred at 1120 hr. Immediately after the firmness of
the docking was assured, Yeliseyev and Khrunov floated into the Soyuz 5
orbital module and began to don space suits for the long awaited crew
transfer (Figure 46).[71]

Volynov returned to the Soyuz 5 command module and closed the orbital
compartment hatch behind him. The exterior hatch of the orbital compartment was then opened, exposing Yeliseyev and Khrunov to the vacuum of
space. Cautiously, the pair peered into space. Finally, Khrunov gently
pushed himself through the open hatch to begin the exchange. Carefully

1. Telemetry halyard
2. Hose connections
3. Manometer
4. Oxygen feed connection
5. Safety halyard
6. Pack suspension system
7. Visor closing bracket
8. Visor filter
9. Space suit window
10. Helmet connecting ring
11. Pack suspension system lock
12. Space suit operating mode selection valve
13. Mirror
14. Pressure regulator valve
15. Life support system control panel
16. Air-tight helmet
17. Life support system pack
18. Emergency oxygen supply cut-in valve lever

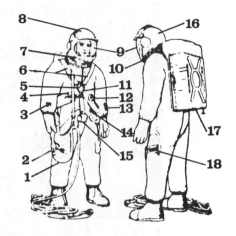

Figure 46   Features of Soyuz space suit with autonomous life support system as depicted in a 1974 Soviet book. Although life support system is shown here on the cosmonauts back, the Soyuz 5 cosmonauts may have worn theirs attached to their legs.

he moved over the handrails which lined the spacecraft, inspecting the mated spacecraft and the docking mechanisms as he went. Along the way photographs were taken and a test was performed to evaluate assembling techniques. Externally mounted television cameras allowed the Soyuz 4 and 5 commanders (Shatalov and Volynov) and ground personnel to monitor the entire procedure. With the aid of his tether the first cosmonaut slowly made his way to the hatch of the Soyuz 4 orbital module and entered (Figure 47). Yeliseyev quickly followed suit until both cosmonauts were safely in Soyuz 4 and the hatch had again been closed. The first in-space crew transfer had been completed. In all, no more than an hour had elapsed, during which time Yeliseyev and Khrunov were outside together for 37 minutes.[72]

Yeliseyev and Khrunov shed their space suits and were warmly greeted aboard Soyuz 4 by Shatalov. Shatalov was presented with newspapers and letters printed since his launch two days earlier. With a full complement of three the new crew of Soyuz 4 began to carry out the remaining experiments assigned to them.

1. Solar panels
2. Propulsion module
3. Orbital module
4. Orbital module side hatch
5. Rendezvous antennae
6. Docking apparatus
7. Portholes

Figure 47   Transfer of the Soyuz 5 cosmonauts to Soyuz 4

At 1555 hr, only four hours and thirty-five minutes after the creation of the four-compartment, 12,924-kg, 18-m^3 "space station", Soyuz 4 and Soyuz 5 undocked. By 1830 hr Khrunov, Yeliseyev, and Volynov had returned to their respective orbital modules for a much-deserved rest. Shatalov meanwhile slept in the command module of Soyuz 4.[73]

In the morning of 17 January both crews continued to make medical and photographic studies. In addition, Soyuz 4 began preparations for the return home. Prior to 0900 hr Shatalov, Yeliseyev, and Khrunov completed storing in the command module those instruments and photographic equipment which were to be returned to earth. Shatalov manually oriented the spacecraft and activated the retro sequence. By 0953 hr the three cosmonauts had safely landed approximately 40 km NW of Karaganda. Immediately, they were surrounded and congratulated by the waiting rescue party. Meanwhile, their fellow traveler, Volynov, continued to pilot Soyuz 5 around the world.[74]

Volynov spent the rest of the day carrying out various experiments, conducting television interviews, and testing the spacecraft control systems. On his thirty-sixth revolution, Volynov again fired the main propulsion engine to place Soyuz 5 into an orbit of 229 km by 201 km. After retiring early, Volynov awoke at 0130 hr on 18 January, his last day in space. Following the lead of Soyuz 4, Volynov brought the Soyuz 5 command module to a successful touchdown about 200 km SW of Kustanai at 1100 hr.[75]

On 19 January Pravda summed up the major accomplishments of the flight which included:

o Successful accomplishment of maneuvers, detection, rendezvous, "mooring" and docking of the spacecraft

o Creation of an inhabited experimental space station in orbit

o Transfer of two cosmonauts from one spacecraft to another--an experiment which has provided the basis for such operations in outer space as the supply of goods, repair, and assembly work, replacement of crew of manned orbital stations or their rescue in case of emergency

o Overall testing and checking of systems, assemblies and components of the spacecraft under the conditions of individual flight and as part of an experimental space station

o Carrying out a large number of scientific and technical and medico-biological investigations, observations, and experiments.[76]

Following the completion of the Soyuz 4/5 mission, Soviet spokesmen emphasized that the techniques exhibited were essential to the construction of large permanent space stations. However, Western observers quickly noted that without major redesign no more than two Soyuz could be docked at one time. Additionally, the necessity of performing an EVA (extra-vehicular activity) to traverse from one compartment to another was considered unacceptable for a true space station.[77]

In spite of these shortcomings space watchers predicted increased activity and further spectaculars in the spring of 1969. Soviet spokesmen and cosmonauts had been talking for over a year about permanent space stations and flights of two, three, or four manned spaceships at a time.[78] Based upon the success of Soyuz 4 and 5 and upon the need to draw attention away from the triumphant Apollo 11 lunar landing, most space experts were amazed to see spring and summer come and go without a single Soyuz mission. Unbelieveably, another nine years would pass before another EVA was attempted.

SOYUZ 6, 7, AND 8

Statements released between late August and early October 1969 suggested
that Soviet cosmonauts would soon take to the skies in record numbers. An
attempt to construct a large orbiting platform was expected. Thus, the
launch of Soyuz 6 with two cosmonauts on board--Georgii Stepanovich Shonin
and Valeriy Nikolaevich Kubasov--at 1410 hr on 11 October was half expected.
Nine nimutes later Soyuz 6 was safely inserted into an orbit of 223 km by
186 km at 51.7°. A single sentence of the launch announcement suggested
that this mission might well surpass that of Soyuz 4 and 5. "During the
course of the flight," it read, "experiments will also be conducted on
the methods of welding of metals in high vacuum and in the state of weightless."[79] The message clearly predicted a test of a space welding-system
technique which had long been deemed essential for the construction in
orbit of large space stations.

Following the pattern set by Soyuz 4 and 5, Soyuz 6 spent the inital
orbits deploying the solar panels, checking spacecraft systems, and adjusting to the new weightless environment. On the seventh revolution,
Shonin oriented the spacecraft and carried out an orbital correction at
2008 hr. There was little doubt that the crew of Soyuz 6 was expecting
company soon.

They did not have to wait long. At 1345 hr the next day Soyuz 7 lifted
off a Baikonur launching pad into a 226 km by 207 km orbit, while Soyuz 6
was orbiting between 230 km and 194 km. Soyuz 7 carried a complete three-
man crew--Anatolii Vasil'evich Filipchenko, Vladislav Nikolaevich Volkov,
and Viktor Vasil'evich Gorbatko. For the first time, there were five
Soviets in space at once. A new announcement accompanying the launch of
Soyuz 7 called only for "navigational investigations jointly with Soyuz
6 in group flight".[80]

Biographical data released indicated that Filipchenko and Gorbatko
had been back-ups for Shatalov and Khrunov, respectively, on the Soyuz
4/5 mission. Combined with the fact that Shonin and Kubasov had been
back-ups for Volynov and Yeliseyev, respectively, the Soyuz 6 and 7 flights
held great promise indeed.

In the early afternoon of 13 October when word was expected of a Soyuz
6/7 docking, Tass announced that a third Soyuz had been orbited (223 km

by 205 km) at 1329 hr Moscow time with a crew of two--none other than Shatalov and Yeliseyev themselves. No other Soviet cosmonauts had flown a second space mission except the late Komarov (Voskhod 1 and Soyuz 1). In the space of three days the USSR had impressively launched three manned spacecraft with a total contingent of seven cosmonauts.

With the arrival of Shatalov (who was named group commander) and Yeliseyev in Soyuz 8, the joint mission objectives were stated in part to be the following:

o Final touches to the complicated system of control for the group flight of three spacecraft simultaneously

o Joint orbital maneuvering to solve a number of problems connected with manned flight.[81]

For the remainder of the day, all crews concentrated on several optical navigational techniques involving the earth, planets, and stars. Emphasis was also placed on extensive manual control of Soyuz orientation and propulsion systems versus reliance on automatic sequencers.[82]

Just prior to the launch of Soyuz 8, Soyuz 6 made another orbital maneuver which brought the spacecraft closer to Soyuz 7. Once in orbit Soyuz 8 also made several maneuvers in the direction of Soyuz 7--possibly even approaching to within 500 meters. On 14 October, the beginning of the second day of the group flight, the expected triple rendezvous did not materialize, but Soyuz 8 did maneuver to within seeing distance of Soyuz 7. Reportedly studies were made concerning observation and photographing of near spacecraft, and light signals were tested to evaluate their usefulness in communications. No further group maneuvers were announced.[83]

The 15th of October 1969 finally saw completion of the triple rendezvous and several dual approaches. All spacecraft were now in an orbit roughly 225 km by 200 km. Entering Soviet radiovisibility at 0650 hr, the recently awakened cosmonauts prepared for the day's activites. First, Soyuz 7 performed acts of space acrobatics while Soyuz 8 observed. Then Soyuz 8 approached Soyuz 7 to a distance of about 500 meters and repeated the visual experiments of the day before. Meanwhile Soyuz 6 was close enough to observe and record the Soyuz 7/8 rendezvous. Later in the afternoon of the same day Soyuz 6 and Soyuz 8 took turns approaching Soyuz 7 to within a few hundred meters. However, no apparent attempt was made to bring the craft closer together or to dock.[84]

In an interview following his flight Shatalov stressed that one of the major goals of the group flight was to develop and check autonomous navigation devices. He stated that due to the multiple rendezvous and close-formation flying the following results could be reported:

o New information had been received regarding the optimal maneuvers for rendezvous with the help of autonomous devices for the determination of the dynamics of relative motion of the approaching spacecraft, as well as methods of coordination between crew

o A large amount of statistical data on fuel expenditure for the different maneuvers with different methods of orientation had been obtained

o Extensive material regarding the most rational distribution of control between man and the automatic machines while carrying out different jobs had been obtained.[85]

After several hours' sleep the three crews awoke together at 0500 hr on 16 October. Following breakfast and exercises, Shonin and Kubasov readied the welding experiments which had been mentioned as one of Soyuz 6's primary objectives on the day of launch. Kubasov was in charge of the experiment which was christened Vulkan and conducted the welding operations himself. The 50 kg instrument consisted of "the welding assembly, with the working units of the welding equipment, and a rotating table with samples of metals to be welded; instrument assembly with power supply unit; shielding case for covering the welding assembly; panel for remote control".[86]

The Vulkan instrument was located in the orbital compartment. After all had been made ready, Shonin and Kubasov retreated to the command module, secured the hatch, and evacuated the atmosphere of the orbital module. Kubasov then tested three methods (low-pressure compression arc welding, electron-beam welding, and consumable-electronic arc welding) of welding using the remote-control panel in the command module. At the conclusion of the tests, the orbital module was repressurized and Kubasov reentered the compartment and performed manual welding experiments. Later the apparatus was dismantled and along with the welding samples was transferred to the command module for return to earth.[87]

When the results of the experiments were disclosed much later, it became obvious that welding in space was more difficult than had been anticipated. Of the three techniques electron-beam welding proved the best, but none was totally satisfactory. Ignition problems and local porosity of the welds were given as some of the problems. As a result Soviet engineers began exploring other techniques employed in welding processes.[88]

The Vulkan experiment took place while Soyuz 6 was making its 77th orbit. Having concluded this experiment and other assigned chores, Shonin and Kubasov prepared to deorbit. Following the 80th orbit Soyuz 6 reentered the earth's atmosphere and made a soft landing 180 km NW of Karaganda at 1252 hr.

Launched at one-day intervals, the three Soyuz spaceships returned the same way. Without further major experiments, Soyuz 7 landed at 1226 hr on 17 October approximately 155 km NW of Karaganda. Soyuz 8 followed suit with a 1210 hr landing on 18 October 145 km N of Karaganda. On their last day in space the crew of Soyuz 8 had participated in a long-distance communications test from their craft to the ship, Kosmonaut Vladimir Komarov, to the orbiting Molniya 1 communications satellite and then to mission control.

Each crew had remained in space for five days of which three were spent in triple-formation flying. What had been the true mission of the monumental Soyuz 6/7/8 undertaking? Almost from the beginning, reports emerging from the Soviet Union were contradictory. Most agreed that Soyuz 6 was not equipped with a docking mechanism because the corresponding weight allowance had been reserved for the Vulkan equipment (Figure 48). However, Soyuz 7 is usually believed to have been equipped with the passive drogue docking collar whereas Soyuz 8 carried the active probe.[89] Tass is even credited with saying on 15 October that Soyuz 7 and 8 were programmed to dock.[90] But further questions after the flight received evasions or outright denials, reminding the questioner that docking had already been performed by Soyuz 4 and 5. A few sources contend that Soyuz 7 and 8 were never intended to dock.[91]

Of course it is entirely possible that the Soyuz 6/7/8 maneuvers were the primary objectives scheduled for the mission. The in-flight control of three spacecraft was in itself a major accomplishment. The problem

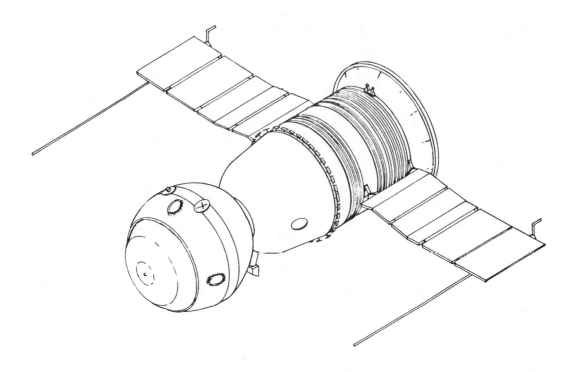

Figure 48   Speculative drawing of Soyuz 6 spacecraft
             (Drawing by R.F. Gibbons)

encountered in analyzing the triple mission is to determine whether it
was related to an upcoming manned lunar flight or whether it was a part
of the future Salyut space-station program.

Several sources believe that Soyuz 6 was to fly in a solo mode in the
spring of 1969, but was postponed due to the concentrated effort surrounding Luna 15. In this scenario Soyuz 7 was being developed to dock with a
boiler-plate Salyut space station scheduled for launch in the summer or
fall of 1969. When the Salyut prototype fell behind schedule, the idea of
flying a joint mission--Soyuz 6, Soyuz 7, and the Soyuz 6 backup as Soyuz
8--was proposed. Although a triple flight would not be directly related
to a Salyut mission, it would correspond to two Soyuz craft docking with
an unmanned space station or "hub". This latter concept was often suggested by Soviet scientists and believed by Western observers to be an
intermediary step for the Soviets until Salyut was ready.[92]

An equally plausible explanation relates the Soyuz 6/7/8 rendezvous
with a manned lunar landing concept. In this scheme a three-component
lunar spaceship would be constructed in earth orbit, and then fired to

164

the moon. This expensive and complicated procedure is believed to have been adopted when the Soviet "superbooster" failed all launch tests in 1968 and 1969. Evidence that the Soviets were still planning a manned lunar adventure can be seen in statements issued during that time period. See the Zond section in *Volume 47, Science and Technology* for further details.

SOYUZ 9

Seven months passed from the completion of the joint flight of Soyuz 6, 7, and 8 to the next manned Soyuz mission. This time no spectaculars were planned. The flight was scheduled to be a long-duration test of man's ability to withstand weightlessness for extended periods. The goal was to surpass the 14-day record held by the US Gemini 7 astronauts.

At 2200 hr on 1 June 1970 the sky around Baikonur lit up as Soyuz 9 lifted off in the world's first manned night launching. On board were two cosmonauts, one a veteran, one a rookie. Andriyan Grigor'evich Nikolaev became the first Vostok cosmonaut to fly also a Soyuz mission. Along with him was Vitalii Ivanovich Sevast'yanov. For this flight, two major modifications were made to the Soyuz spacecraft: (1) The rendezvous and docking equipment was deleted; and (2) the third cosmonaut couch was removed to allow room for added scientific instruments.[93]

Soon after reaching orbit Nikolaev and Sevast'yanov began implementation of a schedule they hoped to maintain for at least the next two weeks. (See Figure 49.) A working day including meals and exercise periods would last for approximately 16 hours with the remaining eight hours designated for rest and sleep. Two sleeping bags were hung in the orbital compartment for this latter purpose. Two strenuous exercise periods per day were scheduled with the cosmonauts occasionally wearing a special weighted suit which simulated the force of gravity on their bodies by exerting a force which the cosmonauts had to overcome. In addition, countless medical and psychological tests were conducted during the mission.

It would of course be impossible to detail here all the events of the flight of Soyuz 9.[94] However, following is a brief summary of the activities of Nikolaev and Sevast'yanov:

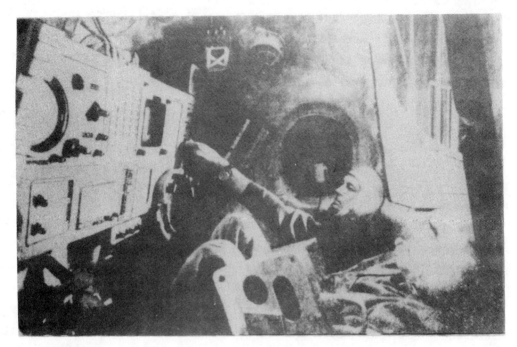

Figure 49   Soyuz 9 cosmonauts in the Soyuz trainer

2 June (Day 1)

Observed and analyzed luminous particles and impurities on windows due to engine firings; raised orbit to 266 km by 247 km.

3 June (Day 2)

Shaved before breakfast using specially designed techniques; on 29th orbit arterial pressure was measured before and after work with a 10-kg force expander as part of extensive medical evaluations for the long-duration flight; visual contrast sensitivity tested.

4 June (Day 3)

Used star Vega as object of spacecraft stabilization sensor for astro-navigation; conducted astronomical and earth observations; investigated sensitivity of vestibular apparatus in weightlessness.

5 June (Day 4)

On 48th and 49th orbits, put Soyuz 9 into a spin-stabilized solar-oriented mode; completed two 50-minute exercise periods.

6 June (Day 5)

Completed medico-biological experiments, including humidity measurements in different parts of the spacecraft; again tested feasibility of spin-stabilization; observed a tropical storm.

7 June (Day 6)

Made astronomical and earth observations; checked the condition of space-craft windows; conducted medical tests of tonicity of skeletal muscles in weightless condition.

8 June (Day 7)

Carried out navigational techniques involving the earth's horizon as a reference; conducted spectrophotography of earth's atmosphere under varying conditions; completed two one-hour exercise periods; monitored various medical states and responses.

9 June (Day 8)

On 96th orbit, calculated spacecraft position very precisely using selected landmarks on earth; continued medical evaluations and exercise.

10 June (Day 9)

Conducted further experiments using Vega as target for star sensor; revealed that Sevast'yanov preferred to sleep in the command module where the temperature was slightly cooler than the 24°C in the orbital module.

11 June (Day 10)

Rest day; played chess and read books; performed house-cleaning chores; continued exercise program.

12 June (Day 11)

Conducted photographic and spectrometric surveys of earth and near-earth space; performed medical experiments aimed at measuring muscular strain and sensitivity of muscles and joints.

13 June (Day 12)

Tested star sensor using Canopus as target; supervised experiments dealing with biological payload on board (insects, bacteria, etc.).

14 June (Day 13)

Jointly with the ship Akademik Shirshov and the Meteor satellite, observed cloud formations in Indian Ocean; saw small meteorites burn up in atmosphere; checked spacecraft window conditions.

15 June (Day 14)

Performed medical checkups and exercises; retested spacecraft orientation and propulsion systems; entered new orbit of 231 km by 215 km; photographed earth formations.

16 June (Day 15)

Surpassed Gemini 7 endurance record for longest space flight; photographed detailed sections of the USSR while aircraft did same; conducted astro-navigation exercises.

17 June (Day 16)

Noticed formation of cyclone near USSR; continued emphasis on medical tests and exercises.

<u>18 June (Day 17)</u>

Concluded planned experiments; began preparations for landing.

<u>19 June (Day 18)</u>

Landed at 1459 hr Moscow time; new endurance record of 424 hours.

With the final command to return to earth, Soyuz 9 was oriented at 1352 hr on 19 June for the reentry burn. At exactly 1417 hr 30 sec the powerful main propulsion engine fired, slowing the spacecraft and decreasing its altitude. The descent was programmed to ensure a deceleration force of no more than 3 g's. After enduring an extended period of weightlessness a minimum amount of strain on the cosmonauts was desired. By 1444 hr the parachute system was activated to the delight of the crew and ground personnel alike. Touchdown occurred some fifteen minutes later at 75 km W of Karaganda.[95]

Quickly rescue personnel rushed to the command module to help the two Soviet heroes out of their craft. After 18 days of weightlessness Nikolaev and Sevast'yanov were unable to get out of their couches. They remarked that their bodies felt as though they were under a force of several g's. This sharply contrasted with the relative ease that the Gemini astronauts had readjusted after their 14-day flight in the much more cramped Gemini capsule. Nikolaev and Sevast'yanov were moved into isolation at Tyuratam to prevent catching an infectious disease in their weakened condition. For several days following the landing, both cosmonauts complained of feeling heavy and being uncomfortable. Only by the tenth day did they experience a return to normalization.[96]

Problems with weightlessness were experienced in orbit, too. By employing the spin-stabilizing technique to conserve fuel while maintaining the solar panels in a sun-fixed orientation, centrifugal forces were set up within the spacecraft. Reportedly, the cosmonauts could feel the varying effects of this force in different sections of the spacecraft, some sections feeling more unpleasant than others.[97]

Overall, though, the flight of Soyuz 9 was very successful. The cosmonauts had proved that man could endure the rigors of space for at least 18 days and probably up to a month without serious, permanent effects. This would be essential if a permanent manned space station was ever to be a reality. The Soviet Union was now ready. Within a year two Soyuz

spacecraft would dock with the orbiting station Salyut 1. The latter of
these missions would spend 22 days on board the station conducting numerous scientific and earth resources experiments.

SOYUZ 12

Following the tragic deaths of the Soyuz 11 cosmonauts, the entire
Soviet manned space program underwent an extensive analysis. There had
been reports that Salyut 1 itself had had design and production problems
delaying its maiden flight to April 1971. Soyuz 10 had successfully
docked with the large space station, but had to return prematurely after
failing to enter Salyut 1. Now the seemingly triumphant flight of Soyuz
11 had brought the entire orbiting laboratory program to a halt when the
returning cosmonauts perished accidently.

A year after the tragedy, Kosmos 496 was flown in an apparent test of
a redesigned Soyuz. However, a subsequent launch of a second Salyut and
manned Soyuz never materialized.[98] Fully another year passed before
Kosmos 573 tested what was to become the standard Salyut ferry craft.
With what appeared to be a successful flight by this unmanned satellite
observers expected to see the launch of the long-awaited second operational
Salyut space station (attempts to launch new Salyut in April and May of
1973 had ended in failure). But three months later it was a manned Soyuz,
Soyuz 12, not a Salyut which took to the heavens. Kosmos 573 had appar-
ently been the precursor flight for Soyuz 12, not the prelude to a new
Salyut/Soyuz mission.

At 1518 hr Moscow time on 27 September 1973, Soyuz 12, carrying Oleg
Grigor'yevich Makarov and Vasiliy Grigor'yevich Lazarev, shot away from
the Baikonur cosmodrome after the longest hiatus in the history of the
Soviet manned space program. From an initial orbit of 249 km by 194 km
the spacecraft performed two orbital corrections and quickly slipped into
a 345 km by 326 km orbit at 51.6°. A brief announcement by Izvestiya
indicated that the mission would last for only two days with the following as primary objectives:

   o Comprehensive testing of improved on-board systems
   o Optimization of manual and automatic controls under various
     flight conditions
   o Spectrophotography of the earth surface.

Soyuz 12 appears to have been originally assigned to dock with a Salyut space station in the spring of 1973. However two successive launches of Salyut (Salyut 2 and Kosmos 557) apparently ended in failure in April and May of that year. With a possible year's delay before another Salyut could be readied, the Soviets appeared to decide to end their 27-month lapse of manned space flight.[99]

Soyuz 12 differed markedly from Soyuz 11. The command module had been redesigned to accommodate only two cosmonauts, but now there was room for the wearing of space suits during launch, docking, and recovery operations. The accident of Soyuz 11 would not be permitted to happen again. Additionally, the characteristic solar wings were now absent from Soyuz. With the Soyuz role now one of crew and supply ferry to Salyut stations, the heavy solar panels were no longer needed, allowing a larger instrument payload capacity for Soyuz.[100]

The short flight of Soyuz 12 was largely devoted to a thorough check of the new on-board systems. The spacecraft life-support system which now occupied the "third" cosmonaut couch was given extensive examination. Automatic and manual orientation and propulsion systems were repeatedly tested (Figure 50). The maneuvers to a high earth orbit (345 km by 326 km) on the first day were later shown to correlate with the orbit flown by Salyut 4 in early 1975.[101] Communications via the Molniya 1 satellite were also tested again.

On the second day Lazarev and Makarov performed the only real scientific experiment of the mission. The two cosmonauts used a multi-spectral camera which took photographs of 100-meter resolution at the earth's surface. This camera actually took photos in nine separate spectral regions (visible to infrared) simultaneously. After analysis these pictures were used "to obtain images of isobaths at different depths (great in the short-wave parts of the spectrum) and to study the spatial structure of contaminated water bodies".[102] In addition, crop and forest conditions could be evaluated from these pictures which also distinguished between dry and moist soils. During part of this experiment aircraft were photographing some of the same regions for comparison with the Soyuz 12 pictures.

Finally on the 32th revolution the retro-engine was ignited and the long descent to earth begun. With Soviet cosmonauts wearing space suits

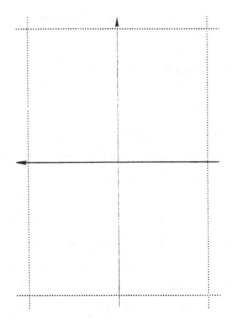

Figure 50   Angular position display for determining the orientation of
the spacecraft from ion sensor inputs. The vertical and
horizontal axes indicate spacecraft position about the pitch
and yaw axes, respectively. In this case the point reflects
both a positive pitch and a positive yaw angle.

during reentry for the first time since Vostok 5 in 1963, Lazarev and
Makarov soft-landed at 1434 hr on 29 September 400 km SW of Karaganda. The
flight was immediately dubbed "flawless".

Soyuz 13

A scant three months after the flight of Soyuz 12, the Soviet Union launched
what was nothing less than a miniature manned orbiting laboratory. Soyuz
13, carrying similar equipment to that first used aboard the much larger
ill-fated Salyut 1, was launched at 1455 hr on 18 December 1973. For the
first time a Soyuz mission seemed almost totally dedicated to scientific
goals.

The announced objectives of the space flight were:
o Research of astrophysical findings in the ultraviolet with the
help of the Orion-2 telescope located on board
o Spectrozonal photography of various sections of the earth's surface for agricultural purposes
o Further testing of the Soyuz spacecraft

o Further perfection of the processes for manual and automatic control, and especially, methods for automatic navigational control under various regimes of flight.[103]

Some early reports thought the mission of Soyuz 13 might be to inspect Kosmos 613 which had been launched less than three weeks earlier. At that time some observers believed Kosmos 613 to be a failed Salyut with Soyuz 13 sent to find out what went wrong. However Soyuz 13 and Kosmos 613 were in different planes, making rendezvous impossible. Later analysis proved Kosmos 613 to be an unmanned Soyuz test.

Initially inserted into a 246 km by 188 km orbit at 51.6°, Cosmonauts Petr Il'ich Klimuk and Valentin Vital'yevich Lebedev maneuvered Soyuz 13 to a higher (273 km by 225 km) orbit on the fifth revolution. Soyuz 13 again possessed the solar panels which had been deleted from Soyuz 12 and was the prototype of the latest variant of Soyuz to be used as orbiting observatories for periods of a week or longer. The rendezvous-and-docking gear was replaced with a complex ultraviolet astrophysical observatory called Orion-2 which is shown attached to Soyuz 13 in Figure 51 (a sister instrument, Orion 1, had been installed on board Salyut 1).

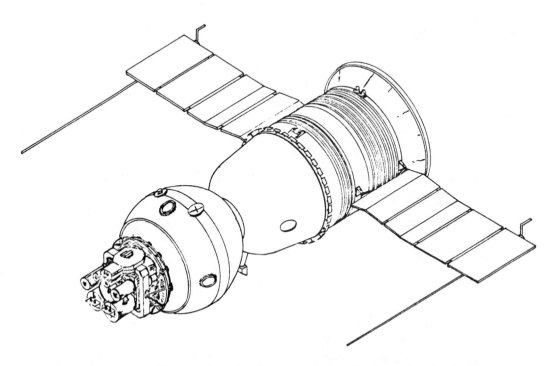

Figure 51   Soyuz 13 outfitted with the Orion-2 astrophysical observatory (protective cover removed)   (Drawing by R.F. Gibbons)

The ensuing eight-day flight of Klimuk and Lebedev was devoted to carrying out several major scientific investigations. Experiments on the agenda included:[104]

1. Orion-2. Described as an ultraviolet meniscus telescope, the Orion-2 complex was designed to yield spectrograms of stars as faint as the twelfth magnitude in the 0.2-0.4 meter wavelength range. These wavelengths are normally blocked by the earth's atmosphere and hence cannot be observed from ground observatories. Mounted externally with a protective dome to prevent severe temperature gradients as Soyuz 13 moved into and out of the earth's shadow, Orion-2 took spectrograms covering an area of more than 20 square degrees. To operate the system Lebedev moved into the orbital compartment where the Orion-2 control panel was located while Klimuk remained in the command module. On command Klimuk would orient the spacecraft to within a few degrees of the subject star. Then Lebedev would adjust the telescope platform to further zero in on the target. Finally, an automatic sensing system would lock the telescope on to a star with an accuracy of a few seconds of a degree, using a second widely displaced star as a stabilizing reference. A shutter over the crystalline quartz window in the protective dome was opened for the desired one-to-twenty minute exposure. Film cassettes could be changed from within the spacecraft so that EVA's were not required. By the end of the flight 16 observation sessions had been completed, producing spectrograms of thousands of stars. For the first time, chromospheres were discovered around cold stars and ultraviolet spectrums were taken of planetary nebula. Instruments attached to Orion-2 also took solar X-ray photographs.[105]

2. Oasis-2. Also housed in the orbital module, Oasis-2 was a self-contained system designed to evaluate the feasibility of producing water, food, and air on board spacecraft via regeneration processes (Figure 52). An earlier model had also been tested on Salyut 1. "Oasis-2 consisted of two round containers with separating membranes. On the ground these containers were filled with nutrient media for hydrogen bacteria and urobacteria. Above the control panel there is a peristaltic pump. During the flight the cosmonauts periodically turned on the 'pump' switch, sending a fresh nutrient medium from the containers to the fermenters. At the same time, a bacterial suspension was taken from the fermenters and fed into the same containers, but on the other side of the membrane. During the flight the pump operated a total of 12 hours and pumped over practically all the prepared nutrient medium. The density of the bacterial mass increased 30 times. In the ground-control version of the test, the increase in density of the suspension was significantly less." [106]

3. Multi-zonal photography. Nine-region spectrophotography was carried out with an instrument similar to that employed by the Soyuz 12 cosmonauts for examining different geographic regions and formations.

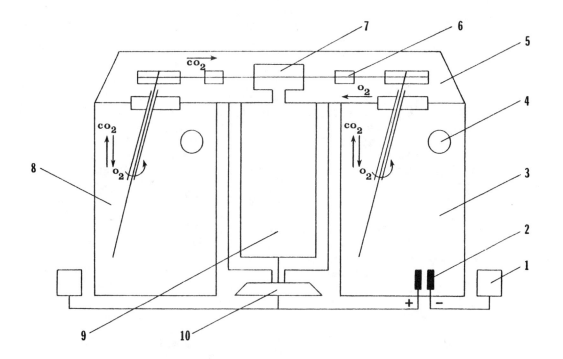

1. Electrolysis monitoring transmitters
2. High voltage electrodes
3. Right-hand cylindrical fermenter
4. Urobacteria and hydrogen bacteria connectors
5. Connecting gas chamber
6. Leakage cutoffs
7. Mixing apparatus
8. Left-hand cylindrical fermenter
9. Motor
10. Magnetic coupler

Figure 52   Prototype of Oasis-2 experiment which was tested on Kosmos 368 (October 1970) for 144 hours

4. <u>Levka</u>. Program designed to measure, through bioelectric potentials in the brain, blood redistribution caused by weightlessness. An increase in blood to the brain is thought to be a probable cause of disorientation felt by most cosmonauts during their first days in space.

5. <u>Observation of Comet Kohoutek</u>. Although the flight of Soyuz 13 had been planned far in advance, the actual launch date may have been affected by the arrival of the much publicized Comet Kohoutek.

6. Samples of chlorella and duckweed were grown to evaluate their reaction to a weightless environment. Initially in a dormant state, the duckweed was revived and its growth processes analyzed by the introduction of a traceable substance.

7. Spectrograms were taken of the earth's horizon to aid in the detection of dust particles and pollution in the atmosphere.

Finally, after eight busy days in space, Klimuk and Lebedev prepared their experimental data and samples for the deorbit burn and descent. At

1150 hr on 26 December the Soyuz 13 command module made a successful landing in heavy snow 200 km SW of Karaganda. Fortunately the landing occurred at the designated area and recovery of the cosmonauts and their payload was immediate.

Soyuz 16

After much negotiation US President Richard Nixon and Soviet Chairman Aleksey Kosygin signed in Moscow on 24 May 1972 a document which, among other things, called for a joint American-Soviet manned space mission in a test flight designed to open new areas of US-USSR cooperation in space. Detailed discussions followed with the final decision to dock a three-man Apollo with a two-man Soyuz in low earth orbit in the summer of 1975. One of the major compromises agreed upon was the creation of a new universal docking mechanism to be used on the joint mission and future spacecraft of each country. By virtue of this common docking mechanism further cooperative missions could be more easily flown in addition to enabling emergency rescues of stranded astronauts by the crews of the other country (Figure 53).

During the next two years the new equipment required to complete the planned mission was engineered and developed. (See Soyuz 19.) Kosmos 638 and 672 were unmanned Soyuz spacecraft flown to test these new systems under actual space-flight conditions. However, the Soviet Union announced that all aspects of the flight would also be tested in a manned Soyuz dress rehearsal before 15 July 1975, the scheduled start of the Apollo-Soyuz Test Project (ASTP). On 2 December 1974 Soyuz 16 assumed that role. Figure 54 shows the Soyuz trainer used in this test project.

Launched at 1240 hr Moscow time into an unusual initial orbit, Cosmonauts Anatolii Vasil'yevich Filipchenko (veteran of Soyuz 7) and Nikolay Nikolayevich Rukavishnikov (veteran of Soyuz 10) quickly prepared for a busy six-day flight.[107] They were scheduled not only to conduct extensive rendezvous maneuvers and simulated docking exercises, but also to complete several biological and astrophysical experiments.

A summary of their major daily chores included:[108]

Day 1

Maneuvered Soyuz 16 to a 223 km by 177 km orbit on the fifth revolution. Reduced spacecraft atmospheric pressure to 540 mm Hg while raising oxygen content to 40% in practice for Apollo docking and crew transfer. Figure

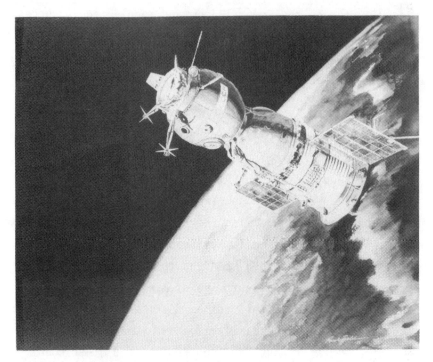

Figure 53   Artist's concept of the Soyuz ASTP
            spacecraft in orbit (Courtesy of NASA)

Figure 54   Soyuz trainer used during the Apollo-Soyuz
            Test Project   (Courtesy of NASA)

176

55 shows the Soyuz orbital module pressure integrity panel. (Normal Soyuz pressure is 760 mm Hg with a 20-22% oxygen content.) Initiated experiment to monitor the growth of microorganisms in space.

Day 2

Again fired the Soyuz propulsion system engine to alter the orbital parameters first to 240 km by 190 km and then to 224 km by 221 km which was then quickly modified to the 225 km circular orbit planned for ASTP . These maneuvers required a 12-second engine burn at perigee to raise the orbit and a shorter retro-burn at apogee to lower the orbit.

Day 3

Observed zone formation in branching fungi to determine if the radiation, weightlessness, and "90 minute day" of space would affect the 24-hour growth ring process seen on earth. This particular experiment was devised to study the phenomenon of biorhythms and their relation to man. On the 32nd and 38th revolutions the new androgynous docking mechanism and associated equipment was tested. Attached to the Soyuz docking collar was a special 20-kg ring which could be pulled away and retracted with the proper force to simulate docking with the Apollo spacecraft (Figure 56). Several different modes of operation were practiced to test various docking situations. Atmospheric conditions were kept at ASTP standards. During the 35th orbit both cosmonauts donned their space suits, sealed the command module, and practiced the maneuvers leading up to docking with Apollo.

Day 4

Continued testing of docking system on revolution 48. Completed tests involving the study of microbe exchange and transfer within the spacecraft. Finished tests concerned with the direction of growth of shoots of higher plants. Zone-forming fungi and microorganism growth experiments continued.

Day 5

Further tested automatic docking system. At the end of the simulated docking sessions, the special ring was blown away by explosives to ensure proper separation of Apollo and Soyuz should the spacecraft be unable to undock under normal operating procedures. Photographed the earth's horizon in polarized light for approximately 30,000 km on the 68th through 70th orbits for the purpose of analyzing atmospheric composition and characteristics. Tested equipment to be used on ASTP artificial solar eclipse experiment in which the Soyuz crew was to photograph the solar corona and background stars when the Apollo spacecraft temporarily blocked out the sun's disc along the Soyuz-sun line. In conjunction with this last experiment, the cosmonauts paid particular attention to the presence around the spacecraft of microscopic particles emanating from Soyuz itself. These particles affect viewing conditions from spacecraft windows and can even form an elongated halo around the ship. Retested the orientation and propulsion systems for retro-burn planned the next day.

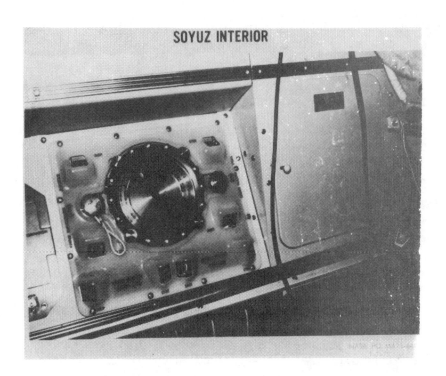

Figure 55   Soyuz orbital module pressure integrity panel
(Courtesy of NASA)

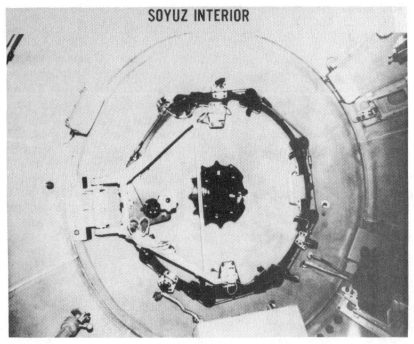

Figure 56   Orbital module hatch leading to the ASTP Docking
Module   (Courtesy of NASA)

<u>Day 6</u>

Completed all biological and astrophysical experiments. Spacecraft atmosphere returned to "Soyuz normal" and space suits donned for reentry (Figure 57). Fired main propulsion engine for 166.5 seconds retro-burn. Landed 300 km N of Dzhezkazgan at 1104 hr Moscow time on 8 December after 96 orbits about the earth.

Following the safe recovery of Filipchenko and Rukavishnikov, Soviet officials proudly announced that the redesigned Soyuz spacecraft and androgynous docking mechanism had performed flawlessly and were ready for the ASTP mission the next July. Although NASA spokesmen congratulated the Soviets on their achievement, some Western critics asserted that Soyuz 16 had not been launched into the proper initial orbit.[109] The cause of this error was suggested to be a malfunction in the upper stage of the launch vehicle which resulted in giving Soyuz 16 an excessive apogee.[110] Coupled with the failure of the previous manned space flight, Soyuz 15, to rendezvous and dock with the Salyut 3 space station, this apparent failure again raised in some US circles the question of Soviet technical capabilities. However, it was noted that Soyuz 16 was able to reach the ASTP orbit despite the assumed launch malfunction.

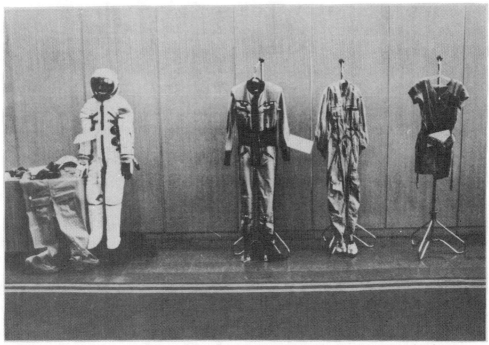

Figure 57   Attire worn by the Soyuz ASTP cosmonauts during the international flight   (Courtesy of NASA)

SOYUZ 19

Soyuz 19 was the Soviet designation of the Soyuz spacecraft which participated in the Apollo-Soyuz Test Project (ASTP). The enormous political and technical ramifications of this historic mission are beyond the scope of this book.[111] However the major activities of the flight are outlined here.

Ever since the ASTP mission began serious preparations after the 1972 US-USSR summit, a wealth of technical information concerning all aspects of the Soviet space program was made available. Although much of the data cited in this book was already available, during this period (1972-1975) the Soviets released a substantial amount of technical data heretofore classified. In particular, new information relating to spacecraft attitude, maneuvering, and life-support systems was revealed for the first time.

For the first time in the history of the Soviet space program, a manned space launching was publicly scheduled and televised live. At 1520 hr Moscow time 15 July 1975 with a world-wide audience Cosmonauts Leonov and Kubasov (Figure 58) blasted off atop an augmented Vostok booster into clear skies toward an historic meeting with a US Apollo spacecraft approximately two days later (Figures 59-60).[112] Inserted into an inital orbit of 221 km by 186 km the cosmonauts immediately deployed the spacecraft solar panels and antennae and began preparations for their part in the planned launch of the US Apollo seven and one-half hours later.

Leonov and Kubasov were presented with many tasks on the first few orbits of which the most important was maneuvering Soyuz 19 into the required 225 km circular orbit. This was accomplished in stages by a 7-second correction burn on the fourth orbit bringing Soyuz 19 to 232 km by 192 km and by a 21-second firing on the 17th orbit for a final orbit of 225 km by 222 km. By the second orbit the cosmonauts had removed their space suits and were inspecting the orbital module atmosphere control systems.

Prior to the Soyuz launch the on-board television system which controlled the four interior and exterior cameras malfunctioned, preventing the planned TV coverage of the Soyuz cosmonauts during launch. Leonov and Kubasov attempted to analyze the problem in Soyuz while ground-support

Figure 58   Cosmonauts Leonov and Kubasov on their way to the launching pad   (Courtesy of NASA/USSR Academy of Sciences)

personnel worked out repair procedures in a Soyuz simulator. By the second day a temporary fix provided the rest of the world with the first
color photos from within the Soyuz 19 spacecraft.

Also during the beginning orbits both cosmonauts initiated the biological experiments tested on Soyuz 16 (zone-forming fungi, embryonic development and fish hatchings, and micro-organism growth). In addition in a
two-hour 34-minute procedure the spacecraft atmosphere was reduced to a
pressure of 540 mm Hg and an oxygen content of 40%.

Meanwhile the Apollo spacecraft, carrying astronauts Stafford, Brand,
and Slayton, was successfully launched from the Kennedy Space Center at
2250 hr Moscow time. Upon reaching orbit, Apollo was approximately 6800
km behind Soyuz. For the next 44 hours both crews were very busy preparing for the long-planned international docking in space.

When the first proposals to attempt a docking of an American Apollo
with a Soviet Soyuz were finalized, several major engineering hurdles had

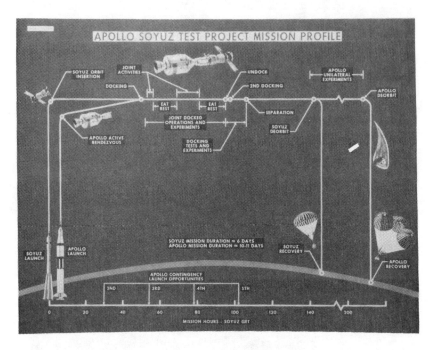

Figure 59   Apollo-Soyuz Test Project Mission Profile
              (Courtesy of NASA)

Figure 60   The Apollo-Soyuz complex in docked configuration
              (Courtesy of NASA)

to be overcome before such a mission would be possible. Incompatible spacecraft atmospheres was one of the two major items to be tackled first. While Soyuz employed conventional atmosphere pressure and composition (nitrogen and oxygen at 760 mm Hg), Apollo was constructed with an almost pure oxygen content at a pressure of 270 mm Hg. Since it would not be practical to redesign either spacecraft to meet the specifications of the other, a compromise solution was reached. Soviet engineers agreed to reduce the cabin pressure to 540 mm Hg and increase the oxygen content to 40%. American engineers agreed to construct and launch with Apollo a docking module in which crew members of either craft could adjust from one atmosphere to the other for the planned crew transfers. The idea is not unlike the decompression chambers used by deep sea divers who have spent extended periods at great depths (high pressures). In fact, without the docking module the astronauts and cosmonauts would have suffered a "bends"-like reaction during transfer. Finally, the Soyuz orbital compartment environmental control system was augmented to handle a total of four spacemen--an event scheduled to take place during the first crew transfer (Figure 61).

The docking module was 3.15 meters long and weighed 2012 kg. Stored under the adapter section of the Saturn IB launch vehicle, the docking module was retrieved by the Apollo spacecraft by the same turn-around procedure used by the Apollo lunar spacecraft when picking up the Lunar Module from the spent Saturn IVB stage. The 1.5-meter diameter interior tunnel could hold two men and contained the necessary TV and communications equipment and the atmospheric control panels.

The second major engineering problem came in developing the docking mechanism to be used. Both countries, after years of design, had developed probe/drogue type docking collars. These, though, were obviously not compatible. With one of the main objectives of the flight to pave the way for future joint missions (especially those of a rescue nature) both sides agreed to develop a new androgynous docking mechanism which would be incorporated as standard equipment on future spacecraft of each nation. The advantage of the androgynous connectors is that each mechanism can play the active or passive role (Figure 62 illustrates the (ASTP) Androgynous docking system). Thus any two spacecraft can dock together. Previously spacecraft had been of two different types, and two ships with similar mechanisms were unable to couple.

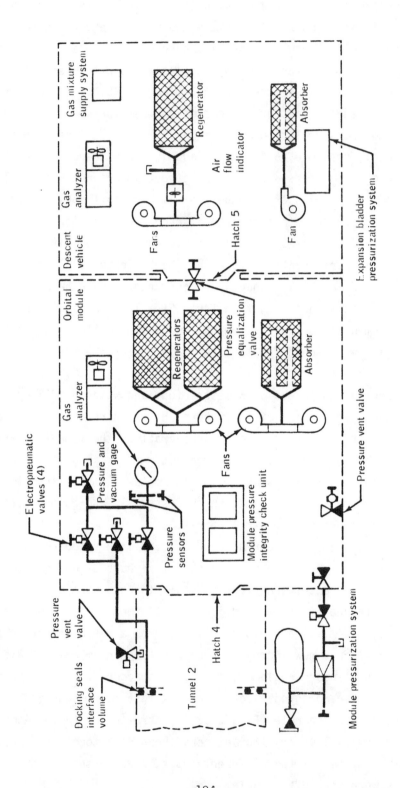

Figure 61   Soyuz environmental control system modified for ASTP

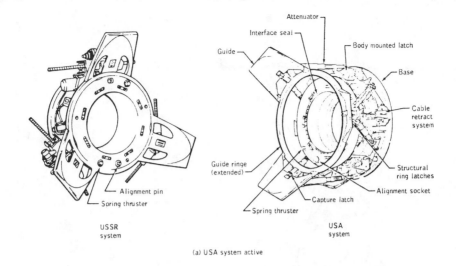

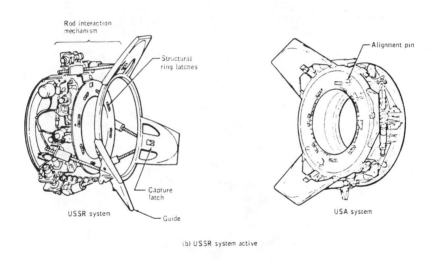

Figure 62   ASTP Androgynous docking system

For the ASTP flight the Soyuz orbital module was outfitted with one of the new docking devices using a compatible docking reference system. Therefore the docking module which is positioned between the Apollo and Soyuz spacecraft (Figures 63-64) carried the androgynous collar on the Soyuz end and an older US drogue type collar for connection to Apollo. A total of four crew transfers was called for by the ASTP flight plan with all five spacemen spending time in the spacecraft of the other country.

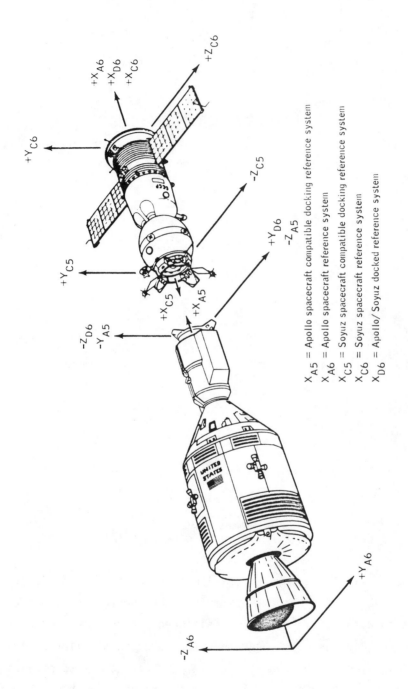

X_{A5} = Apollo spacecraft compatible docking reference system
X_{A6} = Apollo spacecraft reference system
X_{C5} = Soyuz spacecraft compatible docking reference system
X_{C6} = Soyuz spacecraft reference system
X_{D6} = Apollo/Soyuz docked reference system

Figure 63   The Apollo-Soyuz coordinate system

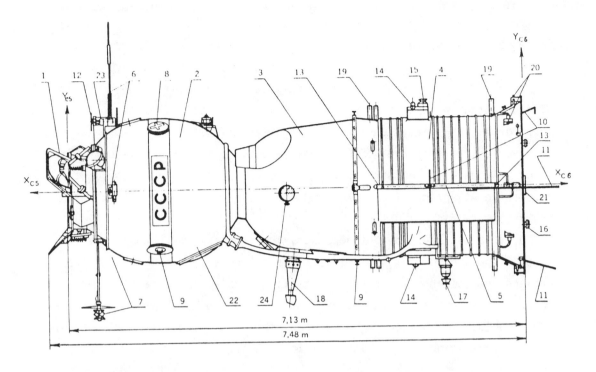

Figure 64   Major components of the Soyuz ASTP spacecraft

1. Docking mechanism
2. Orbital module
3. Command module
4. Propulsion module
5. Solar panels
6. VHF radio antennae (121.75 MHz)
7. VHG radio antennae (259.7 MHz and 296.8 MHz)
8. Radio/TV communications antennae
9. Command radio link antenna
10. Telemetry antennae
11. Communications antenna
12. Docking target
13. Orientation lights
14. Flashing light beacons
15. Sun sensor
16. Ion orientation sensor
17. Infrared orientation sensor
18. Periscope (optical orientation)
19. Approach and orientation engines
20. Orientation engines
21. Main propulsion engine
22. Orbital module side hatch
23. External television camera
24. Window

Several other problems also had to be overcome. To name a few, these included compatible search and rendezvous radar, attitude control of the docked configuration, communications systems, placement of exterior structures to prevent collisions and electronic interference, and beacons and optical markers for docking.[113]

One further aspect of the mission requiring a compromise of US and USSR practices concerned the operational ground communications and control systems. There was of course an obvious need for direct communications between the launching and control centers of the USSR and their counterparts in the US. In accordance with this requirement direct links were established between Moscow, Baikonur, Houston, and the Kennedy Space Center well in advance of the July mission. Additionally, though, each country had standard restrictions placed upon spacecraft activities when not in direct contact with their respective mission controls (i.e. over native territory). Initially considered a significant obstacle, the problem was resolved by drafting the ATS-6 satellite into operation. This satellite relay provided Houston with the needed communications while Apollo was across the Atlantic. Therefore communications requirements by both sides could be met (Figures 65-66).

July 16 was spent by both crews fixing problems which continued to occur. The Apollo crew had difficulties in removing the docking probe between the command module and the docking module. Also causing headaches were the environmental-control system, attitude-control system, and several experiments. Meanwhile the Soyuz crew continued to do battle with their defiant television system with occasional success. Leonov and Kubasov were also able to speak directly with their fellow countrymen who were on board the Soyuz 18B/Salyut 4 combination.

Docking was planned on Soyuz's 36th orbit and Apollo's 29th orbit. With Apollo acting as the active spacecraft and making the closing maneuvers the two space vehicles achieved an easy and successful hard docking at 1909 hr Moscow time (Figures 67-69). Slightly more than three hours later at 2219 hr the final hatch between the docking module and the Soyuz orbital module had been opened, and Stafford and Leonov had clasped hands in a world-wide televised exhibit of cooperation between two old space rivals.

For two days the spacecraft remained in a docked configuration. During this time the crews conducted scientific investigations and fulfilled the obligitory political tasks. These events and others are thoroughly documented in many available publications.[114] In all four crew transfers took place (Figures 70-71).

At 1503 Moscow time on 19 July the two spacecraft undocked and pulled slightly away. Here the artificial solar eclipse experiment practiced on Soyuz 16 was performed. Then a redocking was accomplished at 1534 hr with the Soyuz collar in the active mode and the Apollo collar in the passive

Figure 65   View of the ASTP flight control center at Star City near
Moscow   (Courtesy of NASA/USSR Academy of Sciences)

Figure 66   One of the physical support/power distribution control rooms
at the USSR flight control center   (Courtesy of NASA)

Figure 67   Soyuz 19 as viewed from Apollo (Courtesy of NASA)

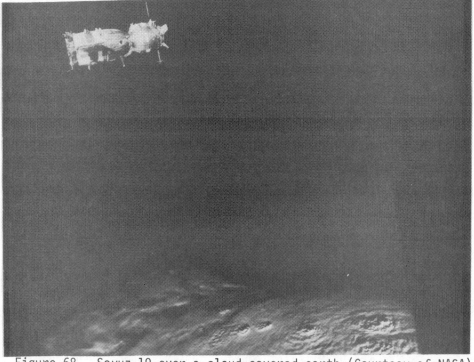

Figure 68   Soyuz 19 over a cloud-covered earth (Courtesy of NASA)

Figure 69   Rear view of Soyuz 19 as seen from Apollo
            (Courtesy of NASA)

Figure 70   Cosmonaut Leonov in Soyuz orbital module with drawing he
            made of Astronaut Thomas Stafford   (Courtesy of NASA)

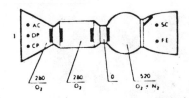

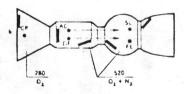

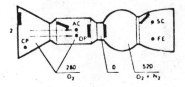

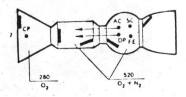

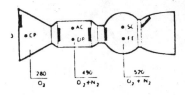

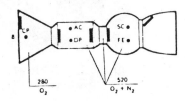

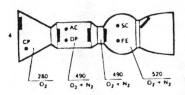

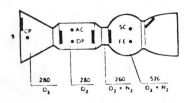

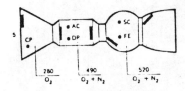

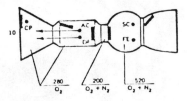

Figure 71   Cabin pressurization and movement
during first crew transfer of the
ASTP mission

192

mode. About three hours later at 1826 hr after reevaluating the docking mechanism and docking procedures the spacecraft separated for the final time. For the next several hours Apollo flew around Soyuz in a station keeping exercise in part to complete additional experiments involving determination of the amounts of atomic nitrogen and oxygen at that altitude by ultraviolet absorption. A few hours later both crews were asleep in their respective spacecraft as they slowly drifted further apart.

The following day (20 July) Leonov and Kubasov spent concluding their scientific experiment packages and preparing for the return to earth. A test firing of the Soyuz propulsion system indicated that all was in order. Finally, at 1310 hr on 21 July, with Leonov and Kubasov back in the command module wearing space suits, the long retro-burn dropping them out of orbit was made. The descent module came to rest 40 minutes later 87 km NE of Arkalyk in a textbook reentry sequence. Within four minutes both cosmonauts were out of their craft greeting the recovery party (Figure 72).

The highly successful ASTP mission came to an end with the safe landing of the Apollo spacecraft in the Pacific Ocean at 0019 hr on 25 July.

Figure 72   Cosmonaut Kubasov autographs the Soyuz 19 command
            module after a successful flight and landing
            (Courtesy of NASA/USSR Academy of Sciences)

SOYUZ 22

Following the return of Soyuz 19 the Soviet space program appeared to resume full concentration on the Soyuz/Salyut space station missions. The Soyuz 18B cosmonauts returned to earth just six days after Soyuz 19's landing after completion of a record breaking 63 day space endurance flight. Between 17 November 1975 and 16 February 1976 an unmanned Soyuz 20 spacecraft (only the second unmanned vehicle to carry the label of a Soviet man in space program) flew a 91-day mission with the then abandoned Salyut 4. Finally, Soyuz 21 which had been launched 6 July 1976 left the Salyut 5 laboratory after 49 days in space amid reports that a 90-day flight had been cut short due to spacecraft malfunctions.[115]

Thus the announcement on 15 September of the 1248 hr Moscow time launch of Soyuz 22 on a solo earth orbital research mission was unexpected. Earlier that year Cosmonaut Klimuk had stated that no further solo Soyuz missions would be flown.[116] However, it is probably significant that Soyuz 22 used the Soyuz 19 backup spacecraft which could be converted for the Soyuz 22 mission with a minimum of effort.

On board were Valeriy Fedorovich Bykovsky (his first flight since Vostok 5) and rookie Vladimir Viktorovich Aksenov. Shortly after takeoff the mission was confirmed to be one designed primarily to evaluate photographic earth-resources techniques and was to be of short duration. The spacecraft entered an unusual orbit of approximately 281 km by 200 km with an orbital inclination of 64.75°.[117] This was the first time in the entire ten-year old Soyuz program that a manned spacecraft had flown at that inclination (all Vostok and Voskhod flights were performed at 65 degrees).

In order to carry out their photographic mission Bykovsky made orbital corrections on the fourth orbit. After two burns of the propulsion system of 20 and 34 seconds duration, respectively, Soyuz 22 entered a more circular orbit of 280 km by 250 km. Further maneuvers on the last revolution of their first 24 hours in space refined the orbit to 257 km by 251 km.

Soyuz 22 carried a wide variety of new equipment and experiments. Paramount was the inclusion of the 204 kg East German multi-spectral MKF-6 camera system. Located at the forward end of the spacecraft in place of the familiar docking mechanism, the system was operated by Aksenov from within the orbital module. (See Figure 73.) The heart of the camera

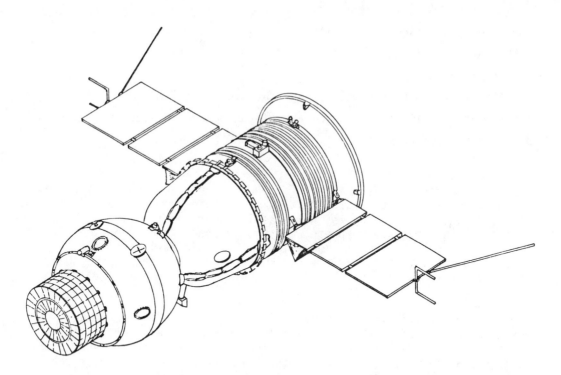

Figure 73   Soyuz 22. Note the MKF-6 multi-spectral camera system
in place of the ASTP docking mechanism (Courtesy of R.F. Gibbons)

system built by the Carl Zeiss People's Enterprise of Jena, East Germany,
over a span of three years were the six (4 visible light and 2 infrared)
lenses enabling the system to obtain six images of a preselected area simultaneously.

To operate, the cosmonauts first opened the exterior housing cover which
protected the instrument when not in use. The camera was then loaded with
film cassettes and readied for shooting. Bykovsky was responsible for the
control and orientation of the spacecraft during photographic sessions
while from the orbital module control panel Aksenov could select single or
multiple exposures. In the multiple exposure mode a variable percentage
of overlap between frames was possible. Within ten minutes almost half
a million square kilometers of the earth could be photographed with a resolution of 20 meters.

As with other multi-zonal cameras employed by previous Soyuz crews, the
comparison of area photographs in different wavelengths permits determination of such items as crop and forest infestation and growth, topographical

formations, and mineral deposits, The camera was first tested on the
15th orbit when it was able to record 19,000 km^2 of eastern Siberia on a
single frame.

Also included on the mission agenda were several medical and biological
experiments. Following is a summary of the major experiments performed
during the Soyuz 22 flight:[118]

16 Sep 1976

Preparations were made to begin MKF-6 photographic sessions. First test
frames were taken on the 15th orbit. These photographs included the region
of the Baikal-Amur railway which was still under construction. The upper
layers of the earth's atmosphere were photographed in conjunction with the
lunar pictures to be shot two days later. The Biogravistat experiment was
begun with the intent to discover the effects of gravitation and dynamic
movements on young plants.

17 Sep 1976

Light and color effects of penetrating cosmic rays on the cosmonauts' optic
nerves were studied. Spacecraft atmospheric samples were collected. Photography covered Siberia to the Sea of Okhotsk in the morning and north-
western USSR later in the day. Further atmospheric pictures were taken.

18 Sep 1976

Photographs were made of the rising and setting moon to evaluate characteristics of the earth's atmosphere and to examine the present cleanliness of
the spacecraft windows. The MKF-6 photographed central Asia, Kazakhstan,
and Siberia primarily to investigate agricultural and geological formations.

19 Sep 1976

Soviet aircraft, carrying a second MKF-6 which could take photographs in
the same spectral frequencies, synchronized their activities with those
of Soyuz 22 over portions of Azerbaydzhan, the southern Urals, western
Siberia, the Baikal-Amur railroad, and other sections of the USSR. These
complementary photographs, when compared, yielded additional geographic
data. Biogravistat operations continued as did the observations of the
fish growth and development.

20 Sep 1976

Northern USSR was photographed by the two orbiting cosmonauts. Later
Soyuz 22 overflew Siberia and European USSR. All biological experiments
continued.

21 Sep 1976

Central Asia, Kazakhstan, eastern Siberia, and southwestern USSR were again
targets for the MKF-6. An AN-30 aircraft of the USSR Academy of Sciences
Institute carrying the sister MKF-6 completed simultaneous aerial photography over East Germany with Soyuz 22. 500 photographs were taken by the
AN-30 on Soyuz's 99th orbit. Visual techniques of manual orientation were
tested. East Germany, the Baltic states, Moscow, and Leningrad were the
subject of some of the final MKF-6 photographs.

Bykovsky and Aksenov concluded the biological experiments and commenced transfer of equipment and samples into the command module for the return to earth. The Soyuz propulsion system was activated and found to be in operational order for the retro-burn. Optical effects of cosmic rays were tested for the final time.

Early in the morning of 23 September, Bykovsky and Aksenov made ready for the final propulsion engine retro-burn. The retro-fire, followed several minutes later by the jettisoning of the orbital and propulsion modules, occurred right on schedule. By 1042 hr the two cosmonauts had gently landed 140 km NW of Tselinograd. Their eight-day international mission had been completed successfully and without incident. In all, over 2400 photographs were returned.

There has been some dispute over the actual purpose of the Soyuz 22 mission. Although no one could question the scientific accomplishments, especially in the field of earth resources, it was also true that unmanned artificial satellites could have done the same job. In fact, some reports suggested that a new series of Soviet earth resources satellites would soon follow based on the experience of Soyuz 22. This alone, though, could hardly justify the expense of the eight-day manned flight.

The return to an inclination of 65° and the reemergence of Bykovsky after thirteen years complicated the puzzle. Bykovsky, a career military officer, was often mentioned in the late 1960's and early 1970's in association with the Soviet lunar landing program. Observers were also quick to point out that an extensive NATO exercise was taking place during this time period which could not be observed at the usual 51.7° inclination. Thus, the conclusion has often been drawn that Soyuz 22 was in effect a manned spy space mission. The validity of this accusation, however, awaits further confirmation.

REFERENCES AND NOTES - SECTION III

1. Vladimirov states that the original design was carried out in 1963. Vladimirov, Leonid, *The Russian Space Bluff*, p. 121. In part this is supported by Dimitriyev, A. Yu., et al., *From Spaceships to Orbiting Stations*, p. 30 and Borisenko, I.G., *Space Launches and Finishes*, p. 29.

2. Remember that this book was published after the cancellation of the Soviet man landing lunar program.

3. *Aviation Week and Space Technology*, 21 Jan. 1974 and 28 Jan. 1974; Wilding-White, T.M., *Jane's Pocket Book of Space Exploration*, p. 15.

4. The command module bears an uncanny resemblance to an early (1961) General Electric design for the US Apollo command module. See *Aviation Week*, 24 Apr. 1961.

5. All weights and measurements given for Soyuz modules are approximate due to modifications arising on different versions of Soyuz.

6. Petrov, G.I., *Conquest of Outer Space in the USSR, 1967-1970*, p. 66.

7. *Flug Revue* Jan. 1977, pp. 17-19; *Aviation Week and Space Technology*, 28 Jan. 1974, p. 37; *Orlando Sentinel Star*, 22 Dec. 1976, p. 6-A.

8. Cosmonaut Feoktistov criticized the number of instrument panels in Apollo saying spacecraft should be more like airplane cockpits (presumably Soviet airplane cockpits). He noted that instruments should be "more simple, logical and therefore more efficient." (*Space World*, Mar. 1970, p. 38.)

9. See *Aviation Week and Space Technology*, 21 Jan. 1974 and 28 Jan 1974 for good description of instrument capabilities.

10. Bumshtein, S.I., *Salyut Space Station in Orbit*, p. 30.

11. Dimitriyev, A. Yu., et al,, *op. cit.*, pp. 51-55; *Aviation Week and Space Technology*, 28 Jan. 1974, pp. 36-41.

12. *Aviation Week and Space Technology*, 28 Jan. 1974, p. 41.

13. Umanskiy, S.P., *Man in Space Orbit*, pp. 44-46; *Aviation Week and Space Technology*, 28 Jan. 1974, pp. 40-41.

14. Only recently (1977) have the Soviets used a pressure-fed propulsion system in their man-in-space programs. See Salyut 6 in this book and Bychkov, V.N., *Liquid Rocket Space Engines*.

15. *Spaceflight,* July-Aug. 1976, pp. 283-284 and Aug. 1974, pp. 300-302.

16. Gatland, Kenneth, *Manned Spaceflight,* pp. 260-261; Petrov, G.I., *op. cit.,* pp. 162-163; *Aviation Week and Space Technology,* 28 Jan. 1974, pp. 36-37.

17. Umanskiy, S.P., *op. cit.,* pp. 48-49; Dimitriyev, A.Yu., *op. cit.,* pp. 38-40. This system was put to the test during the abortive launching of the Soyuz 18A spacecraft. Thankfully, the crew members survived the abort without serious injury.

18. Dimitriyev, A.Yu., *op. cit.,* pp. 47-51.

19. Ponomarev, A.N., *The Years of the Space Era,* p. 239; Kamanin, N. and Rebrov, M., *An Experimental Space Station in Orbit,* p. 91; *Jane's All the World's Aircraft, 1975-1976,* p. 675; Petrov, G.I., *op. cit.,* pp. 57, 161; Dimitriyev, A.Yu., *op. cit.,* pp. 37, 54-55.

20. Umanskiy, S.P., *op. cit.,* p. 80. For further discussions of various systems see: Dimitriyev, A.Yu., *op. cit.,* pp. 21-55; Petrov, G.I., *op. cit.,* pp. 63-68; *Aviation Week and Space Technology,* 21 Jan. 1974, pp. 38-42 and 28 Jan. 1974, pp. 36-41 and 27 Apr. 1970, pp. 70-74; *The Sons of the Blue Planet,* pp. 169-174; Bumshtein, S.I., *op. cit.,* pp. 28-32.

21. See *Soviet Space Programs, 1971-1975* pp. 475-478 for a discussion of Soyuz communications by Geoffrey Perry.

22. Shelton, William, *Soviet Space Exploration: the First Decade,* pp. 266-267; *Aviation Week and Space Technology,* 1 May 1967.

23. *Soviet Space Programs, 1971-1975,* p. 194; Tereshkova later indicated that this flight may have been a failure, *It is I, Seagull,* p. 196.

24. *NASA Authorization for Fiscal Year 1975,* Hearing before the Committee on Aeronautical and Space Sciences, US Senate, p. 242.

25. Gatland, Kenneth, *op. cit.,* p. 234; *Spaceflight,* Mar. 1975, pp. 119-120.

26. *Spaceflight,* May 1974, p. 200; *Aviation Week and Space Technology,* 23 Feb. 1976; *Soviet Space Programs, 1971-1975,* p. 197. Initially *Aviation Week and Space Technology* mistakenly reported Kosmos 613 as a Salyut space station with which Soyuz 13 was scheduled to dock (AWST, 17 Dec. 1973, p. 25).

27. *Aviation Week and Space Technology,* 22 Apr. 1974, p. 21 and 19 Aug. 1974, p. 18; *Soviet Space Programs, 1971-1975,* p. 199.

28. Gatland, Kenneth, *op. cit.*, p. 233; *Aviation Week and Space Technology,* 3 June 1974; *Spaceflight,* July 1975, p. 279.

29. *Soviet Space Programs, 1971-1975,* p. 199; *Aviation Week and Space Technology,* 12 Aug. 1974, p. 22 and 19 Aug. 1974, p. 18.

30. *Aviation Week and Space Technology,* 13 Oct. 1975, p. 11; *Soviet Space Programs, 1971-1975,* p. 214.

31. *Orlando Sentinel Star,* 22 Dec. 1976, p. 6-A; *Flug Revue,* Jan. 1977, pp. 17-19; *Aviation Week and Space Technology,* 13 Dec. 1976, p. 27.

32. Mandrovsky, Boris, *Soyuz 1. Facts and Speculations,* pp. 1-2; Shelton, William, *op. cit.,* pp. 210, 267-268; *Space Technology International,* July 1967, p. 44; *Space World,* June 1974, p. 10; *Spaceflight,* Sep. 1967, pp. 294-298 and May 1977, pp. 183-189; *Soviet Space Programs, 1966-1970,* p. 366; Peterson, R.W., ed., *Space: From Gemini to the Moon and Beyond,* pp. 93-95.

33. *Soviet Space Programs, 1966-1970,* p. 364.

34. Peterson, R.W., ed., *op. cit.,* p. 94.

35. Skuridin, G.A. ed., *Mastery of Outer Space in the USSR, 1957-1967,* pp. 1101-1102; Blagonravov, A.A., et al., *USSR Achievements in Space Research, First Decade in Space, 1957-1967,* p. 593.

36. Mandrovsky, Boris, *op. cit.,* pp. 8-9; *Space/Aeronautics,* "Perspective", May 1967.

37. Skuridin, G.A., ed., *op. cit.,* pp. 1103-1104; Shelton, William, *op. cit.,* p. 274.

38. Skuridin, G.A., ed., *op. cit.,* pp. 1105-1106.

39. Smolders, Peter, *Soviets in Space,* p. 150; Borisenko, I.G., *op. cit.,* pp. 31-32; *Aviation Week and Space Technology,* 1 May 1967.

40. Peterson, R.W., ed., *op. cit.,* p. 87.

41. *Spaceflight,* May 1977, pp. 183-189 and Sep. 1977, pp. 334-335 and Jan. 1978, pp. 39-40.

42   *Spaceflight,* Jan. 1978, pp. 39-40; *Space Technology International,* July 1967, p. 43; *Aviation Week and Space Technology,* 1 May 1967, p. 22 and 15 May 1967, p. 69; Smolders, Peter, *op. cit.,* pp. 147, 157-158; *Space World,* June 1974, pp. 11-12; *Science News,* 6 May 1967; *Spaceflight,* Sep. 1977, pp. 334-335.

43. Hall, Al, ed., *Petersen's Book of Man in Space, Volume 3,* p. 65.

44. Lebedev, V. and Gagarin, Yuri, *Survival in Space*, p. 101; Turnill, Reginald, *The Observer's Book of Manned Spaceflight*, p. 130; Smolders, Peter, *op. cit.*, pp. 155-156.

45. *Nature*, Volume 255, 15 May 1975, p. 87; *Ramparts*, Aug. 1972, pp. 42-43; Gatland, Kenneth, *op. cit.*, p. 140.

46. *Aviation Week and Space Technology*, 19 June 1967, pp. 66 and 71.

47. Petrov, G.I., *op. cit.*, pp. 15-23.

48. *Spaceflight*, Jan. 1968, pp. 17-18; *Aviation Week and Space Technology*, 6 Nov. 1967, p. 16; *The Sons of the Blue Planet*, pp. 186-187.

49. Petrov, G.I., *op. cit.*, pp. 19-20; *Spaceflight*, Jan. 1968, p. 18.

50. The first fuel transfer to a manned space station was accomplished by the Soviets during the Soyuz 26/Salyut 6/Progress 1 mission in Jan.-Feb. 1978.

51. James, Peter N., *Soviet Conquest From Space*, pp. 90-91.

52. See Progress 1 and 2 in this book for problems involved in fuel transfer in space.

53. See Zond 4, *Volume 47, Science and Technology Series* and *Apollo and Zond - Race Around the Moon?* by this author in *Spaceflight*, Dec. 1978.

54. Petrov, G.I., *op. cit.*, pp. 26, 31; *Aviation Week and Space Technology*, 29 Apr. 1968, p. 32.

55. Petrov, G.I., *op. cit.*, pp. 34-35.

56. *Spaceflight*, Sep. 1968, pp. 303-305; Petrov, G.I., *op. cit.*, pp. 28-30.

57. *Interavia*, Dec. 1968, p. 1489; Peterson, R.W., ed., *op. cit.*, p. 142; Borisenko, I.G., *op. cit.*, pp. 34-35; Petrov, G.I., *op. cit.*, pp. 39-40; *Aviation Week and Space Technology*, 4 Nov. 1968, pp. 16-17.

58. *Spaceflight*, Oct. 1976, pp. 369-370.

59. *The Sons of the Blue Planet*, p. 188; Smolders, Peter, *op. cit.*, p. 163; Petrov, G.I., *op. cit.*, p. 69; *Spaceflight*, Feb. 1969, pp. 67-71.

60. Gurney, G. and C., *Cosmonauts in Orbit*, p. 123; *Soviet Space Programs, 1971-1975*, p. 182; Petrov, G.I., *op. cit.*, p. 67; *Jane's All the World's Aircraft, 1969-1970*. However Beregovoi is also quoted as saying Soyuz 2 and 3 were identical and docking was not part of the flight plan. See *Spaceflight*, Feb. 1969, p. 71 and Smolders, Peter, *op. cit.*, pp. 163-164.

61. An unsubstantiated story which places the blame on Beregovoi can be found in *Space World*, Oct. 1974, p. 9.

62. Petrov, G.I., *op. cit.*, pp. 41-47; *Spaceflight,* Feb. 1969, p. 68.

63. *The Sons of the Blue Planet,* pp. 188-189; *Spaceflight,* Feb. 1969, pp. 68-70.

64. Petrov, G.I., *op. cit.,* p. 59; *Spaceflight,* May 1975, p. 170.

65. Kamanin, N. and Rebrov, M., *op. cit.*, pp. 20-21; Petrov, G.I., *op. cit.*, pp. 72-73.

66. Kamanin, N. and Rebrov, M., *op. cit.*, pp. 27-28; Petrov, G.I., *op. cit.*, p. 107.

67. Petrov, G.I., *op. cit.*, p. 107.

68. Kamanin, N. and Rebrov, M., *op. cit.*, pp. 28-32.

69. Kamanin, N. and Reborov, M., *op. cit.*, pp. 32, 51-52; Petrov, G.I., *op. cit.*, p. 107.

70. Herzl, George, G., ed., *Sixth Aerospace Mechanisms Symposium, NASA TM X-2557,* pp. 143-150.

71. These life support packages appear to have been strapped to the cosmonauts' legs instead of being worn as a back pack. See Riabchikov, Evgeny, *Russians in Space,* p. 255; Gurney G. and C., *op. cit.*, p. 129; *Space World,* Feb. 1976, p. 9; Smolders, Peter, *op. cit.*, pp. 172-174; Dimitriyev, A.Yu., *op. cit.,* p. 64; Turnill, Reginald, *op. cit.*, p. 133.

72. Borisenko, I.G., *In Outer Space,* p. 115; Kamanin, N. and Rebrov, M., *op. cit.*, pp. 55-56, 78-79; Petrov, G.I., *op. cit.,* pp. 95, 112-114.

73. *The Sons of the Blue Planet,* p. 226; Kamanin, N. and Rebrov, M., *op. cit.*, pp. 86-87; Petrov, G.I., *op. cit.*, p. 95.

74. Petrov, G.I., *op. cit.*, pp. 89-91.

75. Petrov, G.I., *op. cit.*, pp. 91-94.

76. Petrov, G.I., *op. cit.*, p. 96. For a personal summary of the flight by the cosmonauts see Petrov, G.I., *op. cit.,* pp. 106-116 and *Spaceflight,* May 1969, pp. 173-176.

77. *Aviation Week and Space Technology,* 27 Jan. 1969, pp. 18-19; *Space World,* Feb. 1976, pp. 4-22.

78. *Soviet Space Programs, 1966-1970,* pp. 366-372.

79. Petrov, G.I., *op. cit.*, pp. 116-118; *Soviet Space Programs, 1966-1970,* pp. 376-377.

80. Petrov, G.I., *op. cit.*, pp. 122-125.

81. Petrov, G.I., *op. cit.*, p. 129.

82. This gave rise to some theories that problems appeared in the automatic systems. See *Aviation Week and Space Technology,* 20 Oct. 1969, pp. 190-191 and 27 Oct. 1969, pp. 18-19.

83. *Aviation Week and Space Technology, ibid;* Petrov, G.I., *op. cit.,* pp. 135-136.

84. Ponomarev, A.N., *op. cit.*, p. 237; Smolders, Peter; *op. cit.*, p. 181; Petrov, G.I., *op. cit.*, pp. 138-139, 157-159.

85. Petrov, G.I., *op. cit.*, p. 158.

86. Petrov, G.I., *op. cit.*, p. 159.

87. Dimitriyev, A.Yu., *op. cit.*, p. 77; Petrov, G.I., *op. cit.*, pp. 140, 156, 159-160; *Spaceview,* Mar./Apr. 1977, pp. 23-25; *Aviation Week and Space Technology,* 27 Oct. 1969, p. 19.

88. Dimitriyev, A.Yu., *op. cit.*, pp. 77-78; Gurney, G. and C., *op. cit.*, p. 137.

89. Lewis, Richard S., *From Vineland to Mars,* pp. 222-223; *Soviet Space Programs, 1971-1975,* pp. 184, 495; *Interavia,* Nov. 1969, p. 1747; Gurney, G. and C., *op. cit.*, p. 135; Peterson, R.W., ed., *op. cit.*, pp. 208-210.

90. *Soviet Space Programs, 1971-1975,* p. 184. See also Soyuz 6/7/8 in *Jane's All the World's Aircraft, 1970-1971.*

91. Beard, Robert, *Soviet Space Failures;* Turnill, Reginald, *op. cit.*, p. 135; Smolders, Peter, *op. cit.*, pp. 182-183.

92. *Aviation Week and Space Technology,* 17 Nov. 1969, pp. 26-27 and 30 Apr. 1973; *Space World,* Jan. 1976, pp. 12-13.

93. Petrov, G.I., *op. cit.*, pp. 197-198.

94. For more detailed descriptions of the experiments and work performed see: Petrov, G.I., *op. cit.*, pp. 189-210; Smolders, Peter, *op. cit.*, pp. 186-194; *Soviet Space Programs, 1966-1970,* pp. 238-240; Ponomarev, A.N., *op. cit.*, pp. 241-249; *Investigations of the Upper Atmosphere and Outer Space Conducted in 1970 in the USSR,* pp. 84-87; *Third and Fourth Orbital International Laboratory Symposia,* pp. 63-90, 109-116.

95. Borisenko, I.G., *Space Launches and Finishes,* pp. 45-46; Petrov, G.I., *op. cit.*, p. 198.

96. Riabchikov, Evgeny, *op. cit.*, p. 282; Peterson, R.W., ed., *op. cit.*, pp. 252-253; Smolders, Peter, *op. cit.*, pp. 189, 193; Petrov, G.I., *op. cit.*, p. 204; Borisenko, I.G., *op. cit.*, pp. 46-47.

97. *Aviation Week and Space Technology,* 28 Jan. 1974, p. 41.

98. Kosmos 496 may have been a failure. See Kosmos 496 earlier in this section.

99. *Aviation Week and Space Technology,* 16 Apr. 1973.

100. The winged configuration would be retained for non-Salyut missions.

101. In fact, Lazarev and Makarov were scheduled to board Salyut 4, but their Soyuz 18A spacecraft never achieved orbit due to the only manned launch failure.

102. *Space Research Conducted in the USSR in 1973,* p. 96.

103. *Aviatsiya I. Kosmonavtika,* Volume 16, No. 1, p. 8.

104. See the following for further experiment details: Saydeyev, R.Z., ed., *The Conquest of Outer Space in the USSR 1974,* pp. 73-96; *Aviation Week and Space Technology,* 14 Jan. 1974, pp. 20-21; Borisenko, I.G., *op. cit.,* pp. 56-58; *Spaceflight,* Feb. 1976, p. 74; *Soviet Space Space Programs, 1971-1975,* pp. 198-199; *Space Research Conducted in in the USSR in 1973,* pp. 80-81, 97.

105. Sagdeyev, R.Z., ed., *op. cit.,* pp. 73-78, 80-81; *Space Research Conducted in the USSR in 1973,* p. 97; *Aviation Week and Space Technology,* 14 Jan. 1974, p. 21; *Spaceflight,* Feb. 1976, p. 74 and May 1976, p. 177.

106. Sagdeyev, R.Z., ed., *op. cit.,* p. 83.

107. Various parameters have been given for this initial orbit: *Soviet Space Programs, 1971-1975* - 352 km by 254 km; Turnill, Reginald, *The Observer's Spaceflight Directory* - 254 km by 169 km; Royal Aircraft Establishment - 291 km by 184 km (by 3rd orbit).

108. Sagdeyev, R.Z., ed., *op. cit.,* pp. 263-309; *Spaceflight,* Mar. 1975, pp. 111-112. See also *Apollo-Soyuz,* NASA EP-109, pp. 71-82 for description of those experiments which were also repeated on the ASTP mission.

109. The unmanned ASTP test of Kosmos 672 was launched in Aug. 1974 into a 221 km by 195 km orbit and Soyuz 19 which was the Soviet half of ASTP first entered into a 228 km by 188 km orbit.

110. *Aviation Week and Space Technology,* 3 Feb. 1975, p. 18 and 14 Apr. 1975.

111. For a general description of the flight by each country see *Apollo-Soyuz* by Walter Froehlich, NASA EP-109 and *Soyuz and Apollo,* Moscow 1976. For an in depth analysis of the history of US-USSR space co-operation up to and including the preparations of ASTP see *US-Soviet Cooperation in Space* by Dodd L. Harvey and Linda C. Ciccoritti. *The Partnership, A History of the Apollo-Soyuz Test Project,* E.C. and L.N. Ezell, NASA SP-4209.

112. An entire second Soyuz spacecraft and launcher were readied as a back-up. Preparations on the second vehicle only stopped five hours before launch.

113. See Sagdeyev, R.Z., ed., *op. cit.*, pp. 520-547 for general compatibility discussion. See same source pp. 547-597 for general ASTP preparation procedures.

114. To list a few: Turnill, Reginald, *op. cit.*, pp. 59-84; *Spaceflight*, Oct. 1975, pp. 356-358 and Nov. 1975, pp. 384-391 and Dec. 1975, pp. 427-434; *Apollo-Soyuz* (EP-109); *Soyuz and Apollo, a USSR Publication; Apollo-Soyuz Mission Report*, Volume 34, *Advances in the Astronautical Sciences,* ed., C.M. Lee, American Astronautical Society, 1977.

115. See Soyuz 21 mission in this book.

116. *Spaceflight,* Feb. 1977, p. 62; *Space World*, July 1977, pp. 37-38; *Aviation Week and Space Technology,* 21 June 1976, p. 23.

117. Royal Aircraft Establishment. Also *Spaceflight,* Feb. 1977, p. 62.

118. Details of this flight can be found most easily in *Spaceflight,* Feb. 1977, pp. 61-63 and Mar. 1979, pp. 110-112; Turnill, Reginald, *op. cit.*, pp. 313-314; *Space World*, July 1977, pp. 36-42; *Tass and Izvestiya* releases of 15 Sep.-23 Sep., 1976.

Section IV

SALYUT SPACE STATION

INTRODUCTION TO SALYUT

Since 1971 the USSR man-in-space program has been directed toward the exploitation of space, utilizing the Soyuz spacecraft and long-term Salyut space stations. From the launching on 19 April 1971 of Salyut 1 to the orbiting of Salyut 6 in 1977, the Soviet Union has orbited seven of these large space stations and has perhaps attempted to launch two others. This enormous expenditure of money and manpower reflects the determination of the Soviet Union not only to maintain her presence in space, but also ultimately conquer it.

Serious space-station concepts have appeared in Soviet literature since the early part of this century; however, not until the 1960's, when the reality of manned space flight was proven by Yuri Gagarin aboard Vostok 1, was the specific task of constructing an orbiting laboratory undertaken.[1] Manned operations from an orbiting platform open a wide vista of opportunities: earth resources research, astronomical observation, medical and biological investigations of the effects of weightlessness and radiation, scientific and industrial experimentation of manufacture in a weightless vacuum, and military surveillance.

The 1969 docking of Soyuz 4 and Soyuz 5 in earth orbit was billed by the Soviets as the creation of the world's first experimental space station. Although the configuration did provide a total working volume of 18 m^3 (the largest to that date) and held four cosmonauts, the Soyuz combination remained mated for only a few hours and crew transfer between orbital compartments required extravehicular activity. By definition a space station must be a long-term (months or years) platform within which crew members can easily travel from one compartment to another.

Although eventually bigger space stations will undoubtably be assembled in earth orbit and may take the form of the familiar toroidal stations of

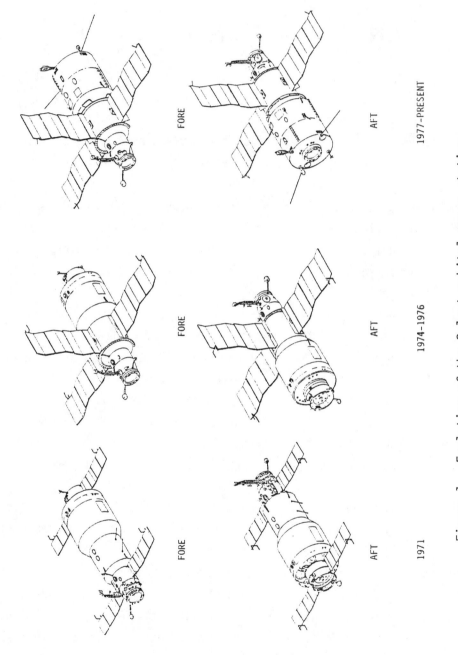

FORE

AFT

1977-PRESENT

FORE

AFT

1974-1976

FORE

AFT

1971

Figure 1   Evolution of the Salyut orbital space station
(Drawings by R.F. Gibbons)

science fiction renown, the earliest stations were restricted to launching in one piece by available conventional rockets. Thus the space stations which to date have been orbited by the US and USSR have by necessity been cylindrical in shape. As early as 1962, Z. Dobrichovsky proposed an elementary Soviet space station capable of supporting four men for a period of sixty days. His three compartment design bears a close resemblance to the subsequent Salyut stations of the 1970s. Dobrichovsky envisioned the forward section as the crew quarters and operations center as well as serving the dual purpose of return ferry. The second compartment consisted of the last stage of the launch vehicle with the remaining fuel pumped out to provide a substantial working and living area. Instrumentation comprised the third and final compartment.

As with the Soyuz spacecraft Salyut has undergone major redesign efforts during its nine-year existence. These improvements in capability and sophistication can be distinguished by first, second, and third generation spacecraft (Figure 1). Additionally, by analyzing the characteristics of each space laboratory, Salyut missions appear to fall into two separate programs: civilian and military.

Figure 2 tabulates the seven known Salyut space stations which have reached earth orbit. This section is dedicated to an in-depth review of these station characteristics and histories. The individual Soyuz missions to these orbiting platforms are discussed in the following section.

SALYUT SPACE STATIONS

Designator	Launch Date	Days In Orbit	Type	Related Missions
Salyut 1	19 Apr 1971	175	Civilian/ Military	2 - Soyuz 10, Soyuz 11
Salyut 2	3 Apr 1973	55	Military	0 - Broke up shortly after orbital insertion
Kosmos 557	11 May 1973	11	Civilian	0 - Apparently experienced major failure after orbital insertion
Salyut 3	25 Jun 1974	214	Military	2 - Soyuz 14, Soyuz 15
Salyut 4	26 Dec 1974	770	Civilian	4 - Soyuz 17, Soyuz 18A, Soyuz 18B, Soyuz 20
Salyut 5	22 Jun 1976	412	Military	3 - Soyuz 21, Soyuz 23, Soyuz 24
Salyut 6	29 Sep 1977		Civilian	23 - Soyuz 25, Soyuz 26, Soyuz 27, Progress 1, Soyuz 28, Soyuz 29, Soyuz 30, Progress 2, Progress 3, Soyuz 31, Progress 4, Soyuz 32, Progress 5, Soyuz 33, Progress 6, Progress 7, Soyuz 34, Soyuz T-1, Progress 8, Soyuz 35, Progress 9, Soyuz 36, Soyuz T-2

Figure 2

Chapter 11

SALYUT PROGRAMS

After the initial design and development of the Salyut space station in the mid- and late-1960s, the USSR man-in-space program broke off into two separate branches: one civilian-oriented, one with military objectives. This is not to say that experiments of military value are not performed during a civilian flight or that cosmonauts on a military mission do not conduct some purely scientific experiments. But the training, mission profiles and, in some cases, Salyut capabilities differ between the two programs.

This delineation between civilian and military objectives is not surprising. While the USSR refuses to acknowledge the military aspect of any of its satellites or manned programs, Western observers have a tendency to go to the other extreme by reading military motives into every rocket launched from the Soviet Union. The true nature of the Soviet space program does, of course, lie somewhere in between. The civilian side is represented by lunar and planetary probes, high orbiting astronomical and astrophysical observatories, biological payloads, and earth-resources satellites, to name a few. On the other hand, the Soviet Union has demonstrated its prowess in perfecting photographic reconnaissance satellites, ocean-surveillance platforms, electronic ferrets, and hunter-killer satellites.

A dual-purpose space program is to be expected. It was after all the military potential of space flight which prompted both the US and the USSR to invest such large sums of money into developing orbital capabilities in the 1950s and early 1960s. The US has never concealed the fact that it maintains two separate space programs: civilian, managed by NASA with launchings at Kennedy Space Center, and military, managed by the USAF with launchings at Vandenberg AFB. The US has in the past sought to develop two purely militarily oriented man-in-space programs: Dyna-Soar (X-20), 1958-1963, and Manned Orbiting Laboratory (MOL), 1963-1969. Both programs were cancelled before operational flights could be initiated due to program limitations, advancing technology, and budgetary problems.

In a parallel to the subsequent Soviet development, MOL and the Apollo Orbital Workshop (which later evolved into Skylab) were being designed at about the same time and with similar capabilities, but of course with different objectives. This duplication of effort--the construction of two entirely different systems with similar capabilities by two federally funded agencies--was the eventual downfall of MOL by a cost-conscious Congress.

Although the Soviet Union is not hampered by the type of funding procedures which have always been a thorn in the side of NASA and the US military, Moscow took a more efficient approach; that is, design the basic space station, ferry, and launch vehicles to meet all needs, then segregate engineers and program managers into two distinct--and in many ways isolated--bureaus.

Figure 2 illustrates the seemingly balanced nature of the Salyut civilian and military programs. Salyut 1 appears to have been a test vehicle for the series to evaluate basic system capabilities and reliability. When Salyut 2 and Kosmos 557 flew in April and May of 1973 their premature demises prevented a clear analysis of their missions. It was noted, however, that Salyut 2 had transmitted in frequencies reserved solely for military reconnaissance satellites and not on the standard Soviet manned-flight-related communication frequencies. Not until after the launch of Salyut 3 and Salyut 4 in 1974 was the dual nature of the Salyut program suspected.

One of the first to recognize the significance of these differences was Sven Grahn.[2] He noted that while Salyut 1, Kosmos 557, and Salyut 4 telemetry transmissions were found on 15,008 MHz and employed continuous wave-pulse duration modulation, Salyuts 2 and 3 had used 19.994 MHz with frequency-shift key-pulse duration modulation. An investigation into these differences brought out other identifying characteristics which have been upheld by Salyut 5 and 6.

Figure 3 indicates that the civilian and military versions of Salyut can be characterized by the following:

CIVILIAN AND MILITARY SALYUT PROGRAMS

Program	Designator	Operational Orbit (average in km)	Telemetry Frequency (MHz)	Crew Composition
Prototype	Salyut 1	270-250	15.008 922.75	Soyuz 10: Shatalov (M, Com) Yeliseyev (C) Rukavishnikov (C) Soyuz 11: Dobrovolskiy (M, Com) Patseyev (C) Volkov (C)
Civilian	Kosmos 557	Never reached operational orbit	15.008 922.75	None. Malfunction and decayed in 11 days
	Salyut 4	350-340	15.008 922.75	Soyuz 17: Gubarev (M, Com) Grechko (C) Soyuz 18A: Lazarev (M, Com) Makarov (C) Soyuz 18B: Klimuk (M, Com) Sevastyanov (C)
	Salyut 6	350-340	15.008 922.75	Soyuz 25: Kovalenok (M, Com) Ryumin (C) Soyuz 26: Romanenko (M, Com) Grechko (C) Soyuz 27: Dzhanibekov (M, Com) Makarov (C) Soyuz 28: Gubarev (M, Com) Remek (Czech) Soyuz 29: Kovalenok (M, Com) Ivanchenkov (C) Soyuz 30: Klimuk (M, Com) Hermaszewski (Polish) Soyuz 31: Bykovsky (M, Com) Jaehn (East German) Soyuz 32: Lyakhov (M, Com) Ryumin (C) Soyuz 33: Rukavishnikov (C, Com) Ivanov (Bulgarian)
Military	Salyut 2	290-260	19.944	None. Malfunctioned and decayed in 55 days.
	Salyut 3	270-260	19.944 143.625	Soyuz 14: Popovich (M, Com) Artyukhin (M) Soyuz 15: Sarafanov (M, Com) Demin (M)
	Salyut 5	270-260	19.944	Soyuz 21: Volynov (M, Com) Zholobov (M) Soyuz 23: Zudov (M, Com) Rozhdestvenskiy (M) Soyuz 24: Gorbatko (M, Com) Glazkov (M)

M = Military
C = Civilian
Com = Commander of mission

Figure 3

1. <u>Civilian Salyut</u>. These orbital laboratories are flown in high
    (350-340 km) orbits to aid in astronomical observations and to
    reduce atmospheric drag, resulting in less fuel consumption to
    maintain altitude. Telemetry is maintained on standard Soyuz
    frequency of 15,008 MHz. Although the commander of the host Soyuz
    has thus far always been military, the accompanying flight engineer
    is civilian.[3] The equipment located in the large conical shell
    within the Salyut aft working compartment is astronomical and
    astrophysical in nature.
2. <u>Military Salyut</u>. Flown in lower (270-260km) orbits, these space
    stations are equipped for high-resolution photo reconnaissance.
    Photographic equipment is installed in the same position as the
    astronomical and astrophysical apparatus on the civilian Salyuts.
    Low altitudes are essential for the detailed military reconnais-
    sance desired, but larger orbital corrections are required. Tele-
    metry is transmitted on 19.944 MHz and in a different format.
    Military Salyut crews are exclusively military officers and mis-
    sions to these stations are usually of shorter duration. Mili-
    tary Salyuts also have the capability to operate in an unmanned
    mode and to periodically eject photographic capsules to be re-
    covered in the Soviet Union.[4]

Salyut 1 does not fit well into either of these categories, having
characteristics of both. Hence, its true mission was probably one of eval-
evaluation of the potentials of both programs.

At this time, the future of the civilian and military Salyut programs
as separate entities is uncertain. The recent increase in activity in
the civilian sector can be assumed to be continued. The advantages of a
manned military observatory with the capabilities of a Salyut over sophisticated unmanned satellites are not so clear. Two possible paths are
available to Soviet space planners.

If the military Salyut program is to be retained, a new orbital station should be launched in the near future. Although one would not expect
to see more than one Soyuz docked to such a vehicle, the latest third
generation, dual-ported Salyut would probably be used. With the recent
advent of the Progress unmanned space tankers, a military Salyut could

be refueled with the station either unmanned or manned.[5] This would relieve the major problem of keeping the large laboratory at a relatively
low altitude and would permit operations in more promising higher inclinations. Longer life stations with only occasional visits by cosmonauts
and an increased film canister ejection capacity should also be incorporated.

Since the Soviets have expressed the desire to maintain a virtually
continuous manned observation from space,[6] one should expect to see two
functioning Salyuts--one civilian, one military--aloft at the same time.
A step in this direction came in 1975 when the Soviet mission control demonstrated its ability to coordinate two simultaneous and separate manned
space flights (Soyuz 18B and Soyuz 19).

A second possibility would be cancellation of the military Salyut program in favor of longer-lived unmanned photographic satellites and a shorter
duration and more versatile Soviet shuttle.[7] There still exists a great
debate among Western experts on the design of the Soviet shuttle and the
date of its maiden flight, but there is little doubt that such a reusable
vehicle is under construction in the Soviet Union. The ability to make
frequent, short forays into space would be extremely valuable to a military program. However, the advent of the Soviet shuttle should also aid,
rather than hinder, the civilian Salyut program.

Chapter 12

SALYUT SPACECRAFT DESIGN

FIRST GENERATION

Following the conclusion of the Soyuz 6/7/8 missions in October 1969, Communist Party Chief Leonid Brezhnev revealed that the Soviet Union was developing an earth orbiting laboratory. The purpose of the laboratory was to provide for "investigations of space technology, space biology and medicine, geophysics, astronomy and astrophysics."[8]

Reports indicate that one month later the Soviets attempted to launch a Proton rocket carrying either a complete Salyut space station or, perhaps, an unfinished Salyut shell to test basic maneuvering, guidance, power, and communications systems.[9] If this rocket was indeed launched it never reached orbit.

A Salyut space station weighs on the order of 19,000 kg; thus making the use of a Proton launch vehicle mandatory. No other known Soviet rocket is capable of placing such a heavy payload into orbit. If indeed a Salyut-related launch was attempted in November 1969, its failure set back the Salyut program at least one year. On 2 December 1970 Kosmos 382 was hurled into orbit on a yet-to-be-resolved mission. Launched by a Proton rocket, Kosmos 382 performed extensive orbital maneuvers including significant perigee and orbital inclination changes. The purpose of the Kosmos 382 flight is usually thought to be associated with either the Salyut program or a manned lunar landing effort.* However, the realization that the early Salyuts employed the same propulsion system as Soyuz places some doubt as to why a mission of this nature would be needed by the Salyut program.[10]

---

*   See Zond Section of *Volume 47, Science and Technology*

SALYUT 1

Finally, one week after the tenth anniversary of the flight of Vostok 1, the unmanned Salyut 1 space station lifted off a pad at Baikonur and entered a 222 km by 200 km orbit at an inclination of 51.6°. At a weight of 18,900 kg Salyut 1 was the most massive payload ever orbited by the USSR. Within four days Soyuz 10 was launched to rendezvous and dock with the orbiting laboratory.[11] (See Figure 4.)

SALYUT 1 CHRONOLOGY

Date	Event
19 Apr 1971	Salyut 1 launched
23 Apr 1971	Soyuz 10 launched
24 Apr 1971	Soyuz 10 docked with Salyut 1, but crew unable to transfer due to docking/hatch malfunction; Soyuz 10 crew returned to earth
6 Jun 1971	Soyuz 11 launched
7 Jun 1971	Soyuz 11 docked with Salyut 1; crew transferred to station
29 Jun 1971	Soyuz 11 undocked after 23-day stay and returned to earth; crew found dead due to accidental depressurization
11 Oct 1971	Salyut 1 destroyed during reentry after 175 days in orbit.

Figure 4

The dimensions of Salyut 1 were impressive: overall length 16 m (including rendezvous antennae, but without Soyuz attached) with a maximum diameter of 4.15 m. The distance measured across the solar panels was 11 meters. The spacecraft consisted of three major sections, two of which were habitable (Figure 5). Running from the forward end to the aft they were (1) the transfer/docking compartment, (2) the working/living compartment, and (3) the unpressurized instrument/propulsion section.[12]

The transfer/docking compartment was itself 3 m long and 2 m in diameter. The forward end held the drogue-docking mechanism to work in conjunction with the probe of the manned-Soyuz ferry. For the very first time provision was made for removing the probe/drogue combination from the tunnel pathway to allow for the internal transfer of the crew members. This

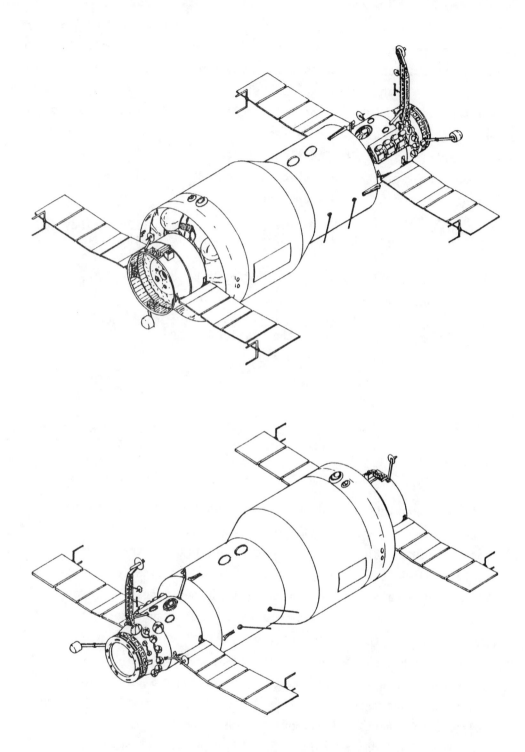

Figure 5   Salyut 1, the world's first manned orbital space station,
launched in April 1971   (Drawings by R.F. Gibbons)

type of docking mechanism has been used on every Soyuz/Salyut mission and is described in section 5.[13] At the far end of the transfer/docking compartment was a second isolation hatch. Within this compartment was the control panel for the Orion stellar telescope (discussed in detail later), some internal components of the Orion telescope, cameras, and biological experiments. An access hatch in the compartment allowed the retrieval of film cartridges from the telescope after exposure.[14]

The exterior of the transfer/docking compartment also housed many important instruments. These included:

1. The external modules of the Orion stellar telescope (They were in a special spherical depression imbedded in the transfer compartment.)

2. Two solar cell panels (left and right)

3. The antennae of the rendezvous radio equipment

4. The optical light for orientation during manual docking of the (Soyuz) spacecraft with the station

5. One of the external television cameras

6. Panels with the heat-regulating system units (the hydraulic pumps, the liquid flow rate regulators, the expansion tanks, and so on)

7. The ion sensors of the station orientation system used to orient the station by the longitudinal-axis with respect to the oncoming ion flux

8. Panels with sensors for studying micrometeorite particles.[15]

The next compartment represented the heart of the Salyut complex. The 9.1-meter-long working compartment was actually composed of two different diameter sections. As the cosmonaut left the transfer/docking compartment he entered a 3.8-m-long, 2.9-m-wide cylindrical area in which was located the main station control panel (the largest of seven such panels). Continuing aft the cosmonauts passed through a short (1.2 m) adapter section to the largest room of the station--4.1 m long, 4.15 m in diameter. This section was dominated by a large conical device which housed varying observational equipment (more to be said later).[16]

An attempt was made to create a frame of reference for the otherwise disoriented cosmonauts. A "floor" ran the length of the station to provide an artificial "down" reference, while the walls, floor, and ends were painted different colors to aid in this deception. Each region of the station was to serve specific purposes. The forward end of the working module was used for dining, recreation, and berthing. Also installed there was the navigational and motion control gyroscopic system along with four of the seven station control panels. The larger portion of the work compartment housed the food and water storage equipment, the sanitation unit, some exercise equipment, and the large observation device (sometimes referred to as the "chimney"). The connection adapter section contained medical supplies and experiments and more exercise equipment.[17]

Running along the exterior "underside" of the small diameter section of the working compartment were an array of instruments and sensors, including vertical and horizon sensors, star finders, an optical orienter, and ion sensors for attitude control (Figure 6). The exterior of the large diameter working compartment was largely devoid of instruments and was covered with a thermal shield for use during launch and once in orbit. One large and several small cutouts appeared in the skin of the compartment to allow penetration of internal instruments. Twelve portholes, radio-equipment antennae, and micrometeorite sensors were also present.

Figure 6   Instrument packed underside of a Salyut space station
(Courtesy of R.F. Gibbons)

The instrument/propulsion compartment completed the Salyut space station and was 2.17 m long with a diameter of 2.2 m. Unaccessible to the cosmonauts, this compartment contained the main propulsion unit, ion sensors, and the attitude-control engines along with the necessary fuel supplies. Two more solar panels were attached 180 degrees apart. A second set of rendezvous antennae extended beyond the compartment skirt. Finally, a second TV camera provided the cosmonauts and earth controllers a view of this portion of the station. One of its functions was to monitor the separation of Salyut from the last stage of the carrier rocket.[18]

The full extent of the duplication of the Soyuz propulsion systems was made evident by a mock-up of a second generation Salyut station at the 1975 Paris air show (Figure 7-8). Identical main propulsion engines are used: 417-kg thrust, single-nozzle primary and a 411-kg thrust, twin-nozzle back-up. In addition four 10-kg thrust engines provide vector control. Surrounding the instrument/propulsion compartment at 90-degree intervals are four sets of six pitch and yaw thrusters. Pairs of roll thrusters complete the attitude-control system units.[19]

The attitude-control system is centered around four ion traps, an infrared vertical detector, a solar sensor, angular-velocity sensors, and the main gyroscopic system. During rendezvous maneuvers the Salyut attitude control system plays the same role as the passive Soyuz vehicle did in earlier Soyuz/Soyuz missions. Initial rendezvous procedures up to 15-30 km require both the Soyuz ferry and the Salyut station to alter orbits in closing the gap. At closer distances, only the orientation of the Salyut station is controlled by the approaching cosmonauts in order to maintain the proper relative alignment of both spacecraft.[20]

Within the station 27 lights provided the proper illumination to all parts of the laboratory and worked in conjunction with the TV and photographic equipment. The remaining two TV cameras of the four total were located within the station. One was fixed such that a view of the Salyut main control panel and the cosmonauts working there was visible (Figure 9). The second was portable and could be used in any part of the station or for viewing through one of the 20 portholes. This latter camera was equipped with both a wide-angle and a telescopic lens. All four cameras recorded 625 lines per frame at 25 frames per second.[21]

Figure 7   Propulsion module of the first two generation Salyuts.
Note the similarity to the Soyuz propulsion engine,
Section 3   (Courtesy of R.F. Gibbons)

Figure 8   Detailed look at the main and back-up nozzles of the
Soyuz/Salyut propulsion system (Courtesy of R.F. Gibbons)

Figure 9   Interior view of the Salyut 1 space station. The photograph
was taken in the adapter section of the working compartment
looking forward. The hatch at the top of the picture separates the transfer/docking compartment from the working
compartment.

As pointed out there were seven discrete control panels throughout
the station for operation of equipment and monitoring of on-board systems:

Station No. 1 is the central control station of Salyut. The control
of the basic on-board systems and, in part, the scientific apparatus
is concentrated here. This station is located in the lower part of
the work compartment (in the small-diameter zone). The station is
equipped with two chairs on which two cosmonauts can operate simultaneously. The cosmonauts' panels, the control arm for the orientation and navigation, the optical viewers of the orientation system,
and ports are located there.

Station No. 2 (astropost) is located in the work compartment (in the
small-diameter zone). It is designed for working out the manual astro-
orientation and astronavigation. At the station there are: a panel,
a control handle for the orientation of the Salyut, means of holding
the cosmonaut in the work position, and a port.

Station No. 3 designed to control the scientific apparatus is located in the control part of the compartment (in the large-diameter zone). Here, provision has been made for control panels for the equipment and a port.

Station No. 4 also serves to control the scientific apparatus and, in addition, it is used for medical research. The equipment of the station is below, in the conical part of the work compartment. The control panels for the scientific apparatus, the port, the chair, and the medical research equipment are located there.

Station No. 5 is designed to control the Orion stellar telescope. Its control panels, the port, the sight and the arm for guiding modules of the stellar telescope to the given star are located in the transfer compartment above.

Station 6 (astropost) is analogous with respect to purpose and composition to Station No. 2, but in contrast to Station No. 2 it has a chair and is located in a bay which, if necessary, can be converted by means of a shutter into an isolated "warm room". All of the equipment of Station No. 6 is located in the working compartment on the port side (in the small-diameter zone).

Station 7 is used to control the scientific apparatus for studying the space about earth. Its control panels for the equipment, port, and means of holding the cosmonauts are on the starboard side in the bay symmetric to the bay of Station No. 6.[22]

A look at the control panels at Station No. 1 immediately tells the observer that Salyut was based on Soyuz technology. In fact, over the console was an almost exact replica of the main control panel in Soyuz. This of course facilitated cosmonaut familiarization and operation of the Salyut space station. The information available and the instruments provided at Station No. 1 included:[23]

1. Control panel for navigational apparatus (orientation, propulsion, etc.)

2. Control panel for life support

3. Control panel for thermal regulation

4. Radio communications

5. Emergency warning indicators

6. Navigation indicator (provided instant location of Salyut above the earth, time of entry into and exit from earth's shadow, status of communications with ground stations, number of orbits made by the station)

7. Cathode-ray display (allowed visual tie with on board TV cameras and display of automated checklists)

8. Chronometers

9. Lighting controls

10. Remote control of various instruments and systems within the system

11. Automatic sequencers for control of on-board systems

12. Stellar globus (provided means of determination of the orientation of the Salyut station with respect to the stars.

The remaining six substations were more specialized in nature. They were designed for the performance of some specific task or experiment such as the operation of the Orion telescope or medical experiment. However, all six substations were equipped to handle communications with ground personnel, and navigation and orientation requirements.

Electrical power for the operation of a Salyut space station is derived from large solar panels. The two pairs of solar panels on Salyut 1 were apparently identical to those used by Soyuz spacecraft. Apart from their similar appearance and dimensions the total active area of solar cells of a combined Soyuz/Salyut 1 was 42 m^2 (three times 14 m^2 for each pair of Soyuz panels). On subsequent models of Salyut the two pairs of wings were replaced by three larger, maneuverable panels which also enabled the Soyuz spacecraft to eliminate its solar panels and fly on battery power alone during its brief launch and reentry solo operations. While docked the Soyuz and Salyut 1 electrical systems were connected allowing the complex to draw on the Soyuz power-generating capabilities. Nickel-cadmium buffer batteries on board Salyut and the buffer battery on Soyuz regulated the electrical output under varying loads and were available in the event of a loss of solar generating capability.[24]

In order to maintain a solar fixed orientation, the attitude-control system, in conjunction with an optical viewer similar to that employed by Soyuz spacecraft, positioned Salyut 1 such that the plane of the solar panels was perpendicular to the sun-Salyut line. Again as with Soyuz the station was placed in a three-degree-per-second rotation about this axis to provide a spin-stabilization mode. This method of solar orientation coupled with the fixed nature of the Salyut 1 solar panels proved to be inconvenient in the operation of ground and space observations. For each observation utilizing fixed sensors the space station had to be reoriented, the experiment performed, and the station realigned with respect to the sun. On the second and third generation Salyut stations the three larger solar panels are movable, allowing a constant solar fix during various orientations of Salyut.[25]

It should be pointed out that when speaking of the Salyut space station, Soviet spokesmen invariably mean the Soyuz/Salyut complex. Thus the Salyut station is often quoted as being 23 m long (16 m Salyut plus 7 m Soyuz) and weighing close to 25,600 kg (18,900 kg Salyut plus 6,700 kg Soyuz). The volume of the complex is given as 100 m^3. Presumably this means that Salyut has a volume of 91 m^3 since Soyuz has an announced volume of 9 m^3.

After docking, the Soyuz does become an intergral part of Salyut. In addition to the mating of the electrical systems already mentioned, the propulsion and attitude-control systems of Soyuz are also available if needed. (In practice though, the Soyuz engine systems are rarely used since they must always be capable of the orientation and retro-burns required for reentry.) For berthing, the cosmonauts often choose the orbital module of Soyuz instead of the spaces provided in the forward end of the working compartment.

Salyut space stations have been manned by crews of two, three, and four cosmonauts while Soviet authorities list six as the maximum number allowed. Salyut 1 was manned by the three-member cosmonaut team of Soyuz 11. Their apparently successful 24-day mission ended tragically when the returning cosmonauts perished during reentry due to an atmospheric leak in their Soyuz spacecraft. All subsequent Soyuz have only carried two cosmonauts as a result of added life-support equipment in Soyuz. Hence, until early 1978 all Salyut space stations were manned by only two cosmonauts. Although some mention has been made in the Western press that later Salyuts (post Salyut 1) were modified from a 3-man to a 2-man design, it is doubtful that any substantial alterations were actually implemented. The dual-docking ported third-generation Salyuts (beginning with Salyut 6) have the capability of supporting four cosmonauts for short periods of time as evidenced by the flights of Soyuz 26/27, Soyuz 26/28. Soyuz 29/30, and Soyuz 29/31. Recent reports also predict a return soon to a 3-man Soyuz spacecraft, indicating that Salyut may once again carry three cosmonauts for extended periods.

The scientific apparatus on board Salyut stations varies with the Salyut type (civilian or military) and, to an extent, with the planned Soyuz missions to each Salyut. The following represents a brief description of some of the major instruments outfitted on board Salyut 1:

1. <u>Orion 1 Telescope</u>. The heart of the astrophysical experiments
   on Salyut 1, this stellar spectrograph was designed to obtain
   spectrograms of individual stars in the 2,000-3,000 Å range. A
   large and a small reflecting mirror of 280-mm and 50-mm diameter,
   respectively, combined to produce an effective focal length
   of 1400 mm. The mirrors were finished with only an aluminum
   coating. This method left open the possibility of resurfacing
   the mirror by the cosmonauts after the mirror had been subjected
   to particle bombardment over a period of time. In fact, this
   technique was used on later Salyut stations. Coupled with an
   intricate spectroscope, resolutions of about 5 Å could be obtained
   in the mid-2600 Å operating range. The tracking system was able
   to maintain a lock on a selected star with an accuracy of ten
   seconds of arc. A telescope sight installed within Salyut permitted the cosmonaut to pick the desired section of the sky and
   aim the Orion complex toward it. To operate, one cosmonaut maintained orientation of Salyut as a second cosmonaut manipulated
   the Orion system. Both crewmen had to work quickly since spectrographs could only be taken for a 30-35 minute period during each
   orbit while Salyut was in the earth's shadow. Film cassettes could
   be replaced in the Orion complex located on the exterior of the
   station by means of a mechanical arm and small airlock near the
   telescope in the transfer/docking compartment.[26]

2. <u>Anna III Gamma Telescope</u>. This instrument could detect gamma radiation in excess of 100 Mev with a resolution of one degree.
   Comprised primarily of a series of scintillation counters and a
   Cherenkov counter, the Anna III complex was only 600 mm by 400 mm
   by 450 mm, weighed 45 kg, and when in operation consumed 14 watts
   of electrical power. The relatively new field of gamma astronomy
   (possible only above the earth's atmosphere) had thus far only
   been investigated by high-altitude balloons and unmanned satellites.
   The prospect of installing a man-operated device on board Salyut
   held a high priority among Soviet astronomers. The purpose of
   Anna III was threefold: (1)"To do detailed studies of the fitness
   of the telescope, (2) to discover the possibilities of investigating

gamma-quanta with different orientation of the orbital station and
(3) to determine the physical conditions of performing the experiment; that is, find the background of mutual and charged particles
both coming in from the outside and occurring inside the station."[27]

3. FEK-7 Photoemulsion Camera. The purpose of this device was to
study the multicharge component of primary cosmic rays. Specific
particles looked for included Dirac monopole, antinuclei, and
transuranium nuclei. Cameras of this type had already been flown
on Kosmos 213, Zond 5, 7 and 8, and Soyuz 5, but for much shorter
periods of time.[28]

4. Micrometeorite Sensors. Although the danger of any manned spacecraft being struck by a meteor of sufficient size to cause significant damage is very slight, the longer range effect of the constant bombardment of micrometeorites must be considered. To this
end, micrometeorite detectors of the capacitor and piezoelectric
type were located on the outer surfaces of the instrument/propul-
sion compartment and the large-diameter section of the working
compartment.[29]

5. Photographic Equipment. Several optical and multi-spectral cameras
were installed on board Salyut 1. The many photographic programs
included geological, meteorological, oceanographical, and astronomical studies. Photographic sessions provided for joint operations
with earth-bound aircraft and orbiting Meteor satellites.[30]

6. Medical Equipment. Of course the primary objective of the first
long-term orbiting laboratory was to investigate the effect of prolonged periods of weightlessness on the human organism. Prior to
the launching of Salyut 1 the longest manned mission had been the
18-day flight of Soyuz 9. Even during this short time, internal
deterioration of certain cardiovascular and skeletal systems indicated that counter-measures would have to be undertaken if man
was to spend periods of a month or more in space. In addition
to a strenuous regime of physical exercise (deep knee bends, etc.)
Salyut 1 carried several devices to keep the cosmonauts in satisfactory physical condition. "Penguin" suits which exerted a
stress similar to gravity on the skeleton and muscles were worn

occasionally by the cosmonauts. A treadmill was installed in the floor of the large-diameter working compartment. The Chibis medical unit capable of reducing the pressure on the lower torso was used by the cosmonauts in the hope of improving circulation in the lower half of the body. Blood, air, optical and many other tests related to the health of the crew were performed regularly.[31]

7. <u>Biological Equipment</u>. Salyut 1 contained the apparatus for performing numerous biological experiments. The development of fertilized frog eggs brought by Soyuz 11, the growth of higher and lower forms of plants and insects, the genetic variations of fruit flies (drosophilla) and the growth of high-order plants in a hydroponic farm (Oazis 1) were all observed.[32]

8. Many other instruments were also available such as a Cherenkov-scintillation telescope for determining charged particle fluxes and the "Era" system for evaluating high-frequency secondary-electron resonance and ionospheric structure.[33]

Figure 10 depicts the Salyut 1 space station during final check-out before mating with the upper stage of the Proton launch vehicle. Apparently, Salyut like Soyuz is ground-tested and mated to the launch vehicle horizontally before transfer to the launch pad. Since the aerodynamic shroud which covered the upper portion of Salyut did not extend around the entire craft, special thermal shields were employed to protect the station during its climb into orbit. Ejectable covers were placed over concealed sensors and telescopic equipment, and were jettisoned once Salyut 1 reached orbit.

Salyut 1 was visited by two Soyuz crews--Soyuz 10 and Soyuz 11. Soyuz 10 docked with the station on 24 April 1971 but could not effect an entry into the laboratory due to a malfunction in the docking mechanism. Soyuz 11 was sent up 43 days later for another attempt. This time the cosmonauts were successful, becoming the world's first crew on board a true orbiting space station. Soyuz 11 undocked with Salyut 1 at 2125 hr on 29 June after a stay of 23 days.

Salyut 1 remained aloft in a powered-down condition for two more months. During this time ground controllers periodically fired the station's engines to combat its natural orbital decay. These procedures were apparently taken to test the longivity of the orbital laboratory and to ensure its availability, should another Soyuz crew be allowed to visit after a brief review

Figure 10   Salyut 1 undergoing final check-out before mating with the Proton launch vehicle. Note the folded solar panels at the forward end and the large "cut-outs" at the right of the picture.

of the Soyuz 11 disaster. Finally on 11 October 1971 after the decision to substantially modify future Soyuz spacecraft was made, Salyut 1 was commanded to make a fiery reentry over the Pacific Ocean.

SECOND GENERATION

1972 LAUNCHES

With the unexpected deaths of the Soyuz 11 crew during their reentry
from Salyut 1, Soviet manned space operations ground to a halt. Preliminary investigations into the accident indicated that a major overhaul of
the Soyuz command module was in order. Meanwhile Salyut designers made
use of this unfortunate delay in their orbital laboratory program to incorporate modifications which had arisen since Salyut 1 was first designed
and from the experience gained with the station by the Soyuz 11 team.

Between 26 June 1972 and 2 July 1972 Kosmos 496, an unmanned Soyuz,
tested the new systems installed as a result of the Soyuz 11 accident.[34]
On 30 July 1972 the Soviet Union is reported to have launched its second
Salyut space station as a prelude to resumption of manned Soyuz flights.
However, according to US sources one of the second-stage engines cut off
before schedule, resulting in a failure of the spacecraft to achieve orbit
and its subsequent destruction during reentry. A back-up Salyut is thought
to have been readied for a flight in September of the same year, but was
postponed due to unresolved launch vehicle problems.[35]

The question of the nature of the Salyut lost on 30 July 1972 now presents itself. The next Salyut, Salyut 2, is thought by some to have been
a second-generation Salyut and was not flown until April 1973. Thus the
July 1972 attempt is roughly mid-way between the Salyut 1 and 2 launches.
However, if one believes the theory that the July 1972 back-up was scheduled for a later cancelled September 1972 mission, then that back-up could
have eventually become Salyut 2 in April 1973. Hence, the July 1972 launch
could well have been the unglorious debut of the second-generation Salyut.

The possibility that all these stations were still first-generation
Salyuts will be discussed following a review of Salyut 2 and Kosmos 557.

SALYUT 2

Almost two years after the launch of Salyut 1, the USSR announced the
launch of Salyut 2 for "the purpose of checking the efficiency of improved

structures, on-board systems, and equipment of the station, as well as with a view to conducting scientific and technical experiments in outer space."[36]

Inserted into a 260 km by 215 km orbit at 51.6° on 3 April 1973, Salyut 2 was quickly brought to a 260 km by 239 km orbit by the next day. Shortly after launch twenty to twenty-five pieces of space debris were tracked by radar in the vicinity of Salyut 2. The origin of the debris is uncertain: It could have been the result of an explosion of the last stage of the carrier rocket or the junk could have been nothing more than the discarded shields used to protect Salyut during launch. All appeared well on board Salyut 2 and the circularization maneuver of 4 April suggested that a Soyuz launch-and-rendezvous mission was imminent. By 8 April the orbit had been raised again, and finally on 14 April the orbit was raised still further. But following the 14 April orbital maneuver Salyut 2 appears to have under-gone a catastrophic failure. The space station tumbled out of control and began breaking up. By 28 May after only 55 days in space what was left of the orbital laboratory disintegrated during reentry into the earth's at-mosphere.[37]

The actual reason for the break-up is unknown outside of Soviet space circles. However, two major theories have been presented. The first as-sumes that when the last stage of the Proton launch vehicle exploded (if indeed it did) Salyut 2 was damaged. The ready Soyuz crew waited until an evaluation as to the extent of damages could be made. The 14 April accident dashed all hope of salvaging Salyut 2 and the Soyuz mission.

The second and perhaps more probable explanation assumes that Salyut 2 was not damaged during orbital insertion. The series of orbital maneuvers carried out between 4 and 14 April indicate that Salyut 2 was functioning normally. A Soyuz crew would not be expected to be launched immediately.[38] In fact, all indications as late as 10 April were that a Soyuz mission was still being prepared.[39] Some believe that solar flare activity on 4 and 5 April delayed an earlier attempt to man Salyut 2. Hence, up until 14 April all systems appeared "go" for Salyut 2.

The suddenness of the malfunction following the orbital maneuver left little evidence as to its origin. The accident could have been caused by some on-board explosion or by a stuck attitude-control thruster (such as that which plagued the US Gemini 8) which sent the laboratory into a wild spin, ripping off communications antennae, solar panels, etc.[40]

The mystery of Salyut 2 deepened when analysis showed that the station did not transmit on frequencies normal for a manned Soviet space flight. Only later was this seen to indicate the military objectives of the ill-fated space station. On 18 April Soviet sources denied any intention of sending men to the orbiting laboratory and even suggested that Salyut 2 was partially related to the Apollo-Soyuz Test Project.[41]

In keeping with the Soviet character on 28 April Soviet news agencies prepared the public for the inevitable decay of Salyut 2 a month later by by announcing that Salyut 2 had completed its mission program. A 1974 Soviet book described the significance of Salyut 2 in the following manner:

> As a result of the successful accomplishment of the Salyut 2 station flight programme, essential experimental information has been obtained, which confirms the correctness of adopted design and circuitry principles, as well as selected characteristics of the basic systems and on-board equipment of the space laboratory. These data will be utilized in constructing new space vehicles.[42]

KOSMOS 557

Even while Salyut 2 was falling out of the sky, the USSR launched what at first appeared to be nothing more than another satellite with the unimpressive name of Kosmos 557. It was soon obvious that this was not the case. Rocketed into orbit atop a Proton launcher on 11 May 1973, Kosmos 557 was found the next day circling the earth in an orbit ranging between 243 km and 214 km at 51.6°. Communication frequencies and radar data finally concluded that Kosmos 557 was indeed a Salyut space station.[43]

The fact that the spacecraft had been quickly given the Kosmos designator instead of the name Salyut 3 suggests that a malfunction very early in flight had rendered the station useless. No subsequent orbital maneuvers were detected, implying that the station propulsion or on-board command sequencer system had failed. Left in that low earth orbit, Kosmos 557 rapidly decayed and reentered the atmosphere on 22 May, six days before Salyut 2.[44]

The characteristics of the short-lived Kosmos 557 were closer to those of Salyut 1 (and the later Salyuts 4 and 6) than they were to Salyut 2. This has been shown to indicate Kosmos 557 was probably intended to carry

on the work of Salyut 1 under the civilian Salyut program. If this was
so, then Kosmos 557 was not, as some assume, hastily launched as a mere
back-up to Salyut 2 in order to beat the US Skylab launch scheduled for
May of that year. Kosmos 557 must have already been ready for continuation of the civilian Salyut program. It is possible that had Salyut 2
been successful, Kosmos 557 would have flown in late May or early June
as Salyut 3. Having two operational Salyuts in orbit simultaneously would
have taken the sting out of the much larger and versatile US Skylab, which
was launched only three days after Kosmos 557.

Within the space of two months, two sophisticated and highly expensive
orbital laboratories had been totally lost. Were they in fact the first
of the second-generation Salyut space stations or were they sisters of
Salyut 1? The answer to both questions may be yes.

In the summer of 1973 a mock-up of the second-generation Salyut was
put on display at the cosmonaut training center near Moscow (Figure 11).[45]
This was the first indication that the 1971 model Salyut had undergone
serious modification. Considering Soviet past practices, the exhibition
of this new design would indicate that the initial second-generation

Figure 11   The second generation Salyut trainer

Salyuts had already been built. Hence the inference is that at least Salyut 2 or Kosmos 557 was of this new breed. Another report suggests that Salyut 2 was one of the new orbiting laboratories based on optical tracking of its solar panels.[46] But the Royal Aircraft Establishment lists both spacecraft as having four solar panels, the trademark of Salyut 1.

Three possibilities exist:

1. Salyut 2 and Kosmos 557 were both similar to Salyut 1. This would imply that, in accordance with Soviet desires for standardization, several spacecraft were made along with Salyut 1. Salyut 2 and Kosmos 557, therefore, represented the use of spacecraft already in the "pipeline" when redesign was initiated. This view is supported by the Royal Aircraft Establishment data on the solar panels. The 30 July launch attempt of the previous year would then be of the Salyut 1 variety also. The display of a second generation Salyut in 1973 may have been an attempt to save some face (if only for the cosmonauts) in the wake of the disasters of Salyut 2 and Kosmos 557 and the ultimate success of Skylab. Furthermore, no wingless Soyuz variant had yet flown under either the Kosmos or Soyuz programs. Flight of a solar-paneled Soyuz to a second generation Salyut would be unlikely, while one unmanned or manned test of the new wingless Soyuz would be expected before use on a Salyut mission.

2. Salyut 2 and Kosmos 557 were different generation space stations - one old, one new. The US optical tracking data supports the theory that Salyut 2 was second generation. If that was the case, then Kosmos 557 was of the older type which supports the idea of eventual use of the back-up of the July 1972 failure. Since there is no data to suggest the type of mission of the 1972 launch, in this instance one could infer that it was civilian in nature. This would also explain why two Salyuts were ready for launch in the space of little more than a month. There is no significance to the fact that the newer model was launched before the older one since both were obviously undergoing check-outs simultaneously.

3. Salyut 2 and Kosmos 557 were both second generation Salyuts. This seems reasonable in light of the two-year pause since Salyut 1. We have already seen the evidence that Salyut 2 might have been a second-generation Salyut. Similar evidence for Kosmos 557 comes from the fact that Soyuz 12 which is believed to have been scheduled for a Kosmos 557 mission probably could not have flown on a mission involving a first-generation Salyut since this Salyut ferry had no solar panels. What then became of the back-up to the July 1972 attempt, assuming such a craft existed? It was probably either scrapped for parts (unreasonable due to the expense of the station) or was modified to the second generation format. The latter would also involve a great deal of expense and effort and would seem unnecessary since apparently no serious fault had been found with Salyut 1. A third possibility exists that the station eventually found its way into the role of a ground mock-up for the later Salyut missions.

In December 1978 this question became even more cloudy with a report in *Aviation Week and Space Technology* that the Salyut 3 and Salyut 5 military Salyuts were structurally different from the models and photographs of the civilian Salyuts displayed by the Soviets. According to this report the docking collar for the military Salyuts was located at the aft end of the station with a peripheral propulsion system similar to Salyut 6. In addition, the solar panels of these stations were reported to be located on the large diameter section of the station, perhaps giving rise to erroneous interpretations of the reflections of the ill-fated Salyut 2. Confirmation of this theory will probably have to await acknowledgement by Western space officials since, if true, the Soviets would hardly admit to a seven-year deception.

SALYUT 3

On 25 June 1974 almost three years after the Soyuz 11 tragedy, Salyut 3 was successfully lifted into orbit by a Proton launcher to become the Soviet Union's second operational space station and the first of the military Salyuts. From an initial orbit of 270 km by 219 km at 51.6°, Salyut 3 had been maneuvered by 28 June into a more circular operating orbit of 269 km by 266 km. The orbiting space laboratory was then in a position to receive its first Soyuz crew. Five days later at 2151 hr Moscow time Soyuz 14 rocketed away from the same Baikonur cosmodrome which had launched Salyut 3. Twenty-six hours later the two craft had docked, and the Soviet Union's space station program was revived (Figure 12).

Salyut 3 contained a number of significant modifications over the Salyut 1 prototype model.[47] The overall dimensions of the station had not changed: The three progressively larger cylinders of 2 m, 2.9 m, and 4.15 m diameter were joined to form a structure stretching 16 meters long (including fore and aft rendezvous antennae). Outwardly the solar array arrangement had been drastically altered (Figures 13-14). Whereas Salyut 1 had two pairs of fixed solar wings (one pair on the transfer/docking compartment and the other on the instrument/propulsion compartment), Salyut 3 sported three larger, rotatable solar panels affixed at 90-degree intervals to the smaller diameter (2.9 m) forward section of the working compartment. The major advantage of this modification was to allow the solar panels to track the sun while the space station maintained a fixed attitude with respect to either the earth or outer space.

SALYUT 3 CHRONOLOGY

Date	Event
25 Jun 1974	Salyut 3 launched
3 Jul 1974	Soyuz 14 launched
5 Jul 1974	Soyuz 14 docked with Salyut 3; crew transferred to station
19 Jul 1974	Soyuz 14 undocked and returned to earth after a stay of 15 days
26 Aug 1974	Soyuz 15 launched
28 Aug 1974	Soyuz 15 failed to dock with Salyut 3 and returned to earth
23 Sep 1974	Capsule ejected from Salyut 3 reentered atmosphere and was recovered in USSR; believed to contain high-resolution photographic material
25 Dec 1974	Announced end of Salyut 3 operations
24 Jan 1975	Salyut 3 destroyed during reentry after 214 days in orbit

Figure 12

In addition to being movable, the new solar panels were much larger than the older Soyuz arrays. The total area of the panels was 60 m^2 with each of the three panels measuring approximately 3 m wide and 7 m long.[48] This compares with the total collecting area of 42 m^2 for the Soyuz/Salyut 1 combination. This increase in area allowed every Soyuz docking with a second- or third-generation Salyut to dispense with its own solar wings. In these cases Soyuz operates solely on battery power during the one-day rendezvous maneuvers and during the short reentry phase of the flight. The elimination of these heavy panels allows Soyuz to bring added supplies and scientific equipment to Salyut.

A second major capability of Salyut was the confirmation of an airlock in the transfer/docking compartment to permit an extravehicular activity (EVA) in the event of a needed repair or scientific operation. Surprisingly enough, although this capability existed, no EVA was performed on Salyuts 3, 4, or 5. Although EVA's were planned, these experiments were always cancelled prior to the launch of Soyuz spacecraft. Not until December 1977, did the USSR perform its first EVA since the Soyuz 4/5 flight of January 1969. It is not clear whether the Soyuz 11/Salyut 1 combination permitted EVA. Recent photographic evidence indicates that Salyut 1 may also have had an EVA hatch.

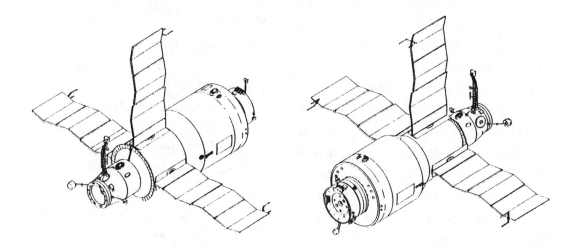

Figure 13   The second-generation Salyut space station. The larger and
movable solar panels enabled Soyuz ferry craft to dispense
with their own heavy solar wings (Drawings by R.F. Gibbons)

Figure 14   Soyuz and Salyut mock-ups on display at the Kosmos Pavillion
in Moscow   (Courtesy of R.F. Gibbons)

The new arrangement of solar panels permitted Salyut 3 to maintain a constant earth-oriented attitude. This allowed full use of the high-resolution reconnaissance camera system which was installed in place of the solar and astronomical equipment in the aft working compartment of Salyut 1. The Soviets described the camera system as having a ten-meter focal length for earth-resources observation work. A US analysis of the system concluded that the apparatus was better suited for high-resolution photography of a military nature, including detection of ground objects as small as 30-45 cm. These same analysts correctly predicted seven months in advance the Salyut added capability of ejecting a small, recoverable film canister months after a Soyuz crew had vacated the station.[49]

Meanwhile the USSR has ignored these accusations of military motives of earth-resources work, stressing instead the scientific and environmental benefits obtained. A Soviet report to the international COSPAR (Committee on Space Research) in 1975 stated the following:

> Among the practical problems which were solved using the complex of photographic equipment were: study of tectonic structures for the purpose of planning a search for materials; study of ore controlling structures and detection of areas promising for the search for minerals (ore and petroleum- and gas-bearing regions); creation and revisions of maps (geological, topographic, soils); observation of the ice cover of the ocean; observation of the contamination of water in rivers, lakes, and seas; inventory of forests and agricultural fields; study of the coastal zone of seas and oceans; detection of sources of ground water; investigation of lands subjected to salinization.[50]

The Soviets emphasized the interior redesign of the working compartment into three sections: living, control, and instrumentation. The difference, however, appears to be more in name only. The "floor" was reported painted in a dark color whereas the walls were a light, paler shade, even though Salyut 1 had utilized color-coded walls, ends, and floor three years earlier. Sleeping gear, medical supplies, an auxiliary life-support control panel, table with food, heater, and hot and cold water, tape library, books, radio, and chess set were all located in the forward section. The center "control section" contained the same main and auxiliary control panels as designed with Salyut 1. The aft end of the working compartment housed the majority of on-board systems: electric, communication, life support, telemetric, etc. Also included were the physical exercise apparatus, hygienic facilities, tools, spare parts, and scientific experiments.[51]

Other modifications included improvements to the control, stabilza-
tion, electric-supply, autonomous-navigation, heat-regulation, life-support, radio-communication, and on-board computer systems as well as scientific instruments.[52] The individual experiments performed by the Soyuz
14 crew will be outlined in the next section.

Another innovation in the Salyut program was the running of a sister
station in simulation in the Soviet Union. If problems arose in space or
if the cosmonauts wished to deviate from their flight plan, the operation
was first carried out on earth, the results evaluated, and a "go" or "no
go" decision given to the cosmonauts.

The announced three primary objectives of Salyut 3 consisted of:

1. Investigations of geological-geographic features on the earth's
    surface, atmospheric formations, and phenomea for the purpose
    of obtaining data for solving problems in the national economy

2. Investigation of the physical characteristics of space

3. Biomedical investigations for evaluating the influence of space
    flight, factors on the human body and determining rational
    schedules for crew work.[53]

Soviet statements gave the operational lifetime of Salyut 3 to have
been on the order of three months. This seems a rather short time for
such an expensive undertaking. In actuality, Salyut 3 remained aloft for
seven months. Following the successful 15-day stay on board the orbital
laboratory by the Soyuz 14 crew, a second visit was prepared. Five weeks
later, Soyuz 15 was launched on what may have been a scheduled longer-
duration mission. Unfortunately Soyuz 15, equipped with a new automatic
rendezvous and docking system, was unable to dock with Salyut 3, forcing
the crew to return after only two days in space. A "Soyuz 16" flight has
been reported as a proposed subsequent attempt, but apparently the fix to
the new rendezvous system lasted beyond a time considered safe for reoccu-
pation of the aging Salyut station.[54]

On 23 September the previously mentioned photographic pod was automatically ejected from Salyut 3. After a controlled reentry, the capsule
was recovered on Soviet territory. During the period prior to this event
the unmanned space station was used in a program to determine ballistic
and aerodynamic characteristics and the influence of gravitational forces
and moments on changes in position of the solar arrays.[55]

In late December 1974, the Soviets stated the scientific mission of Salyut 3 was completed and issued a brief summary of its performance through Christmas Day. During this time 400 scientific experiments were carried out, 8,000 control commands were transmitted to the ship, more than 200 dynamic operations were performed, and 70 television and 2500 telemetric sessions were conducted. Perhaps the most impressive figure of all was the fact that the Salyut 3 stabilization engines had been fired one-half million times![56]

After a highly successful career Salyut 3 met a fiery death and a watery grave after 214 days in space when on 24 January 1975 a command from ground control sent it plunging into the Pacific Ocean.

SALYUT 4

On 26 December 1974, the day following the completion of Salyut 3's scientific mission, Salyut 4 was launched into orbit signaling the USSR's determination to proceed with its orbital laboratory program. To this point the record was less than satisfactory. Of the four Salyuts which had reached orbit (at least another probably failed during launch) two had experienced catastrophic failures early in flight before a Soyuz crew could be sent. Four Soyuz missions had been flown to the remaining two Salyuts (Salyut 1 and 3), but only one was a success. The first flight (Soyuz 10) docked, but could not enter Salyut 1, whereas the second crew (Soyuz 11) perished during reentry. Finally, Soyuz 14 flew a successful 15-day mission with Salyut 3, but it was followed by Soyuz 15 which was unable to dock with the same space station. Thus, the launching of Salyut 4 before Salyut 3 had reentered was unexpected.

Salyut 4 was inserted into an initial orbit of 270 km by 219 km at 51.6°, identical to that of Salyut 3. However, Salyut 4 was part of the civilian Salyut program, whereas the mission of Salyut 3 had been militarily oriented. As expected, Salyut 4 quickly began maneuvers raising its orbit to reduced drag altitudes. By 30 December 1974 the apogee had been lifted to 349 km with a corresponding perigee of 276 km. This orbit was circularized to 355 km by 343 km by 6 January 1975. With less atmospheric drag at these higher altitudes and the new trackable solar panels the orbiting lab used less fuel reserves, extending its operational life, and provided a better platform for astronomical observations. Four days later, the first manned Soyuz mission to Salyut 4 was launched (Figure 15).

SALYUT 4 CHRONOLOGY

Date	Event
26 Dec 1974	Salyut 4 launched
11 Jan 1975	Soyuz 17 launched
12 Jan 1975	Soyuz 17 docked with Salyut 4; crew transferred to station
9 Feb 1975	Soyuz 17 undocked and returned to earth after a stay of 29 days
5 Apr 1975	Soyuz 18A launch aborted; crew rescued
24 May 1975	Soyuz 18B launched
25 May 1975	Soyuz 18B docked with Salyut 4; crew transferred to station
26 Jul 1975	Soyuz 18B undocked and returned to earth after a stay of 62 days
17 Nov 1975	Unmanned Soyuz 20 launched
19 Nov 1975	Soyuz 20 docked with Salyut 4
16 Feb 1976	Soyuz 20 undocked and returned to earth after a stay of 89 days
3 Feb 1977	Salyut 4 destroyed during reentry after 770 days in orbit.

Figure 15

The areas of study of the Salyut 4 space station and its Soyuz crews were stated to be "the sun and other celestial sources of electromagnetic radiation of various ranges, the physical and optical characteristics of the atmosphere, the refinement of methods for determining and monitoring the natural resources of the earth, medical and biological research, technical experiments, and the refinement of new space-technology facilities."[57]

The overall structure of Salyut 4 did not differ markedly from that of Salyut 3.[58] However the variety and sophistication of the scientific apparatus on board was significantly improved. These included the OST-1 orbital solar telescope, the AO-1 and AO-2 astronomic orienters, the MMK-1 micrometeorite detector, the Silya-4 spectrometer, the Filin-2 X-ray spectrometric telescope, the RT-4 X-ray telescope, the KDS-3 diffraction spectrometer, the KSS-2 solar spectrometer complex, the ITS-K infrared spectrometric telescope, the Delta autonomous-navigation orbital radio altimeter, the Stroka* teletype equipment, the Spektru upper atmospheric analyzer, the Emissiya interferometer, the BA-3K star camera, the KATE-140 and KATE-500 multi-spectral cameras, the Polynon installation for recording vital functions of the cosmonauts, the Amak-3 blood analyzer, the Plotnost bone-tissue density monitor, the Rezeda-5 pulmonary ventilation recorder, the Levka-3 brain blood-vessel monitor, the Tonus-2 muscular microelectro-stimulator, the Chibis physical-conditioning device, the Bioterm-2M, Bioterm-3, and Bioterm-4 apparatus used to evaluate mutational stability under weightless conditions, the Oazis++ plant growth experiment, the KM microbe cultivator, the FKT cellular division experiment, the Vshk-2 and LV-1 optical orienters of the station attitude-control system, the S-2 sextant, the Fakel photometer, the Neytral velocity vector detector, the Vektor ionic angular position indicator, the Ion mass spectrometer, the VPA-1 visual polarimetric analyzer, the Ya-2 luminescence meter, the Kaskad star-sensing and navigation instrument, and the Freon installation for investigating liquid behavior under weightless conditions. Details of these apparatus can be found in the references listed at the end of this section.[59]

Of the new instruments, the Orbiting Solar Telescope (OST-1) drew the most attention. Located in the large conical enclosure in the aft section of the working compartment, OST-1 was designed to capture solar radiation in the range of 800-1300 Å. The basic construction was a logical extention of experience gained with the Orion-1 telescope carried by Salyut 1 (Figure 16). With a focal length of 2.5 meters for the main parabolic mirror both photographs and spectrographs (with a resolution of 1Å)of the sun were taken simultaneously. Provision was also made for refurbishment of the mirror surfaces with and aluminum spray after the telescope had been exposed to micrometeorite bombardment for several weeks.[60]

Soyuz crews aboard Salyut 4 usually devoted most of each day to a particular area of investigation (biomedical, solar, earth resources, Figure 17 roughly outlines the number of days related to the indicated

---

* *Stroka means "line" in Russian.*

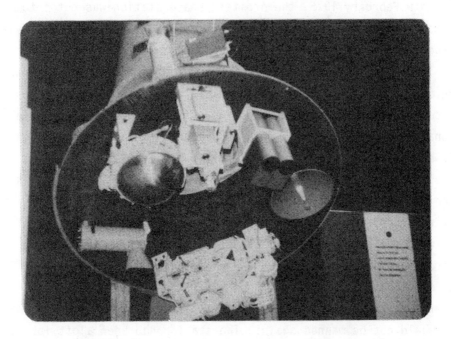

Figure 16   The Salyut 4 OST-1 Orbiting Solar Telescope (Courtesy of
R.F. Gibbons)

scientific discipline by the Soyuz 17 and Soyuz 18B crews. The remaining
days of each flight were spent loading and unloading equipment and for
relaxation.

ACTIVITIES OF SALYUT 4

Activity	Number of Days Devoted	
	Soyuz 17	Soyuz 18B
Research		
Solar	3	6
X-ray Sources	3	8
Infrared Sources	2	-
Atmosphere	4	2
Natural Resources	3	11
Biomedical	5	9
Technical Experiments	3	6

Figure 17

Following the 30-day mission of Soyuz 17 to Salyut 4 between 11 January 1975 and 9 February 1975, the orbiting space station was put into a powered-down mode until the next Soyuz crew arrived. On 5 April 1975, Soyuz 18A was rocketed away from the Baikonur cosmodrome to continue the work of Soyuz 17.[61] To the astonishment of the Soyuz crew and launch controllers alike, a malfunction in the launch vehicle during the second-stage separation caused the world's first--and thus far only--manned launch failure. Fortunately, both cosmonauts were recovered in relatively good health after their harrowing experience.[62]

Seven weeks later, Soyuz 18B succeeded in docking with Salyut 4 and remained for 62 days, setting a new Soviet space-endurance record. After their return on 26 July 1975, Salyut 4, the only Soviet space station to host two Soyuz crews, was again deactivated. Designed to sustain a two-man crew for 95-110 days Salyut 4 had housed Soyuz 17 and Soyuz 18B for a total of 91 days.

With the return of Soyuz 18B most Western observers assumed that Salyut 4 would not be manned again. The station had been aloft for seven months and had been used to its full potential. Therefore, four months later when the Soviet Union announced that Soyuz 20 had been launched on 17 November 1975 on a mission to Salyut 4, speculation as to its purpose was high. The Soviets quickly announced that Soyuz 20 was unmanned (only the second unmanned Soyuz spacecraft to carry a Soyuz designator) and was testing an automatic rendezvous and docking procedure in the development of an unmanned Salyut supply vehicle.[63] Two days later, Soyuz 20 carrying a small biological payload docked with Salyut 4.

Although no supplies or fuel were actually transferred from Soyuz 20 to Salyut 4, the ability to provide orbiting cosmonauts with new materials was proven. There was also a second purpose to the mission. Soyuz 20 remained attached to Salyut 4 for 89 days before being commanded to return to earth. Hence, by automatic means, the integrity of the Soyuz spacecraft was tested for a total of 91 days, paving the way for manned flights of similar duration.[64]

Following the return of Soyuz 20 on 16 February 1976, Salyut 4 again continued its unaccompanied, never-ending flight around the world. Four months later in June 1976 Salyut 5 was orbited, but Salyut 4 sailed along

on its unprecedented mission. Finally on 3 February 1977 after 770 days
in orbit, Salyut 4 was ordered to fire its propulsion engines and reenter
over the Pacific Ocean. Without doubt the flight of Salyut 4, almost
single-handedly, salvaged the faltering Salyut program and opened the door
to more ambitious projects.

SALYUT 5

The last of the second-generation Salyut stations made its debut on
22 June 1976 when it was inserted into an orbit of 260 km by 219 km. Unlike Salyut 4, Salyut 5 did not move into a higher orbit. Almost as if
the two programs were taking turns, the mission of Salyut 5 was soon revealed to be military-related. This orbiting reconnaissance laboratory
remained in the relatively low orbit to conduct both earth-observation
and earth-resources studies.[65]

Prior to the launch of Salyut 5, Cosmonauts Klimuk and Sevas'tyanov
had stated that future Salyuts would have two docking facilities and could
accommodate unmanned resupply craft. Thus, when Salyut 5 did take to the
skies,Western observers assumed the orbital station had this capability.
Initially, Soviet spokesmen refused to confirm or deny these suspicions.
Later in the flight it was announced that Salyut 5, like the other second-
generation Salyuts, had but one docking port. Both of these predicted
features did not appear until the next Salyut, the civilian Salyut 6,first
of the third-generation Salyuts.[66]

Since Salyut 5 was largely dedicated to military objectives the amount
of astronomical and astrophysical equipment carried was much less than
that of Salyut 4. The Orbiting Solar Telescope of Salyut 4 was again replaced with a high-resolution earth-observation camera system similar to
the one employed by Salyut 3. However, a number of new processing type
experiments were conducted.

Some of the specific objectives of the Salyut 5 station were:

Survey of Soviet territory below 52°N and visual observations of
natural formations; compilation of one-millionth and one-500,000th
scale maps; analysis of tectonic structures of selected areas with a
view to finding places likely to contain oil, gas and ore deposits;
exploration of areas adjacent to hydro-engineering structures now in
the drafting stage; taking pictures for a comprehensive exploration
of areas adjacent to the eastern section of the Baikal-Amur trunk
railway now under construction; study of seismic activity and an

understanding of mud-current and avalanche danger in mountainous districts; observation of the formulative stages of storms and hurricanes; and observation and immediate transmission of information of fire hazards in forests and on fires.[67]

A device named Sfera* was tested to evaluate the melting and resolidifying characteristics of such metals as bismuth, lead, tin, and cadmium. A portable spectrograph RSS-2M enabled the on-board cosmonauts to detect smoke, dust, and other pollutants at various altitudes in the earth's atmosphere. The Crystal experiment was conducted to monitor the growth of crystals in a weightless environment. The results of the on-board experiment was later compared with crystals grown in an identical apparatus on earth. Production of a homogenous alloy of dibenzyl and tolane was the object of the Diffusia device. An experiment named Reaction involved the smelting of high grade nickel and manganese solder and the soldering of stainless-steel pipes. The Potek instrument was designed to evaluate the feasibility of building "cosmic capillary pumps which do not need electricity." This experiment relied on capillary and surface-tension forces to move a liquid from one vessel to another. Other experiments involving fish, plants, and fruit flies were also conducted.[68]

Two weeks after the orbital insertion of Salyut 5, Soyuz 21 rocketed into space for a prolonged stay aboard the station. Forty-nine days later, the two Soyuz 21 cosmonauts made what is regarded as a hasty departure from Salyut 5 and returned safely to earth. It has been suggested that a malfunction of the Salyut 5 environmental control system forced the early return. If this is true, the problem must have been corrected by ground controllers, since two more Soyuz missions were attempted. (See Figure 18.)

On 14 October, Soyuz 23 was launched to continue the work begun by Soyuz 21. Unfortunately, the next day a malfunction in the automatic rendezvous equipment prevented the spacecraft from reaching Salyut 5 closely enough for a manual docking attempt. As a result the Soyuz spacecraft made an immediate return to earth. With their bad luck still holding strong the two cosmonauts landed in a Soviet lake, late at night during a heavy snowstorm, making the USSR's first (and unplanned) manned water recovery.

---

* *Sphere*

SALYUT 5 CHRONOLOGY

Date	Event
22 Jun 1976	Salyut 5 launched
6 Jul 1976	Soyuz 21 launched
7 Jul 1976	Soyuz 21 docked with Salyut 5; crew transferred to station
24 Aug 1976	Soyuz 21 undocked and returned to earth after a stay of 48 days
14 Oct 1976	Soyuz 23 launched
16 Oct 1976	Soyuz 23 failed to dock with Salyut 5 and returned to earth; first Soviet manned water recovery
7 Feb 1977	Soyuz 24 launched
8 Feb 1977	Soyuz 24 docked with Salyut 5
9 Feb 1977	Soyuz 24 crew transferred to station
25 Feb 1977	Soyuz 24 undocked and returned to earth after a stay of 16 days
26 Feb 1977	Capsule ejected from Salyut 5 reentered atmosphere and was recovered in USSR
8 Aug 1977	Salyut 5 destroyed during reentry after 412 days in orbit.

Figure 18

A final mission to Salyut 5 was begun on 7 February 1977 with the launch of Soyuz 24. This time a docking was successful and the two cosmonauts transferred to the orbital lab for a stay of 16 days. Soyuz 24 returned to earth uneventfully on 25 February.

Curiously, the day following the return of Soyuz 24, Salyut 5 ejected a pod similar to that ejected by Salyut 3. This capsule, like its predecessor, was guided through a controlled reentry and was recovered in the Soviet Union. It is not clear why the capsule which is assumed to have contained photographic materials was returned only one day after the departure of Soyuz 24. Possibly the object was merely to retest the retrieval system for use on future Salyuts or other spacecraft.

On 5 March 1977, Salyut 5 was placed in a new 265 km by 251 km orbit in what one US aerospace periodical suggested might be an attempt to send yet another crew to the station.[69] This never came to pass. At the time, Salyut 5 was almost nine months old and possibly contained a questionable environmental control system. Therefore, the orbit alteration may have been simply engineered to prolong the life of Salyut 5 for automatic reliability testing in the months ahead.

Finally, on 8 August 1977, Salyut 5 fired its propulsion engines for the last time and began a planned destructive reentry over the Pacific Ocean. After 412 days and 6630 orbits Salyut 5 may have come to a premature end, for waiting in the wings was the long-expected third-generation Salyut space station.

THIRD GENERATION

SALYUT 6

The first-generation Salyut, Salyut 1, had performed well, although the program was dealt a severe blow by the deaths of the returning Soyuz 11 cosmonauts. The second-generation Salyuts had gotten off on a shaky start with Salyut 3, but Salyut 4 and 5 confirmed the versatility of the station complex and provided the experience necessary for further modifications. Before the launch of Salyut 5, cosmonauts had already begun to talk of a new station with dual-docking ports and of the development of an automated space-cargo ship. As the twentieth anniversary of the dawn of the Space Age, the launching of Sputnik 1, drew near, reports indicated that a major Soviet undertaking was about to be unveiled.

Riding the fire and thunder of the Soviet Union's largest rocket, Salyut 6 swiftly climbed into a 275 km by 219 km orbit with an inclination of 51.6 degrees on 29 September 1977. By 7 October Salyut 6's orbit had been raised and circularized to 352 km by 336 km. Obviously a manned Soyuz mission was imminent (Figure 19). In the leap-frogging civilian and military Salyut programs the orbital parameters also indicated that this new space observatory was on a civilian mission.

Two days later, the ambitious Soyuz 25 mission was begun. Launch and the initial catching-up maneuvers went smoothly. Right on schedule the Soyuz 25 cosmonauts began the final approach on their 17th orbit. However, for the fourth time in 11 Salyut missions, a successful docking could not be accomplished. Soyuz 25 was apparently able to make contact with Salyut 6, but a firm docking did not ensue. As with previous failed missions, Soyuz 25 was forced to return immediately to earth since the battery--powered spacecraft has only slightly more than a two-day lifetime without the electrical power of a Salyut station.

SALYUT 6 CHRONOLOGY

Date	Event
29 Sep 1977	Salyut 6 launched
9 Oct 1977	Soyuz 25 launched
11 Oct 1977	Soyuz 25 failed to dock with the Salyut 6 forward port, and returned to earth
10 Dec 1977	Soyuz 26 launched
11 Dec 1977	Soyuz 26 docked with the Salyut 6 aft port, and crew transferred to station
20 Dec 1977	EVA performed to inspect forward docking port; first Soviet EVA in nine years
10 Jan 1978	Soyuz 27 launched
11 Jan 1978	Soyuz 27 docked with the Salyut 6 forward port, and crew transferred to station; first simultaneous dual-mission to a Salyut station
16 Jan 1978	Soyuz 27 cosmonauts undocked Soyuz 26 spacecraft and returned to earth after a stay of 5 days
20 Jan 1978	Progress 1, first unmanned automatic resupply vehicle, launched
22 Jan 1978	Progress 1 docked with the Salyut 6 aft port
7 Feb 1978	Progress 1 undocked from Salyut 6 after a stay of 16 days; Progress 1 destroyed the next day during reentry
2 Mar 1978	Soyuz 28 launched; first international crew
3 Mar 1978	Soyuz 28 docked with the Salyut 6 aft port, and crew transferred to station
10 Mar 1978	Soyuz 28 undocked with Salyut 6 and returned to earth after a stay of 7 days
16 Mar 1978	Soyuz 26 cosmonauts undocked Soyuz 27 spacecraft and returned to earth after a record breaking 95-day stay
15 Jun 1978	Soyuz 29 launched
17 Jun 1978	Soyuz 29 docked with the Salyut 6 forward port, and crew transferred to station
27 Jun 1978	Soyuz 30 launched; second international crew
28 Jun 1978	Soyuz 30 docked with the Salyut 6 aft port, and crew transferred to station
5 Jul 1978	Soyuz 30 undocked and returned to earth after a stay of 7 days
7 Jul 1978	Progress 2 launched
9 Jul 1978	Progress 2 docked with the Salyut 6 aft port

Figure 19

Figure 19 (Cont'd)

2 Aug 1978	Progress 2 undocked and destroyed during reentry after a stay of 24 days
8 Aug 1978	Progress 3 launched
10 Aug 1978	Progress 3 docked with the Salyut 6 aft port
21 Aug 1978	Progress 3 undocked after a stay of 11 days; Progress destroyed 3 days later during reentry
26 Aug 1978	Soyuz 31 launched; third international crew
27 Aug 1978	Soyuz 31 docked with the Salyut 6 aft port, and crew transferred to station
3 Sep 1978	Soyuz 31 cosmonauts undocked Soyuz 29 spacecraft and returned to earth after a stay of 7 days
7 Sep 1978	Soyuz 29 cosmonauts undocked Soyuz 31 spacecraft from aft port and redocked with forward port of Salyut 6
4 Oct 1978	Progress 4 launched
6 Oct 1978	Progress 4 docked with the Salyut 6 aft port
24 Oct 1978	Progress 4 undocked after a stay of 18 days; Progress destroyed 2 days later during reentry
2 Nov 1978	Soyuz 31 spacecraft with Soyuz 29 cosmonauts on board undocked; cosmonauts landed safely after a record 140-day space mission
25 Feb 1979	Soyuz 32 launched
26 Feb 1979	Soyuz 32 docked with the Salyut forward port and the crew transferred to the station
12 Mar 1979	Progress 5 launched
14 Mar 1979	Progress 5 docked with the Salyut 6 aft port
3 Apr 1979	Progress 5 undocked after a stay of 20 days; Progress destroyed 2 days later during reentry
10 Apr 1979	Soyuz 33 launched; fourth international crew
11 Apr 1979	Soyuz 33 propulsion system malfunctioned; mission aborted
12 Apr 1979	Soyuz 33 returned safely to earth
13 May 1979	Progress 6 launched
15 May 1979	Progress 6 docked with the Salyut 6 aft port
6 Jun 1979	Soyuz 34 launched unmanned
8 Jun 1979	Progress 6 undocked after a stay of 23 days; twelve hours later Soyuz 34 docked with Salyut 6 aft port
10 Jun 1979	Progress 6 destroyed during reentry
13 Jun 1979	Unmanned Soyuz 32 spacecraft undocked and returned to earth
14 Jun 1979	Soyuz 32 cosmonauts undocked Soyuz 34 spacecraft from aft port and redocked with forward port of Salyut 6

Figure 19 (Cont'd)

28 Jun 1979   Progress 7 launched

30 Jun 1979   Progress 7 docked with the Salyut 6 aft port

18 Jul 1979   Progress 7 undocked after a stay of 18 days; 10 meter diameter radio telescope deployed from Salyut 6 aft port

20 Jul 1979   Progress 7 destroyed during reentry

15 Aug 1979   Soyuz 32 cosmonauts perform Extra-Vehicular Activity to untangle and discard experimental radio telescope

19 Aug 1979   Soyuz 34 spacecraft with Soyuz 32 cosmonauts on board undocked; cosmonauts landed safely after a record 175-day space mission.

The Soyuz 25 failure left doubt as to the actual design of Salyut 6. The Soviets released virtually no data concerning the new Salyut and did not mention the existence of a spare docking port. Not until after the successful docking of Soyuz 26 with Salyut 6 in December 1977 did details of this third-generation vehicle begin to emerge.

Outwardly, Salyut 6 closely resembled the Salyut 3-5 space stations (Figure 20). However, under closer examination the aft end of the laboratory where the instrument/propulsion compartment had been located had undergone a radical alteration. On older Salyuts the large diameter (4.15 m) section of the working compartment was 4.1 meters long followed by the 2.17 m long unpressurized instrument/propulsion compartment with a diameter of 2.2 m. The new design called for lengthening of the large diameter section to approximately 6 m (the combined length of the large diameter section and the instrument/propulsion compartment).

The total length of Salyut 6 remained about the same as that of the first two generations of Salyut (16 m). The interior pressurized volume also remained essentially the same (91 m^3). But behind the aft bulk head, the propulsion-system engines and fuel tanks were shifted to the periphery of the compartment to allow for a second docking port along the axis of the station.

The second docking port had been long awaited, but its placement at the rear end of the station was unexpected to most (Figure 21). The US Skylab space station had dual docking ports at right angles to one another at the forward end. This was what had been expected with the modified Salyut. An arrangement of this nature permits the construction of only one transfer compartment and does not impede the operation of the space station's

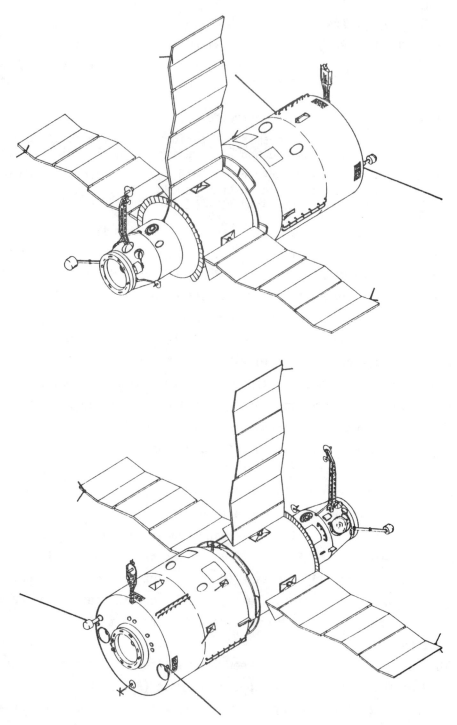

Figure 20   Salyut 6, the latest version of the Salyut space station.
Launched in September 1977, this orbiting laboratory has
hosted 7 manned missions and 7 unmanned Progress cargo
ships.   (Drawings by R.F. Gibbons)

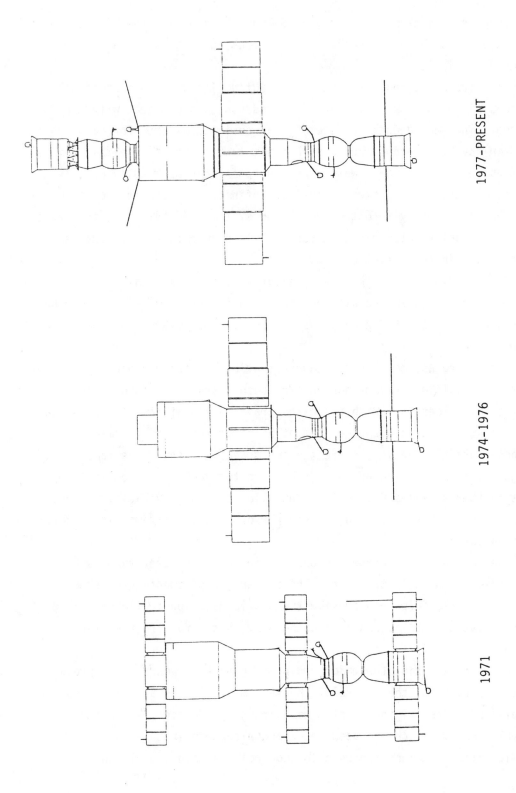

1977-PRESENT

1974-1976

1971

Figure 21   Relative sizes and configurations of the three Salyut generations (Drawings by R.F. Gibbons)

own propulsion system. In fact, if Salyut had employed the single, large-nozzle propulsion system design, a rear docking port would have been extremely difficult.

In retrospect, however, the new Salyut design was the best of all solutions with many advantages and few disadvantages compared with the Skylab system. The second docking assembly was designed as much for cargo as it was for use by a second manned spacecraft. While it is true that movement of supplies such as food, water, and equipment can be handled equally well at either end, the transfer of fuel is infinitely easier if the cargo ship can connect directly into the propulsion system. In this way, the transfer is virtually automatic with very little danger to the cosmonauts. This is possible in the Salyut design.

Vehicle dynamics of the Soyuz/Salyut system are also simplified with the Soyuz or cargo spacecraft located along the station axis rather than at right angles to it. Rendezvous and docking maneuvers, too, become simpler.

One of the assumed disadvantages--that of temporary blockage of the station propulsion system--has in fact been transformed into an advantage in the Salyut design. With the cargo craft docked at the aft end of Salyut the station's main engines cannot be fired for fear of damaging the attached craft. However, since the two spacecraft share the same axis, the cargo ship's propulsion engine can be used to maneuver the entire complex. This further utilizes the full potential of the cargo vehicle. An operation of this nature has already been performed several times in conjunction with Salyut 6.

The second disadvantage of constructing dual transfer tunnels has been minimized in the Salyut design. The aft end compartment is extremely small and does little more than provide the double hatch protection required of such a system. EVA access is located only in the forward transfer compartment.

While undertaking the major engineering task of rearranging propulsion system components, the nature of the system itself was also improved and simplified. The original system was virtually identical to the Soyuz propulsion unit which has been described elsewhere in this book. The new configuration combines the reaction control and main propulsion systems.

Whereas the former employed hydrogen peroxide and the latter relied on hydrogen-peroxide-driven pumps to supply hydrazine and nitric acid, both systems now work on common pressure-fed unsymmetrical dimethylhydrazine and nitrogen tetroxide reserves. This design not only simplifies fuel and oxidizer line arrangement, but also is considered more reliable than the turbine-driven pumps in the older propulsion system. Salyut 6 apparently carries three fuel and three oxidizer tanks which are connected to a high-pressure (3234 psi) nitrogen supply of feed pressure. At least two of both sets of tanks are refillable in orbit. Total thrust of the new propulsion system has been quoted at 600 kg in comparison with a previous maximum thrust of 417 kg.[70]

The capability of either a Soyuz or a cargo vehicle docking at either port was demonstrated between December 1977 and February 1978.[71] In early December 1977 Soyuz 26 was launched to salvage what, up to that time, had been a totally unsuccessful Salyut 6 flight. Fearing the forward docking port was damaged during launch or during the Soyuz 25 docking attempt, Soyuz 26 performed a textbook rendezvous and docking with the Salyut 6 aft port. Although the cosmonauts could perform most of the flight program, refueling was impossible with their spacecraft at the aft port. Following an EVA later that month that proved the forward port was not damaged, plans were formulated to send up a second Soyuz crew for a short visit and send them home in the Soyuz 26 spacecraft, which, in effect, moved Soyuz from the aft end to the forward end and opened the rear port for a later cargo ship.[72]

In January 1978 Soyuz 27 docked with the already orbiting Soyuz 26/ Salyut 6 combination in just such a feat (Figure 22). The Soyuz 27/Salyut 6/Soyuz 26 complex was roughly 30 meters long and weighed close to 32,300 kg. Shortly after the return of the Soyuz 27 cosmonauts in the Soyuz 26 spacecraft, the first unmanned automated resupply mission was carried out using the Progress 1 spacecraft. A description of the new Progress class vehicles is provided later in this section.

Salyut 6 incorporated many systems on an operational basis which had been described as experimental on earlier Salyuts. In addition, new systems and further refinements of old ones could be found on Salyut 6. A total of six television cameras were now carried by the Salyut station:

one color and two B/W internal cameras and three B/W external cameras.
Two of the external cameras were located just above the two docking ports
to aid in docking maneuvers. This is especially important during the automated docking of a resupply craft at the aft port. Daily inspections
of the Salyut 6 exterior were also made with these cameras.

Other equipment and experiments now standardized or being tested for
the first time included: the Delta automatic navigation system, the Medusa
cosmic radiation biological experiment, the Resonance station dynamics test,
the MKF-6M multispectral camera (part of Raduga experiment), the Splav 1
electric furnance (brought to Salyut 6 by Progress 1), the BST-1M infrared
telescope, the Czechoslovakian Morava smelting experiment, the Extinctia
atmospheric micrometeoroid dust layer experiment, the Chlorella algae growth
experiment, the Polynon 2 and Chibis medical equipment, the Czechoslovakian
Oxymeter, a refined water regeneration system, an enclosed cosmonaut shower
unit, the Sirena semi-conductor manufacturing test, and the Relaks psychological experiment to improve rest conditions in the orbital station.[73]

Also introduced was a newly designed EVA space suit with which Cosmonaut Grechko performed only the third Soviet space walk on 20 December 1977.[74]

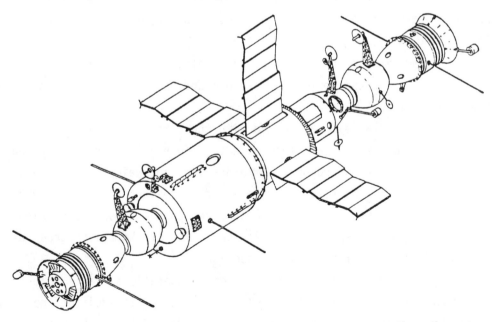

Figure 22   Salyut 6 with a Soyuz spacecraft docked at each port. Eight
             day Interkosmos flights make regular visits to Soviet cos-
             monauts on long-duration space flights (Drawing by R.F. Gibbons)

(The first had been in March 1965 during Voskhod 2 and the second had taken place during the Soyuz 4/5 crew exchange in January 1969.) The new flexible suits permitted greater mobility, ease of donning, and came in a standard size. Equipped with a self-sustaining life support package a tether was used only for safety purposes.

Salyut 6 opened a whole new era of Soviet manned space flight. In the year following the launch of Salyut 6, no less than 11 space missions had been conducted in conjunction with the orbital laboratory, seven manned Soyuz spacecraft along with four unmanned Progress supply ships. Salyuts 4 and 5 had seen only three visits each. Three of the Soyuz missions carried international crews with Polish, Czech, and East German cosmonauts accompanying their Soviet comrades. The Soyuz 26 cosmonauts broke the world's space endurance record by remaining aloft for 96 days. This remarkable achievement itself was shattered only a few months later by the Soyuz 29 crew and more recently by the epic 6 month flight of Soyuz 32. The wide range of experiments and activities of the Salyut 6 crews indicates that the USSR has decided to deepen its already strong commitment to the conquest of near-earth space.

What then can be expected in the future? This topic is addressed more fully in the next section, but the potential of the Salyut space stations themselves can be examined here. Two major advances on the Salyut complex are now widely discussed both inside and outside the Soviet Union.

The first is the enlargement of the Salyut station from the present approximately 19 tons to a more spacious 25-ton model.[75] In a July 1975 report the Soviets envisioned this larger orbital laboratory with the same two-man crew now utilized. However, following the Salyut 6 demonstration of its ability to handle four cosmonauts for up to eight days, the actual crew size may be flexible. One of the limiting factors is the amount of consumable supplies needed by larger cosmonaut contingents. But the development of the Progress resupply vehicle may put this problem to rest.

A 25-ton Salyut would be useful not only in earth orbit, but also valuable on lunar orbit missions. At the present time many believe that Soviet manned lunar expeditions will begin with lunar orbital flights employing a lunar Salyut to be followed later with manned lunar landings.[76]

The fate of a 25-ton or larger Salyut may rest on the development of the Soviet G-type launch vehicle. After initial tests of this super-rocket failed miserably in 1969-1971, the program was apparently abandoned. Rumors have surfaced in recent years, however, that development has been resumed. An alternative solution to a larger booster would be redesigning the Proton launcher with high-energy fuels. This, too, has been reported in the making.

A second method of enlarging the scale of Salyut operations is by connecting two or more Salyuts in orbit (Figure 23). The Soviets have long

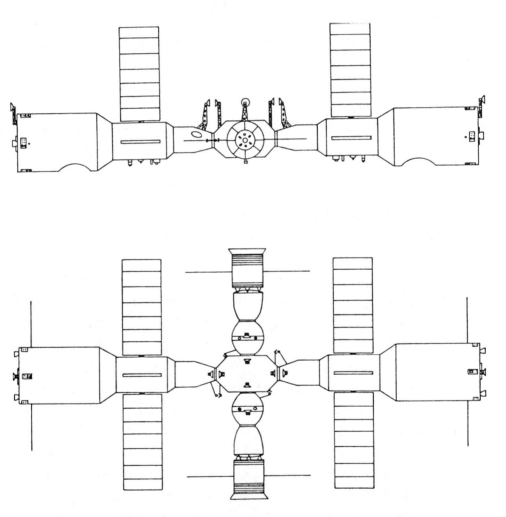

Figure 23   Speculative drawing of two Salyut space stations connected by a special Soyuz docking module. Additional Soyuz or Progress spacecraft could dock at the aft end of each station.

spoken of such constructions. In fact, the Soyuz 6/7/8 joint space flights are thought by some to have been associated with an early effort at examining the potential of such a complex. Several Salyut stations could be joined around a central, independently launched hub. The hub itself could provide additional docking ports for arriving Soyuz spacecraft or Soyuz ships could dock at the aft ports of Salyut 6 type vehicles. Recent flights of some Kosmos satellites suggest that a space tug, invaluable in putting such large pieces together, may be now under development and testing. Finally, plans are also under consideration for a joint Salyut-US Shuttle docking mission.[77]

Chapter 13

PROGRESS SPACECRAFT

Prior to January 1978, earth-orbital space stations of both the US and USSR programs had severely limited operational lifetimes. The major contributing factor to this situation was the replacement of life-support consumables (food, water, air) and maneuvering fuel. Visiting spacemen could bring along small quantities of food and water, but by far most of these exhaustible supplies had to be loaded into the space station before its orbital insertion. The development of unmanned robot cargo transports could sharply reduce the cost of resupply and make in-space fuel transfers possible.

The advent of the Progress spacecraft, therefore, opened a new door to the short- and long-term colonization of space. The appearance of Progress 1 on 20 January 1978 was far from unexpected. Ever since the automatic dockings of Kosmos 186/188 and 212/213 in 1967 and 1968 the Soviet Union had stressed the versatility of such craft and their implementation into future space projects. More recent indications had led many Western observers to predict cargo craft in conjunction with Salyut 4 and 5.

Progress 1 itself was based to a great extent on existing Soyuz hardware (Figure 24-25). Outwardly, Progress vehicles closely resemble their Soyuz sisters: length 8 m, base diameter 2.7 m, and weight of 7000 kg.

The forward compartment of Progress (formerly the orbital compartment) is latticed with racks for the storage of food stuffs, clothing, experimental apparatus, etc. After Progress has docked with a Salyut station, the on-duty cosmonauts may enter this forward compartment to unload the valuable merchandise. When all articles have been removed, the cosmonauts

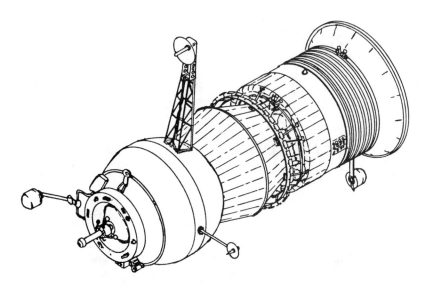

Figure 24   The Progress resupply spacecraft. Note the strong
dependence on Soyuz hardware. (Drawing by R.F. Gibbons)

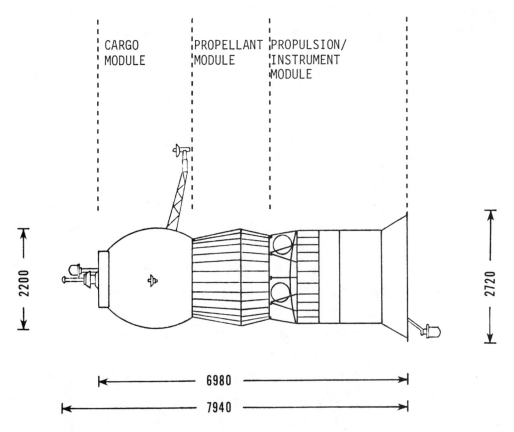

Figure 25   Configuration of the Progress vehicle. All dimensions are
in millimeters.   (Drawing by R.F. Gibbons)

begin reloading the module with waste from the orbiting lab. Thus, when
the transfer is complete, Progress becomes a space garbage scow and is
sent to a fiery reentry in which the ship is destroyed.

The Soyuz command module has been entirely replaced with a fuel/oxi-
dizer stowage compartment. It is here that the unsymmetrical dimethylhydrazine and nitrogen tetroxide are each stored in two tanks for later
transfer to the Salyut propulsion and attitude-control systems. The fuel
and oxidizer connections between Salyut and Progress are located in the
docking ring.

The actual fuel transfer process can be performed under the direction
of the cosmonaut crew or automatically by ground control (Figure 26). This
latter option allows refueling without interrupting crew activities or
even while the station is temporarily unmanned. After verification of
line integrities, the pressure of the Salyut fuel and oxidizer tanks is
lowered by pumping nitrogen of the pressure feed system back into the nitrogen storage tanks. This process is completed very slowly over a span
of several days in order to minimize the large drain of the nitrogen compressor on the Salyut electrical system. With the internal pressure reduced to three atmospheres the unsymmetrical dimethylhydrazine is pressure-
fed from Progress to Salyut by Progress' own compressed nitrogen supplies.
Upon completion of the fuel transfer, the nitrogen tetroxide oxidizer is
forced into the Salyut tanks. Both fuel and oxidizer lines are purged
following the operation to prevent spillage during the Progress undocking
maneuver.[78]

Total payload weight of a Progress vehicle is approximately 2300 kg.
This number is broken down into 1000 kg for propellant and oxygen and
1300 kg for dry supplies in the Progress 1 spacecraft. Since each cosmonaut consumes approximately 15-30 kg of materials per day, a two-man crew
would require a resupply mission every three-to-six weeks. However, these
weights are highly flexible. During the Progress 2 mission only 600 kg
of propellants were transferred while apparently no fuels were off-loaded
by Progress 3 which was sent to Salyut 6 immediately after Progress 2 had
departed. This versatility in the nature of the payload allows the ship-
ment of large quantities of food and scientific equipment to the orbital
laboratories if refueling is not necessary.[79]

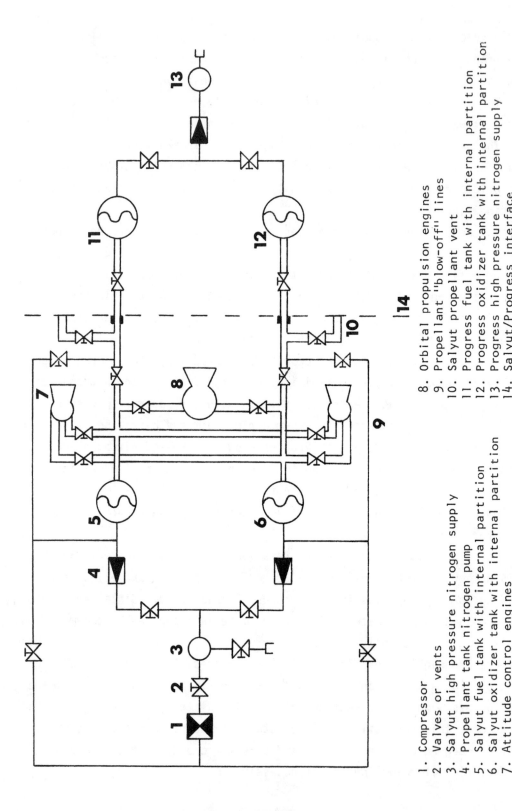

1. Compressor
2. Valves or vents
3. Salyut high pressure nitrogen supply
4. Propellant tank nitrogen pump
5. Salyut fuel tank with internal partition
6. Salyut oxidizer tank with internal partition
7. Attitude control engines
8. Orbital propulsion engines
9. Propellant "blow-off" lines
10. Salyut propellant vent
11. Progress fuel tank with internal partition
12. Progress oxidizer tank with internal partition
13. Progress high pressure nitrogen supply
14. Salyut/Progress interface

Figure 26   The Salyut/Progress refueling system

The propulsion module also resembles that employed by Soyuz spacecraft. Fourteen 10-kg and eight 1-kg thrusters provide attitude control during rendezvous and deorbit maneuvers. As with all Salyut-oriented Soyuz since Soyuz 11, Progress ships rely solely on battery power and do not carry large solar panels. The rendezvous and tracking antennae are also identical to those of Soyuz design.

The time interval between the launch of a Progress vehicle and its docking with a Salyut space station is just over two days as compared to the normal 24-hour period taken by a manned Soyuz spacecraft. The additional 24 hours permits more time for ground controllers to analyze the results of each rendezvous burn. The final docking procedures can be controlled by the Salyut cosmonauts or by the Soviet mission control with the aid of the externally-mounted cameras on both Progress and Salyut.

Progress 1 was launched on 16-day mating with Salyut 6 during the Soyuz 26 mission (Figure 27). The next three Progress flights were in conjunction

PROGRESS PROGRAM

Progress	Launch Date	Reentry Date	Comments
1	20 Jan 1978	8 Feb 1978	First unmanned resupply and re-fueling mission to manned space station; docked with Salyut 6 on 22 Jan while Soyuz 26 cosmonauts were on board
2	7 Jul 1978	2 Aug 1978	Docked with Salyut 6 on 9 Jul while Soyuz 29 cosmonauts were on board
3	8 Aug 1978	24 Aug 1978	Docked with Salyut 6 on 10 Aug while Soyuz 29 cosmonauts were on board
4	4 Oct 1978	26 Oct 1978	Docked with Salyut 6 on 6 Oct while Soyuz 29 cosmonauts were on board
5	12 Mar 1979	5 Apr 1979	Docked with Salyut 6 on 14 Mar while Soyuz 32 cosmonauts were on board
6	13 May 1979	10 Jun 1979	Docked with Salyut 6 on 15 May while Soyuz 32 cosmonauts were on board
7	28 Jun 1979	20 Jul 1979	Docked with Salyut 6 on 30 Jun while Soyuz 32 cosmonauts were on board

Figure 27

with Soyuz 29, whereas Progress 5-7 were associated with the recent Soyuz 32 mission. Details of each of these unmanned cargo deliveries are found in the following section under the associated Soyuz flight.

The use of unmanned Progress cargo transports is expected to remain high. Their ability to bring much needed material and equipment has lengthened the operational lifetime of a Salyut space station from three to nine months to a predicted five years. Even the introduction of a Soviet shuttle in the next few years would probably not affect the Progress program. Most present estimates of a Soviet reusable manned spacecraft do not provide for large cargo or fuel payloads of the type seen in Progress vehicles.

REFERENCES AND NOTES - SECTION IV

1. See the "Soyuz-Salyut Future Operations" Chapter in Section 5 for a review of these and other concepts.

2. *Spaceflight,* Oct. 1974, pp. 392-393 and Mar. 1975, p. 118. See also *Aviation Week and Space Technology,* 29 July 1974, p. 11, and *TRW Space Log, 1974,* pp. 14-15.

3. In the case of Soyuz 28, 30, 31, and 33 the flight engineers were East European. Even if these foreign nationals had military ties in their own countries, they would most certainly be regarded by the USSR as civilians (not permitted in military Salyut). Although the commander of Soyuz 33 was a civilian, a military cosmonaut was already in command of Salyut 6.

4. The apparent unawareness of this capability of cosmonauts associated with civilian Salyuts is a further indication of the lack of communication between the two Salyut programs. See *Aviation Week and Space Technology,* 21 June 1976, pp. 23-24.

5. Both modes of refueling have been tested on board Salyut 6. During fuel transfer with Progress 1 the on-board cosmonauts took an active role. During the Progress 2 refueling operation almost total control was retained by ground personnel.

6. *Aviation Week and Space Technology,* 2 Jan. 1978, pp. 20-21.

7. This is similar to the approach which is being taken by the United States.

8. Bumshtein, S.I., *Salyut Space Station in Orbit,* p. 3. See also *Spaceflight,* 1973, pp. 288-291.

9. Gatland, Kenneth, *Manned Spacecraft,* p. 229; *Aviation Week and Space Technology,* 30 Apr. 1973, and 25 Feb. 1974, p. 38. Soyuz 7 is thought by some to have been originally scheduled for rendezvous with a similar Salyut prototype. See Soyuz 6/7/8 mission in this book

10. Royal Aircraft Establishment, *Table of Earth Satellites, Volume 2, 1969-1973,* p. 243; *Spaceflight,* Feb. 1974, p. 238 and Nov. 1976, p. 415 and Apr. 1977, pp. 159-160; *Aviation Week and Space Technology,* 25 Feb. 1974, p. 38. Cosmonette Tereshkova believed it to be a failed Salyut in her book *I am Seagull,* p. 194.

11. Bumshtein, S.I., *op. cit.,* pp. 7 and 37.

12. Bumshtein, S.I., *op. cit.,* pp. 7-8.

13. It is believed that future Salyut space stations will utilize the ASTP androgynous docking mechanism. This would facilitate the proposed US Shuttle/Salyut mission.

14. Bumshtein, S.I., *op. cit.*, p. 8.

15. Bumshtein, S.I., *op. cit.*, p. 9.

16. Bumshtein, S.I., *op. cit.*, pp. 9-10.

17. Bumshtein, S.I., *op. cit.*, pp. 9-11.

18. Bumshtein, S.I., *op. cit.*, pp. 11 and 21.

19. *Aviation Week and Space Technology,* 7 July 1975.

20. Bumshtein, S.I., *op. cit.*, pp. 14-16.

21. Dmitriyev, A. Yu., et al., *From Spaceships to Orbiting Stations,* p. 94; Bumshtein, S.I., *op. cit.*, pp. 7, 20-21.

22. Bumshtein, S.I., *op. cit.*, pp. 10-11.

23. Bumshtein, S.I., *op. cit.*, pp. 11-17.

24. Ponomarev, A.N., *The Years of the Space Era,* p. 261; Bumshtein, S.I., *op. cit.*, pp. 17-19.

25. Bumshtein, S.I., *op. cit.*, pp. 8 and 16.

26. Further specifications and capabilities of Orion 1 can be found in Bumshtein, S.I., *op. cit.*, pp. 52-57. See also *Aviation Week and Space Technology,* 24 July 1972, and *Russian Report to COSPAR Session, 15th,* pp. 71-72; *Spaceflight,* May 1976, p. 177.

27. Bumshtein, S.I., *op. cit.*, pp. 57-60 provides finer details of Anna 3 construction. See also *Russian Report to COSPAR Session, 15th,* pp. 72-75.

28. *Russian Report to COSPAR Session, 15th,* pp. 75-77; Bumshtein, S.I., *op. cit.*, pp. 62-64.

29. Bumshtein, S.I., *op. cit.*, pp. 64-65.

30. Detailed discussion of these programs can be found in *Russian Report to COSPAR Session, 15th,* pp. 77-79 and Bumshtein, S.I., *op. cit.*, pp. 65-87. See also actual operations performed by Soyuz 11 cosmonauts in this book.

31. Bumshtein, S.I., *op. cit.*, pp. 42-47.

32. Bumshtein, S.I., *op. cit.*, pp. 47-50. See also Soyuz 11 results.

33. *Russian Report to COSPAR Session, 15th,* pp. 70-71, 79; Bumshtein, S.I., *op. cit.,* pp. 61-62.

34. See Kosmos 496 in this book concerning the questionable success of this mission.

35. Turnill, Reginald, *The Observer's Book of Manned Spaceflight,* p. 98; *Spaceflight,* Mar. 1975, pp. 119-120, and Apr. 1975, p. 159; *Aviation Week and Space Technology,* 9 Apr. 1973, p. 21.

36. Zhemchuzhin, N., et al., *Meet Aerospace Vehicles,* p. 41.

37. *Soviet Space Programs, 1971-1975,* pp. 194-195; *Jane's All the World's Aircraft, 1973-1974,* p. 650; Gatland, Kenneth, *op. cit.,* p. 234; *Aviation Week and Space Technology,* 9 Apr. 1973, p. 21; Turnill, Reginald, *op. cit.,* p. 100; *Spaceflight,* Aug. 1973, p. 293.

38. The time between the launch of a Salyut and the first Soyuz mission has been 4, 8, 15, 14, and 10 days.

39. *Soviet Space Programs, 1971-1975,* pp. 194-195; *Spaceflight,* July 1975, p. 280. A minority feel that Salyut 2 was not intended to be manned; *Spaceflight,* Apr. 1975, p. 159 and *Aviation Week and Space Technology,* 3 Sep. 1973, p. 11

40. *Aviation Week and Space Technology,* 30 Apr. 1973, p. 21 and 7 May 1973, pp. 22-23 and 14 May 1973.

41. *Aviation Week and Space Technology,* 3 Sep 1973, p. 11; *Astronautics and Aeronautics, 1973 (NASA),* pp. 102-103, 196.

42. Zhemchuzhin, N., et al., *op. cit.,* p. 41

43. An initial confusion as to the nature of Kosmos 557 led some to think that it was a Soyuz craft placed in orbit to inspect the disabled Salyut 2 or to serve as a target for an upcoming Soyuz 12. See *Aviation Week and Space Technology,* 21 May 1973.

44. Turnill, Reginald, *op. cit.,* p. 101; *Soviet Space Programs, 1971-1975,* pp. 195-196; *Aviation Week and Space Technology,* 28 May 1973; p. 25.

45. Photographs were finally released in early 1974 before Salyut 3 flew. *Aviation Week and Space Technology,* 25 Feb. 1974.

46. *Aviation Week and Space Technology,* 25 Feb. 1974, p. 36.

47. *Aviation Week and Space Technology,* 15 July 1974, pp. 292-293 and 22 July 1974, p. 15.

48. These measurements are derived using supporting figures and diagrams released after Salyut 4 was orbited. See Feoktistov, K.P., *The Salyut 4 Space Laboratory,* pp. 3-5.

49. *Aviation Week and Space Technology*, 25 Feb. 1974, p. 38.

50. *Space Research Conducted in the USSR in 1974, COSPAR Report, 18th Session*, p. 77.

51. *Space Research Conducted in the USSR in 1974, COSPAR Report, 18th Session*, pp. 74-75.

52. *Space Research Conducted in the USSR in 1974, COSPAR Report, 18th Session*, p. 76.

53. *Space Research Conducted in the USSR in 1974, COSPAR Report, 18th Session, ibid*.

54. *Space Technology*, Volume 4, No. 21; *Space Research Conducted in the USSR in 1974, COSPAR Report, 18th Session*, p. 78.

55. Sagdeyev, R.Z., ed., *The Conquest of Outer Space in the USSR 1974*, pp. 250-252, 257; *Aviation Week and Space Technology*, 30 Sep. 1974.

56. Sagdeyev, R.Z., ed., *op. cit.*, p. 259.

57. Feoktistov, K.P., *op. cit.*, p. 1.

58. Feoktistov, K.P., *op. cit.*, pp. 2-4.

59. Feoktistov, K.P., *op. cit.*, pp. 5-18; See also *Aviation Week and Space Technology*, 27 Jan. 1975, pp. 18-19; *Space World*, Nov. 1976, pp. 4-29, and Feb. 1977, pp. 94-95; *Soviet Space Programs, 1971-1975*, pp. 208-213; *Spaceflight*, June 1975, pp. 219-225 and Jan. 1976, pp. 13-18; Bono, Philip and Gatland, Kenneth, *Frontiers of Space*, pp. 130-133. See also Soyuz 17 and 18 flights in this book.

60. Feoktistov, K.P., *op. cit.*, pp. 6, 10-11.

61. The USSR does not recognize the 5 Apr. 1975 launch abort as a "Soyuz" flight. Thus when the next launch came on 24 May 1975, it was called Soyuz 18. The designations 18A and 18B are used throughout this book and in many journals and publications to differentiate the flights. Soyuz 18A is also sometimes called the "April 5th Anomaly".

62. See Soyuz 18A of this book for further details of this nearly fatal flight.

63. The first such vehicle, Progress 1, did not fly until February 1978.

64. Of the three USSR manned missions to date which have exceeded 63 days (Soyuz 26 and 29) replacement spacecraft have been provided by other cosmonaut crews. Therefore, no cosmonaut crew has yet to rely on a Soyuz which has been in flight in excess of two months.

65. It has been pointed out that during the Soyuz 21 mission major military and sea maneuvers were being conducted by Soviet forces. Soyuz 21 may have been placed in orbit to evaluate manned orbital observations of such movements.

66. This may illustrate the lack of communication between the USSR military and civilian man in space programs. Klimuk and Sevas'tyanov may not have known of the impending launch of Salyut 5. In addition at the same conference the two cosmonauts also asserted that all future Soyuz missions would be flown in conjunction with Salyut stations. However in Sep. 1976 Soyuz 22 flew a solo mission on what is thought by many to have been a militarily-oriented flight. See *Aviation Week and Space Technology*, 21 June 1976, pp. 23-24.

67. *Spaceflight,* Oct. 1976, p. 342.

68. *Spaceflight,* Sep. 1976, p. 331 and Oct. 1976, pp. 341-342 and Nov. 1976, pp. 381-382, 396 and Apr. 1977, pp. 138-145; Turnill, Reginald, *The Observer's Spaceflight Directory,* pp. 311-312. See also Soyuz 21 and 24 in this book.

69. *Aviation Week and Space Technology,* 28 Mar. 1977.

70. *L-5 News,* Apr. 1978, p. 9; *Aviation Week and Space Technology,* 1 May 1978, p. 19 and 17 July 1978, p. 19.

71. Although the Progress automated vehicle can be docked at the forward port, fuel can only be delivered via the aft port.

72. The alternate maneuver - undock from the aft port and redock at the forward port - was performed during the Soyuz 29/Salyut 6/Soyuz 31 mission in Sep. 1978.

73. See monthly progress reports beginning with February 1978 Spaceflight. See also weekly updates in *Aviation Week and Space Technology* and *Flight International* during this period.

74. Apparently Soviet EVA's had initially been planned for earlier Salyut flights but had been cancelled prior to the Soyuz launches. See *Aviation Week and Space Technology*, 21 June 1976, p. 24.

75. *Aviation Week and Space Technology,* 28 July 1975, p. 22 and 21 June 1976, p. 24.

76. See also related thinking in the Zond section of Volume 47, *Science and Technology Series*.

77. *Flight International,* 1 Apr. 1978; *Spaceflight,* July 1978, p. 267.

78. *Flight International,* 8 Apr. 1978, p. 996; *Aviation Week and Space Technology,* 20 Feb. 1978 and 1 May 1978, p. 19.

79. *Flight International,* 4 Feb. 1978, p. 289; *Aviation Week and Space Technology,* 9 Oct. 1978, p. 55.

Section V

SOYUZ-SALYUT MISSIONS

INTRODUCTION TO
SOYUZ-SALYUT MISSIONS

The spurt of Soviet manned space activity in 1969--the in-space crew transfer from Soyuz 5 to Soyuz 4 and the impressive triple rendezvous and welding experiments of Soyuz 6, 7, and 8--was followed in June 1970 with the 18-day Soyuz 9 mission, the longest manned orbital flight to that date. Initially, these events were interpreted as signaling the initiation of a manned lunar effort. But as the Apollo expeditions advanced beyond simple technological feats to extensive scientific and research lunar forays, talk of a Soviet manned lunar program was replaced with a new emphasis on the construction of long-term earth orbital stations. Finally on 19 April 1971, Salyut 1, the world's first true orbital laboratory, was launched into earth orbit some two years before the planned American Skylab counterpart.

Since that day, virtually the entire Soviet manned space program has been directed toward developing Salyut station capabilities and laying the ground work for even larger and more permanent orbital habitations. No fewer than 21 manned Soyuz missions have been directed to the five operational Salyut stations with an additional two flights dedicated to testing Soyuz/Salyut hardware. These figures also do not include the many unmanned Soyuz spacecraft, nine Progress cargo spaceships, and at least two failed Salyut stations belonging to the overall Salyut space exploration program.

As illustrated in the previous section in which the different Salyut space stations were described, the Soviet orbiting laboratory program has gradually evolved to the point where the USSR is now considered by many to be the major space power. Since 1967 the Soviet Union has been the leader in yearly space launches, steadily increasing its launches by 50% while the US has decreased its launches by an equal percentage. The Soviet

SOYUZ-SALYUT MISSIONS

Soyuz	Date Launched	Days in Orbit*	Salyut (mission)	Mission Results
10	23 Apr 1971	2	1 (prototype)	First rendezvous and docking with orbiting space station; crew transfer failed
11	6 Jun 1971	24	1 (prototype)	First operational manned orbiting laboratory mission; crew perished during reentry
14	3 Jul 1974	16	3 (military)	First successful Soyuz-Salyut mission; first operational military Salyut
15	26 Aug 1974	2	3 (military)	Failed to dock; crew returned to earth
17	11 Jan 1975	30	4 (civilian)	First civilian Salyut mission; set new Soviet endurance record
18A	5 Apr 1975	0	4 (civilian)	First manned launch abort; crew rescued
18B	24 May 1975	63	4 (civilian)	Set new Soviet endurance record
20	17 Nov 1975	(91)	4 (test)	Unmanned long-duration test of Soyuz spacecraft while docked with Salyut 4
21	6 Jul 1976	49	5 (military)	Military mission; probably terminated prematurely
23	14 Oct 1976	2	5 (military)	Failed to dock; crew returned to earth
24	7 Feb 1977	18	5 (military)	Planned short military observation mission
25	9 Oct 1977	2	6 (civilian)	Failed to dock; crew returned to earth
26	10 Dec 1977	97	6 (civilian)	First successful Soyuz to third generation Salyut; set new Soviet endurance record; first Soviet EVA in nine years
27	10 Jan 1978	5	6 (civilian)	First manned resupply mission; completed first Soyuz/Salyut/Soyuz link-up
28	2 Mar 1978	8	6 (civilian)	First international crew; Soviet-Czech
29	15 Jun 1978	140	6 (civilian)	New Soviet and world duration record of 140 days set; most active Soyuz-Salyut mission to date
30	27 Jun 1978	8	6 (civilian)	Second international crew; Soviet-Polish
31	26 Aug 1978	8	6 (civilian)	Third international crew; Soviet-East German
32	25 Feb 1979	175	6 (civilian)	Longest manned space flight to date
33	10 Apr 1979	2	6 (civilian)	Fourth international crew; Soviet-Bulgarian; failed to dock with Salyut 6
34	6 Jun 1979	(74)	6 (civilian)	Unmanned Soyuz ferry sent to return Soyuz 32 cosmonauts to earth

*Relates to Soyuz crew stay in space, not the associated Soyuz spacecraft stay which is sometimes different. Parentheses indicate lifetime of unmanned Soyuz mission.

Figure 1

Union now holds the record for not only the greatest number of man-days in space, but also the longest manned flight in history--175 days by the Soyuz 32 cosmonauts.

The purpose of this section is to review the initial faltering and later more confident steps of the Soviet Salyut space station program. Figure 1 represents a brief overview of the magnitude of this remarkable space undertaking. At the conclusion of this section an attempt has been made to bring together the statements of Soviet spokesman and Western observers for the sake of predicting the probable path of Soviet manned space exploration in the decades ahead.

Chapter 14

OPERATIONAL SOYUZ-SALYUT
FLIGHT MISSIONS

SOYUZ 10/SALYUT 1

The world was still guessing at the nature and exact purpose of Salyut 1 launched on 19 April 1971, when the Soviet Union announced the launching at 0254 hr on 23 April of the Soyuz 10 spacecraft (Figure 2). On board were now three-time space-flight veterans Shatalov and Yeliseyev, accompanied by rookie Cosmonaut Nikolay Nikolayevich Rukavishnikov. The presence of these three spacemen underscored the importance attached to the Soyuz 10/Salyut 1 mission. Shatalov had commanded Soyuz 4 in January 1969 whereas Yeliseyev was part of the world's first crew transfer from Soyuz 5 to Soyuz 4. Nine months later, Shatalov and Yeliseyev were again paired in Soyuz 8 and together they commanded the triple rendezvous of Soyuz 6, 7, and 8. With Soyuz 10 they were the first Soviets to make three space flights. Although Rukavishnikov was on his first space mission, he was described as a designer and expert on Salyut systems. A more qualified crew for earth's first orbital laboratory could not be found.

Moscow reported Soyuz 10's orbit at 1200 hr Moscow time as 246 km by 208 km at an inclination of 51.6°. Slightly higher than planned, the orbit was adjusted by Shatalov with the first of several orbital maneuvers at 1355 hr in his search for the orbiting Salyut laboratory. Following the procedure set forth and tested by Soyuz 4-5 and Soyuz 6-7-8, Soyuz 10 and Salyut 1 made complementary maneuvers with the aim of docking approximately twenty-four hours after the launch of Soyuz 10.[1]

Early in the morning of 24 April, following a six-and-one-half hour rest, the final rendezvous maneuvers were carried out. Under the watchful

Figure 2 Mock-up of the original Soyuz ferry for Salyut space stations. Note the solar panels which are no longer carried
by current Soyuz ferries. (Courtesy of R.F. Gibbons)

eye of Shatalov the automatic tracking and rendezvous equipment brought
the two craft to within 180 meters. At this distance Shatalov assumed
control and inched the vehicles closer together. At 0447 hr Soyuz 10
and Salyut 1 made a firm mechanical link-up, creating a 23-m long, 25,600-
kg space station complex. A new stage in space exploration appeared about
to begin.[2]

A quick systems check-out and crew transfer to Salyut 1 was predicted.
Unexpectedly, only five and one-half hours later Soyuz 10 undocked and
pulled away from the Salyut station. A brief photo reconnaissance of
Salyut 1 was conducted before preparations were made to return Soyuz 10
to earth. Almost exactly two days after Soyuz 10 had started on what was
thought by all to be a record-breaking space spectacular, the crew returned
safely to earth in the USSR's first night landing. At 0240 hr on 25 April
the three cosmonauts landed 120 km NW of Karaganda some 50 meters from the
edge of a lake from which they were saved at the last moment by a gust of
wind.[3]

The Sovietsimmediately issued statements that the entire Soyuz 10 program had been fulfilled. Later, the purpose of the Soyuz 10/Salyut 1 joint flight was given as providing "for complex checking of the improved on-board systems of the ship, testing of the manual and automatic systems for control, orientation, and stabilization of the ship in different flight regimes and carrying out a series of biomedical investigations."[4]

The Soviets acknowledge that a new docking mechanism was being tested on the flight. The only previous Soviet manned docking had occurred in January 1969 with Soyuz 4-5. On that flight two cosmonauts were required to perform an EVA to move from one ship to the other since the docking mechanism did not provide an internal transfer tunnel. Soyuz 10 was to test an improved version of the docking collar which eliminated this problem. Even though a rigid docking apparently did take place between Soyuz 10 and Salyut 1 the available evidence points to a failure of the tunnel mechanism as the cause of the cancellation and early return to earth of Soyuz 10.

Figures 3 and 4 are photographs of the active (probe) and passive (drogue) docking mechanisms of the type used during the Soyuz 10/Salyut 1 mission. Note the symmetry of the electrical and hydraulic connections and the docking latches around the two docking collars. Soviet spacecraft engineers purposely designed the docking system in this manner to allow for relatively easy (albeit on the ground) modification from an active mechanism to a passive one or vice versa.

The schematic diagrams of Figures 5 and 6 illustrates the operation of the docking mechanisms. During the final moments of the rendezvous process, the Soyuz commander refined the relative alignment of the Soyuz spacecraft and the Salyut space station and edged the probe of his ship into the receiving cone of Salyut.

"The shock absorption of the collision is realized as a result of displacement of the stem of the docking mechanism and rocking of it with respect to the base on a ball hinge. When seating the stem, a spiral spring twists, and first the electromechanical brakes and spring mechanisms which return the system to the initial position after the shock. After capture of the head by the recess of the receiving cone and damping of the relative oscillations, the drive of the docking mechanism is connected to the drawing and equalization of the docking surfaces of the joined objects."[5]

Figure 3   Docking mechanism for the Salyut space station   (Courtesy
of R.F. Gibbons)

Figure 4   Docking mechanism for the Soyuz spacecraft   (Courtesy of
R.F. Gibbons)

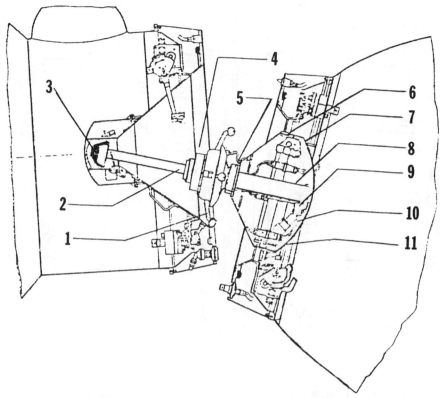

1. Linkage assembly
2. Probe
3. Head
4. Electric Drive
5. Ball and socket joint
6. Locking mechanism
7. Electromechanical damper
8. Probe guide
9. Capture-latches release drive
10. Lateral shock absorber
11. Explosive bolt

Figure 5   Schematic diagram of the Soyuz/Salyut docking process

The actual rendezvous and docking maneuvers between Soyuz 10 and Salyut 1 were described by Soviet spokesmen as emotionally taxing. The cosmonauts described the final docking procedure as similar to bringing an engine into a train depot due to the relative sizes of Soyuz and Salyut. Although references were made regarding the increased complexities in coordinating the maneuvers of a Soyuz/Salyut rendezvous versus a Soyuz/Soyuz rendezvous, subsequently released data have shown that early Salyuts employed Soyuz propulsion and attitude-control systems and did indeed perform as would a Soyuz target vehicle.

Phillip S. Clark has shown a relationship between launch and recovery times and mission duration for Soyuz spacecraft.[6] Applying these results

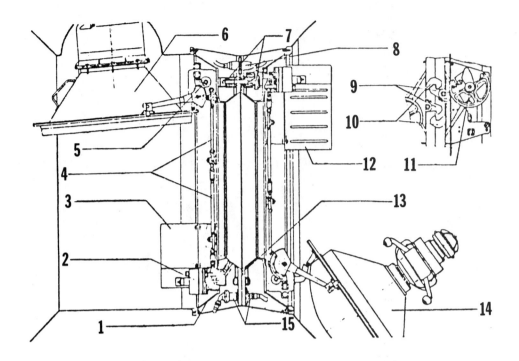

1. Docking ring
2. Hatch pressurization drive
3. Automatic instrument
4. Battening-down element rod
5. Hatch drive
6. Stored drogue assembly
7. Peripheral latch
8. Electrical connector
9. Active hooks
10. Passive hooks
11. Eccentric mechanism
12. Automatic instrument
13. Interface seal
14. Stored probe assembly
15. Hydraulic connector

Figure 6   Soyuz/Salyut docking mechanism in crew transfer mode

to the Soyuz 10 mission, a stay of 30 to 40 days on board Salyut 1 is predicted. This analysis further confirms the supposition that the early
return of Soyuz 10 was not planned.

Another hypothesis suggests that Soyuz 10 was scheduled to remain aloft
for only two weeks for the purpose of activating Salyut 1. Soyuz 11 was
then to have followed soon afterward for the first long-duration mission.[7]

A further note which is sometimes connected with the assumed failure
of the Soyuz 10 crew to man Salyut 1 is the reported space sickness of
Rukavishnikov. The reasoning here is that the rookie cosmonaut became
too ill to continue the mission, forcing Soyuz 10 back to earth. Although
several US and USSR spacemen have experienced some disorientation early

in space flight, none have been seriously incapacitated to the degree requiring termination of the flight. This disorientation usually disappears in 24 to 48 hours. A similar story of space sickness surfaced after the one-day flight of Voskhod 1. However, in both these instances the question of crew health is thought by some to have been initiated by the Soviets themselves to draw attention away from other mission shortcomings.

An unsubstantiated article in 1974 also placed the blame for failure of the mission on the new docking system.[8] This report went on to state that difficulty was encountered in undocking the two spacecraft and that the oxygen supply on board Soyuz was sufficient for only 48 hours. The validity of these later assertions is questionable in the light of factual errors in the Soyuz 10 account and considering known spacecraft design features of the early model Soyuz.

The significance of the return of Soyuz 10 after only two days is probably slight other than to point out the failure of the crew to transfer to Salyut 1. Although Soyuz 10 was of the first-generation Soyuz spacecraft and almost certainly was capable of remaining aloft longer, the crew was trained to work on board Salyut not Soyuz. Virtually all the experimental apparatus and necessary supplies were on board Salyut. The cosmonauts were in space, but they had nothing of value to do unless they could enter the orbiting laboratory. An EVA was out of the question since no space suits were carried and Salyut 1 may not have had the separate EVA hatch which later Soviet space stations would incorporate. Hence, following the photographic survey of Salyut 1 after undocking, the Soyuz 10 crew had no other option but to return to earth.

SOYUZ 11/SALYUT 1

Following the failure of the Soyuz 10/Salyut 1 mission, the USSR space program managers moved quickly to salvage the fledging orbital laboratory program by readying another manned Soyuz mission. The origin of the composition of the subsequent crew of Soyuz 11 has been the subject of much debate.[9] Their untimely deaths in the concluding minutes of the historic flight has only served to deepen rather than to clarify this question.

Most Western observers of the Soviet space program believe that a Soyuz 11 crew was in training when Soyuz 10 was launched to dock with and activate Salyut 1. Regardless of the length of stay of Soyuz 10 (14 to 40 days?), Soyuz 11 is considered to have been planned as the first long-duration space-station flight whose mission would be solely to utilize the facilities and resources of Salyut 1 readied by Soyuz 10. With the unexpected return of Soyuz 10 before the station could be demothballed, this flight plan was in need of revision.

Two possible schemes for recoupling from this unfortunate setback are thought likely. The first would have been to prepare the Soyuz 11 crew then in training to activate the Salyut systems and to perform the other vital tasks formerly assigned to Soyuz 10. After completion of these chores, Soyuz 11 would remain aloft as long as deemed safe, completing as many of their original experiments as possible. It is thought that the six-week delay between the launchings of Soyuz 10 and Soyuz 11 may have permitted such an undertaking.

The second alternative would have been to ready the Soyuz 10 back-up crew for Soyuz 11 and shift the Soyuz 11 crew to the next planned flight, Soyuz 12. (Reflying the Soyuz 10 crew was out of the question since this would prove that Soyuz 10 had failed--something the USSR has always strongly denied.) For several reasons this scenario seems more likely. The Soyuz 10 back-up cosmonauts were well versed in all the required Salyut setup operations, they had long trained along side the Soyuz 10 crew, and re-training of the planned Soyuz 11 crew might not be possible in the few weeks available.

In addition, the final makeup of the Soyuz 11 cosmonauts lends credence to the theory that they were once the Soyuz 10 back-ups. When Soyuz 11 finally blasted off from the Baikonur Cosmodrome toward the orbiting Salyut 1 on 6 June 1971 on board were rookie Command Pilot Georgiy Teimofe'-yevich Dobrovolskiy, Soyuz 7 veteran Vladislav Nikola'yevich Volkov, and rookie Test Engineer Viktor Ivanovich Patsayev. Considering the importance of the first missions to Salyut 1 and the reserve of anxious veterans in the cosmonaut corps, one would not imagine the first mission to exploit fully Salyut 1's potential to be manned by two rookies.[10] Furthermore, Volkov's position as flight engineer parallels Yelise'yev's similar role on Soyuz 10. Due to their similar experience and work together during Soyuz 7-8 Volkov might well have been expected to be Yelise'yev's back-up. Finally, although not certain, it appears that Dobrovolskiy and Patsayev had not fulfilled back-up roles prior to their flight in Soyuz 11. As a rule, Soviet cosmonauts train as back-ups before being assigned to their own missions.

Assuming the Soyuz 11 crew were indeed last-minute substitutes, the question which is thus hotly debated is who were the cosmonauts originally scheduled to fly Soyuz 11. Although speculation varies, Leonov and Kubasov are regarded as two of the prime candidates. The importance of these members lies in the possible effect on the Soviet space program, had they been killed aboard Soyuz 11 instead of Dobrovolskiy, Volkov, Patsayev. With Gagarin's fatal air crash in 1968, the death of Leonov, who had assumed Gagarin's place in cosmonaut popularity, would have dealt the USSR orbiting laboratory program and the man-in-space program in general a severe blow.

At five minutes before eight o'clock on the morning of 6 June 1971, a roar thundered across Tyuratam as the engines of the Soyuz 11 launch vehicle ignited and slowly lifted the three-man spacecraft skyward (Figure 7). After weeks of intensive training and analysis of the new docking mechanism a second attempt was being made to man the slowly decaying Salyut 1. Nine minutes later, Soyuz 11 entered a low earth orbit. At 1350 hr that day the first orbital maneuver was performed placing Soyuz 11 into an orbit of 217 km by 185 km at an inclination of 51.6°.[11]

The first day in space was devoted to calculating the respective orbits of Soyuz 11 and Salyut 1 and to planning the docking maneuvers scheduled for early the following day. Although some initial discomfort due to weightlessness was reported by the crew, these symptoms vanished quickly. Dobrovolskiy noted that a large amount of dust had appeared after orbital insertion and was removed using a wet towel and circulation fan. A minor repair was made to the fan when its blades began striking the protective grating. By 1830 hr Dobrovolskiy and Volkov had retired to the orbital module of Soyuz while Patsayev slept in the command module.[12]

Final rendezvous maneuvers were begun at 0720 hr on 7 June. A 20-second burn of the Soyuz 11 propulsion engine at 0727 hr narrowed the 6-km gap between the spacecraft and Salyut 1. At a distance of 100 meters and a relative velocity of 0.9 m/sec Dobrovolskiy took over manual control of the rendezvous process. Contact was made at 0749 hr with complete electrical and mechanical docking at 0755 hr, exactly 24 hours after the

Figure 7   Lift-off of a Soyuz manned spacecraft
(Courtesy of NASA)

launch of Soyuz 11. The three cosmonauts immediately set about checking
and rechecking all seals and systems. The historic boarding of the world's
first orbital laboratory was begun some three hours later at 1045 hr.[13]
Thus began man's first extended stay in earth orbit for scientific purposes.

The next few days were devoted to activating various Salyut systems and experiments (Figure 8). Dynamic tests to evaluate the docked Soyuz/Salyut configuration were performed. At 1102 hr on 8 June a burn of the Salyut engine lifted the vehicles to an orbit of 265 km by 239 km. A second burn of 73 seconds at 1006 hr the next day raised the orbit still higher to 282 km by 259 km.[14]

The major experimental equipment on Salyut 1 have already been mentioned in the preceding section. Following is a brief highlight of the crew's activities on a day-by-day basis:[15]

7 June: Docking systems check out; transfer of materials from Soyuz 11 to Salyut 1

8 June: Orbital correction; television broadcast; settlement into Salyut 1; activation of Salyut systems and equipment

9 June: Deactivation of certain Soyuz 11 systems; orbital correction; first use of Penguin weighted suit; radiation and micrometeorite measurement equipment activated; atmospheric composition checked repeatedly; wide angle solar and planetary viewer tested

10 June: Physical exercises, including use of treadmill, conducted; cardiovascular system evaluated under varying conditions; bone-density experiments performed; blood samples taken; television broadcast

11 June: Spectrographic measurement of earth and atmosphere; gamma telescope used to measure intensity, angular distribution and energy spectrum of primary cosmic gamma radiation (see Figure 9); Molniya 1 satellite and research ship Akademik Sergei Korolev used for communications relay

12 June: Dosimetric readings studied in conjunction with radiation control problems of long space flights; medical experiments of the human cardiovascular, respiration, and visual systems conducted; photographic sessions; television broadcast; physical exercises; ports inspected

13 June: Geological observations and photography; primary cosmic radiation recorded; hydroponic farm tended; Oasis apparatus monitored

14 June: Autonomous navigation experiments conducted; spectrographic measurements of earth taken; joint observations of weather patterns with Meteor satellite; television broadcast; visual checks performed

15 June: Simultaneous space and aircraft aerial photography performed; agricultural, geodesic, and cartographic spectral readings taken; transmission of cloud cover in conjunction with Meteor satellite; dosimetric control checked; cardiovascular systems checked; cosmic ray particles recorded; television broadcast; aircraft trails and ship wakes observed

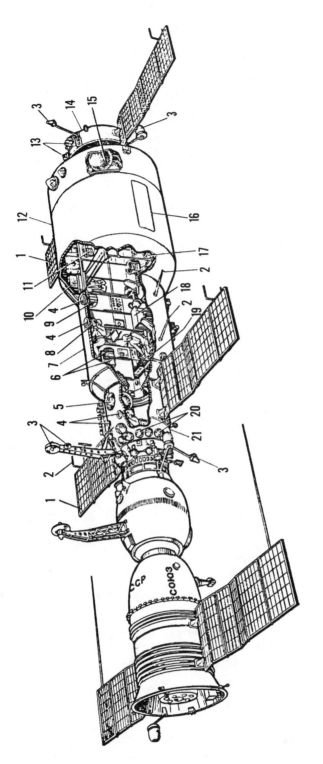

1. Solar panels (2 pairs)
2. Telemetry antennae
3. Rendezvous antennae
4. Portholes
5. Orion stellar telescope
6. Atmospheric regeneration equipment
7. Forward section of working compartment
8. Movie camera
9. Photographic camera
10. Apparatus for biological research
11. Food refrigeration unit

12. Aft section of working compartment
13. Attitude control engines
14. Propulsion compartment and main engine
15. Propellant tanks
16. Micrometeorite detector
17. Treadmill
18. Work table
19. Central control post
20. Compressed gas spheres
21. Docking/transfer compartment

Figure 8   Design of the Salyut 1 space station

294

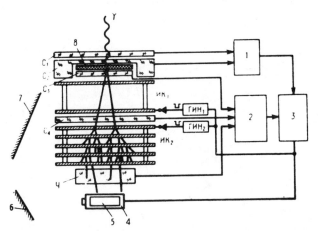

1. adder
2. triple comparison circuit
3. gamma quanta selection circuit
4. photorecorder

5. removable cassette
6. mirror
7. mirror
8. lead converter

$ИК_1$, $ИК_2$: spark chambers

$ГН_1$, $ГН_2$: high voltage pulse generators

$C_1 - C_4$: scintillation counters

Ч : directional Cherendov counter

Figure 9   Block diagram of the Anna III telescope

16 June: Spacecraft control systems evaluated; accuracy checks of manual and automatic orientation instruments; observed photometric effects of engine operations; atmospheric composition measured by radio-frequency mass spectrometers

17 June: High-frequency electron resonance experiment conducted for evaluation of transmitting antenna design; ion and electron densities at Salyut altitude measured; day of rest; medical experiments

18 June: Orion observatory activated; six spectrograms of Beta Centauri obtained; television broadcast (see Figure 10)

19 June: Horizon experiments performed to measure amount of aerosol particles and other optically active components of atmosphere; gyroscopic system evaluation; visual and cardiovascular systems and bone densities again checked; Patsayev's birthday; meteorological observations

20 June: Salyut 1 completed 1000th orbit; television broadcast; photographic sessions; day of rest

21 June: Orion observations: nine spectrograms of Alpha Lyrae; primary gamma radiation, local electron density, and charged particle spectrums measured.

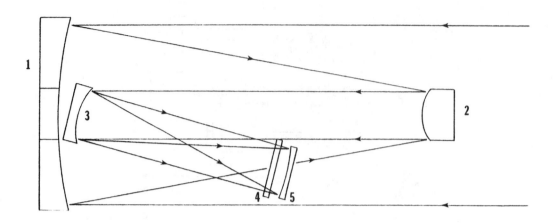

1. Large parabolic mirror
2. Slitless spectrograph
3. Small mirror
4. Diffraction grating
5. Photographic film

Figure 10   Schematic diagram of the Orion telescope

22 June: Manual spectrograph used for horizon studies during sunrise and sunset; polarization of light reflected by earth studied; cyclones and other meteorological events observed; Oazis apparatus monitored

23 June: Wide-angle viewer tested for orientation purposes; port inspected; engine firings observed; photography of USSR conducted

24 June: Space-endurance record set, breaking 18-day record held by Soyuz 9 crew; stellar and earth photographs taken under different orientation regimes; typhoon observed; physical exercises continued with many lasting up to one and a half hours; observed dust particles near Salyut

25 June: Multi-functional Era experiment continued; preparations for return started; experimental results and apparatus stored in Soyuz 11; television broadcast

26 June: Charged particle intensities and spectrum measured; micro-meteorite measurements; exercises and strenous activity undertaken in preparation for landing

27 June: Soyuz 11 system checked out; television broadcast; sleep periods altered to bring all three cosmonauts to same schedule for return to earth; cyclone observed

28 June: Medical experiments repeated for return to earth; reactivation of Soyuz systems

29 June: Final preparations for departure from Salyut 1; undocking at 2128 hr.

The flight of Soyuz 11/Salyut 1 was one characterized by experimentation and evaluation. Although the programmed routine had been thoroughly practiced on earth there was no way to know if such operations could be conducted as expected under weightless conditions. In general, most work schedules fell behind, due to more time being needed for each experiment. The Soyuz 11 cosmonauts made numerous comments on how to improve existing systems and proposed the addition of others. Psychologically and physiologically the crew did not feel hampered.

Figure 11 shows a breakdown of daily rations provided on Salyut 1.

Some of the scientific results gleaned from the Soyuz 11 mission included:

1. Detection of high-frequency secondary electron resonance in space

2. Spectrograms of Beta Centauri and Alpha Lyrae in 2000-3800 Å range clearly showed several absorption lines including the Balmer series

3. Gamma quanta flux from the earth with energy >100 Mev was measured as a reference for primary cosmic gamma quanta

4. Charged particle (proton) flux near Salyut with energy >300 Mev was determined

5. Improved processing techniques for Meteor weather information as a result of joint Salyut/Meteor experiments were found

6. Numerous earth resources data obtained through ordinary and spectrographic photography.

On 25 June the crew announced that preparations had begun to conclude their operations and return to earth. Exercise periods were more strenuous and were lengthened. The task of verifying the Soyuz 11 spacecraft systems and loading the command module with logs, tapes, etc. was also started. After 23 days on board Salyut 1 in the evening of 29 June the cosmonauts closed down the station systems and entered the orbital and command modules of Soyuz 11. If all went according to plan, three more cosmonauts would soon return to carry on the work started by Dobrovolskiy, Volkov, and Patsayev.

Mission control instructed Volkov at 2115 hr to close the Salyut space station/Soyuz orbital module hatches for the last time. After the hatch was sealed the descent module hatch was opened and the seals checked again. All signal lights indicated proper closure. The disengage command was given at 2125 hr, and three minutes later Soyuz 11 pulled away from the

SALYUT 1 DAILY RATIONS

	No. 1	No. 2	No. 3
Early Breakfast: (705-756 kilocalories)	Sausages (entrecote, ham, meat pate) Borodino bread Chocolate Coffee with milk	Carbonate (ham, meat pate) Borodino bread Sweet (praline) Coffee with milk	Sliced bacon (veal, liver pate, sausage meat) Borodino bread Candied fruit Coffee with milk
Late Breakfast: (600-700 kilocalories)	Russian cheese Riga bread Candied fruit	Beef tongue (pork tongue, sausage meat) Riga bread Creamed cheese Cheese with apple puree	Creamed cottage cheese Blackberry puree
Lunch: (798-928 kilocalories)	Vobla (Caspian fish) Sorrel Soup Chicken (ham, meat pate) Table bread Prunes with nuts Blackberry juice	Vobla Borshich Veal (liver pate, sausage) Table bread Captial cookies Blackbury juice	Vobla Kharcho Chicken (ham, meat pate) Table bread Prunes with nuts
Dinner: (593-743 kilocalories)	Pureed meat Table bread Honey cake	Pureed poultry Table bread Prunes	Pureed poultry Borodino bread Russian cheese

Figure 11

298

orbital laboratory. For the next few hours Soyuz 11 remained in the vicinity of Salyut 1, stowing all equipment and double-checking the reentry
procedures. By 0135 hr on 30 June the spacecraft was in position, and
retro-fire took place right on schedule. The seemingly routine process
of reentry now lay before them. In forty minutes they would return to
their native soil as heroes.[16]

Separation of the orbital and propulsion modules quickly followed.
The fiery reentry ensued and by 0202 hr Moscow time the parachute system
was activated. Thirteen minutes later at 0215 hr the capsule gently landed
under the eyes of the waiting rescue party. But, to the horror of all
present, when the command module hatch was opened Dobrovolskiy, Volkov,
and Patsayev lay peacefully in their seats--dead.

The Soviet Union along with the rest of the world was shocked. Speculation as to the cause of death was high. Whereas some believed an accidental hatch leak had suffocated the cosmonauts, others thought the
sudden force of gravity after so many days in space may have been the
cause. If the latter were true, man might well be confined to earth forever except for short forays into space or the use of artificial gravity
might be mandatory for long stays in space.

Within two weeks Soviet spokesmen revealed the truth: the descent
cabin had accidentally lost its vital atmosphere. Soyuz was not equipped
to combat a leak of this magnitude, and the crew did not have available
pressure suits which could have saved their lives. The cosmonauts apparently died from a combination of lack of oxygen and the effects of low
pressure on the oxygen/nitrogen mixture in their lungs. As a result of
the Apollo-Soyuz Test Project mission agreed upon a year later, the United
States pressed the Soviet Union for the cause of the spacecraft leak.
NASA officials would not allow US astronauts in an orbiting Soyuz unless
they could be assured that a repeat of the Soyuz 11 disaster was impossible.

The failure apparently came when the orbital module was explosively
separated from the command module following the retro-burn. The shock
set up by this event is thought to have prematurely triggered a command
module vent valve designed to open after parachute deployment. Complete
cabin atmosphere was lost in approximately 40-50 seconds. Indications
are that the cosmonauts soon realized what was happening and began to close

299

the vent manually. Unfortunately, the mechanism was hard to reach and slow in activation. The cosmonauts perished before the valve could be half closed.[17]

The Salyut space station program which had been the hope of the Soviet Union for the 1970s had been dealt a devastating blow. The setback of Soyuz 10 and the tragic end of Soyuz 11 brought a halt to all Soviet manned operations for 27 months. For the second time in six years the Soviet man-in-space program was in limbo while an extensive self-analysis took place. No one could suspect that three years would pass before the Soviet space station program would recover.

SOYUZ 14/SALYUT 3

Before Soviet cosmonauts could again return to the folds of space, drastic modifications to the Soyuz life-support system had to be implemented. The investigation of the Soyuz 11 tragedy revealed, among other things, that provision would have to be made to allow cosmonauts to wear full pressure suits during critical operations (launch, docking, reentry) and to provide emergency oxygen and nitrogen supplies. The prospect of an early return to manned Salyut missions vanished with the Salyut launch failures in July of 1972 and in April and May of 1973 mentioned in the previous section. Finally, by the summer of 1973 two unmanned orbital tests of the redesigned Soyuz (Kosmos 496 and 573) had requalified the spacecraft for a human crew. In September 1973, Soyuz 12 with Cosmonauts Lazarev and Makarov flew a brief two-day mission to evaluate the new life-support systems and the new battery-powered ferry version of Soyuz. For the first time in eight and one-half years Soviet cosmonauts were dressed in space suits during takeoff and landing.

Following an apparently successful flight of Soyuz 12, the Salyut space station program was once again believed to be near resumption.[18] However, a delay in the Salyut schedule resulted in the eight-day Soyuz 13 solo mission in December 1973. The purpose of this last venture was to test certain components and experiments destined for Salyut stations while awaiting the successful placement of a new orbital laboratory about the earth.

Almost seven more months elapsed before Soviet spacemen would man a Salyut station. The stage was set on 25 June 1974 when the first of the second-generation Salyut laboratories was successfully inserted into earth orbit. Many advances had been made in the space station since the launch of Salyut 1 three years earlier. Eight days later, Vostok veteran Pavel Popovich and rookie Cosmonaut Yuri Petrovich Artyukhin followed the station into space.

Launched at 2151 hr Moscow time on 3 July, Soyuz 14 was some 3500 km behind Salyut 3 upon orbital insertion (Figure 12). Over the course of the next day, four separate orbital maneuvers were performed, bringing the two spacecraft to within 1 km of each other. Here, the automatic search and rendezvous system was engaged, and the separation was quickly narrowed. At a distance of 100 meters Popovich disengaged the automatic equipment and completed the rendezvous manually. At exactly midnight on 4 July a firm docking had been achieved after the relative speeds had been reduced to 0.3 m/sec.

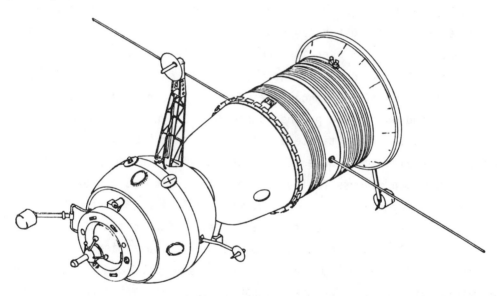

Figure 12   The wingless Soyuz ferry used to transport two-man
crews to Salyut space stations since 1974
(Drawing by R.F. Gibbons)

A quick check of the docking mechanism and seals, pressure equalization, and electrical connectors followed. With all procedures verified on the ground by telemetric data, the cosmonauts were given permission to enter Salyut 3. This process took four and one-half hours, allowing Artyukhin to open the Salyut entrance hatch at 0430 hr on 5 July. The orbit of Soyuz 14/Salyut 3 was now approximately 276 km by 265 km.[19]

Salyut 3 was the first of the militarily oriented operational Salyut stations.[20] Although evaluation of manned earth photo-reconnaissance techniques was one of the primary tasks, the USSR which refuses to admit military motives in space exploration released a broad four point goal for the mission:

1. Testing an improved system for design of the station and also on-board systems and apparatus

2. Study of the physcial characteristics of space

3. Investigation of geomorphological features on the earth's surface, atmospheric formations and phenomena

4. Biomedical investigations for the study of the influence of space flight factors on the human body and determination of rational work regimes of the crew aboard the station and many other experiments.[21]

During the next two weeks Popovich and Artyukhin conducted various experiments and tested the new systems of Salyut 3. One of the major improvements of Salyut 3 over its predecessors was ability of the stations' solar panels to remain sun-oriented under most regimes of station attitude. This of course permitted longer periods of uninterrupted earth surveillance.

As pointed out in the preceding section, Salyut 3's photographic equipment was capable of legitimate earth resources work as well as high-resolution reconnaissance. Some of the data provided during photographic sessions aided such diverse fields as ore, petroleum, and gas exploration, geologic and topographic map making, water pollution, preservation of agricultural resources, flood control, and oceanic ice formation.

In particular, the cosmonauts returned film containing "more than 100 spectrograms of the twilight aureole, daytime horizon and different types of natural features. Each spectrogram after processing makes it possible to obtain 40-50 spectra of individual sectors of the earth's surface or atmosphere at different altitudes. Spectra were obtained for different types of vegetation, soils, fields, agricultural crops, river valleys, lakes, and sectors of the world ocean surface. These data are the basis for a detailed study of the peculiarities of reflection spectra and the development of a method for global evaluation and monitoring of the state of the environment."[22]

The following synopsis highlights the two cosmonauts' stay on board Salyut 3:[23]

5 July: Docking; crew transfer; activation of Salyut systems

6 July: Continued activation of Salyut; medical examinations of cosmonauts, including electrocardiograms

7 July: Rheograph used to measure blood circulation in the brain and arteries; physical exercises begun using Salyut gym; Penguin suits worn

8 July: Observation of polarization of sun light reflected by the earth's surface and atmosphere for the purpose of earth resources evaluation and Salyut automatic navigation

9 July: Radio communications checks; station atmospheric checks; horizon observations made during twilight, day and night in order to study the dynamics of development of optic phenomena in the atmosphere in its interaction with solar radiation and to detect structural characteristics of radiation in the upper atmosphere.

10 July: Pulmonary ventilation examined in conjunction with determining cosmonaut energy expenditures

11 July: Indication that mission will only last one more week; spectrographs taken of horizon during twilight and day to plot vertical profiles of atmospheric brightness and to measure aerosol components of the atmosphere; used new apparatus to test water regeneration from atmospheric moisture condensate; tested new Salyut thermo-regulation system under varying conditions

12 July: Cardiovascular and vestibular examinations performed; continued regular monitoring and cultivation of on-board biological payloads; partial rest day; checked manual control systems; made further atmospheric light polarization tests

13 July: Photographic sessions of geological and morphological formations; Soyuz 14 examined; new solar-planetary orientation instrument checked

14 July: Photographed Soviet Central Asia for ore deposits; charted glacier movements

15 July: Further earth resources photography; observation of cloud formations; tested astronavigation using earth horizon and dust layers as reference

16 July: Spectroscopic photography of earth; Priboy regeneration apparatus again tested; observations by Salyut 3 cosmonauts and Meteor satellite of Atlantic in cooperation with international Tropex-74 program

17 July: Preparations to leave Salyut 3 begun in earnest; Soyuz 14 systems thoroughly checked; documents, etc. transferred to Soyuz 14; vibrational effects on pendulums examined

18 July: Final preparations for the return to earth made; temporary mothballing of Salyut 3 started.

Communications with Salyut 3 were reported to be continuous, relying on research ships (Kosmonaut Yuri Gagarin,Kosmonaut Vladimir Komarov), scattered ground stations, and relay satellites. To aid in tracking down problems which arose on Salyut 3 an exact duplicate of the orbital laboratory was manned in a special laboratory in the Soviet Union. If the cosmonauts wanted to deviate from planned operations, the proposed action could first be tested and verified on the ground before permission was granted to the orbiting spacemen.[24]

Solar flares occurring on 4, 6, and 8 July caused some consternation for the cosmonauts' safety. However, a careful watch of radiational effects revealed that the Salyut 3 crew was not in immediate danger. Solar activity returned to relative calm on 9 July.[25] Daily inspection of Salyut 3's exterior was conducted via the externally mounted cameras.

One aspect of the military nature of the flight came when a leading aerospace periodical reported the orbiting cosmonauts often used code words and participated in observation of targets placed on the ground near Tyuratam.[26]

The Soyuz 14 mission finally came to a close on 19 July. After transferring all necessary gear into the Soyuz descent module and donning space suits, the two cosmonauts entered their spacecraft and sealed the hatch to Salyut 3. Undocking took place precisely at 1203 hr after which Soyuz 14 flew along side Salyut 3 for one more orbit while descent instructions were verified. At 1432 hr retro-fire was begun, followed 28 minutes later by orbital and propulsion module separation. Touchdown came at 1521 hr, 140 km SE of Dzezhkazgan after a flight of 377.5 hours.

Upon landing Popovich and Artyukhin felt the temporarily unpleasant effects of gravity after 16 days of weightlessness. Low blood pressure and low pulse contributed to their overall weakness. Although they were able to walk without assistance their gait was not regularized for four to six hours. Sudden head movements and strenuous activity such as climbing stairs proved taxing. However, within a few days body systems returned to normal.

Thus, after three years and the failure of Soyuz 10 and 11, the first truly successful Soviet space station mission had ended. Although the two-week stay could not compare with the three-month record set by US astronauts earlier that year, Western observers predicted a quick return to Salyut 3 with longer flight durations.

SOYUZ 15/SALYUT 3

The world did not have long to wait to see a second attempt at manning
Salyut 3. Six weeks after the return of Soyuz 14, the Soviet Union proudly
announced the launch of Soyuz 15 for the purpose of continued experiments
in conjunction with Salyut 3. On 17 August 1974, TASS had given the orbital parameters of Salyut 3 as 278 km by 260 km at 51.6°. Nine days later
at 2258 hr on 26 August Soyuz 15, carrying Cosmonauts Gennadiy Vasilyevich
Sarafanov and Lev Stepanovich Demin, blasted off the Baikonur Cosmodrome.[27]
Their initial orbit was reported to be 230 km by 180 km at 51.6°.

Just as Soyuz 14 had done the month before, Soyuz 15 performed orbital
maneuvers during the morning of 27 August raising the orbit to 275 km by
254 km. The three previous flights to Salyut stations had docked within
24 to 26 hours. It was now expected that Soyuz 15 would engage Salyut 3
between 0000 and 0100 hr on 28 August. Surprisingly no word of a docking
came at the predicted time. Instead TASS subsequently reported that by
0800 hr on 28 August Soyuz 15 had completed 22 revolutions and was preparing to return to earth. In the short announcement TASS went on to say,

> "According to the second day program, cosmonauts Sarafanov and Demin
> carried out experiments to perfect the technique of piloting the
> craft in various flight regimes. In the process of maneuvering the
> Soyuz 15 they repeatedly approached the Salyut 3 station. The cos-
> monauts controlled the operation of all systems of the craft, made
> observations of the stages of approach with the station. As the
> manned spacecraft approached the station the cosmonauts conducted
> an inspection of it."[28]

Amid speculation of numerous types of failures, Soyuz 15 made preparations to return to earth at the next opportunity for the standard recovery
area. Since the Soyuz 15 spacecraft was one of the new ferry versions of
Soyuz which did not carry solar panels, the crew was limited to a maximum
2-to-2.5-day flight without Salyut 3. Retro-fire came at 2224 hr that
day with a safe landing in darkness 48 km SW of Tselinograd at 2310 hr.
The command module was spotted within one minute and a rescue helicopter
had landed with ten minutes.[29]

Although the true nature of the Soyuz 15 mission was undoubtably docking and work with the Salyut 3 space station, the actual cause of failure
is still not positively known despite repeated (and differing) statements
by the USSR. Immediately after the return of Soyuz 15 Soviet press releases

implied that a docking and crew transfer had not been scheduled. In addition the nighttime landing was billed as a planned exercise.[30]

Later NASA officials again pressed the USSR for a complete explanation of the flight, since the US agency was motivated by the ASTP mission scheduled for the next year. This time veteran and now head cosmonaut Shatalov explained that Soyuz 15 had been testing a new automatic rendezvous and docking system to be used by future robot supply ships. He went on to say that whenever Soyuz 15 was within 30-50 meters of Salyut 3, the automatic system would fire an excessive correction burn. After several attempts at docking the mission was called off. According to Shatalov, the cosmonauts could have taken over at any time to complete the maneuver, but that only automatic docking was to be tested and no plans had been made for the cosmonauts to enter the station.[31]

This explanation, however, does not ring true.[32] Foremost is the fact that sending cosmonauts along merely to test a new automatic rendezvous system without transfer to Salyut 3 seems highly inefficient. In fact, slightly more than a year later an unmanned Soyuz, Soyuz 20, did just such a docking without the benefit of an idle crew. Although it remains possible that Soyuz 15 did carry a new rendezvous system, after one or two failures the cosmonauts would surely have been instructed to complete the maneuver manually. In that case at least the rest of the mission could still be salvaged.

It may be coincidental that Sarafanov and Demin have not flown again after 18 manned Soyuz missions, or it could be an indication of a failure on their part during this mission.[33]

The evidence does point to a failure in the spacecraft control system when in the vicinity of the Salyut station with the malfunction occurring in the automatic and/or manual systems. However, since Soyuz carries only a limited supply of maneuvering fuel (excluding the emergency reserve supply), after the first few attempts to dock had ended in failure enough fuel probably did not exist for further attempts which forced Soyuz 15 to land under unfavorable night conditions.[34]

The failure of Soyuz 15 to dock with Salyut 3 destroyed Soviet plans to reuse the orbital laboratory. With an estimated planned stay for Soyuz 15 of thirty days, a subsequent flight probably would not have been planned before the end of October. With a designed lifetime of only 90 days and no one on board monitoring systems since the return of Soyuz 14 in July, Soviet space managers might well have decided a third mission to be too risky, even if the malfunction of Soyuz 15 could be corrected. In the end, Salyut 3 drifted in orbit until its programmed destruction on 24 January 1975--two weeks after the beginning of manned operations with its successor, Salyut 4.

SOYUZ 17/SALYUT 4

Although Salyut 3 did not reenter the earth's atmosphere until a month later, on Christmas Day 1974 the Soviets announced the formal end of its operations. Then to the surprise of Western specialists Salyut 4 was launched the very next day, 26 December 1974. Initially placed in the usual orbit of 270 km by 219 km at 51.6 °, Salyut 4 was moved to a higher orbit of 355 km by 343 km by 6 January 1975. Such an orbit had already been predicted for the next civilian Salyut space stations.[35] This higher orbit allowed better use of astrophysical equipment and reduced the need for orbital corrections due to the decreased atmospheric drag at that altitude.

The expected Soyuz launch came at 0043 hr Moscow time on 11 January 1975. The very early launch time indicated an intended stay of thirty days or more. This can be shown by projecting the time when a recovery could be made in the standard Soyuz recovery zone during the usual landing hours. On board Soyuz 17 were rookies Lt. Col. Aleksey Aleksandrovich Gubarev and civilian Georgiy Mikhaylovich Grechko. This crew makeup reaffirmed the suggestion that Salyut 4 was to become the first operational civilian Salyut (Salyut 1 had been a prototype, whereas Salyut 3 was part of the military Salyut program).[36]

From an initial orbit of 260 km by 190 km by its fifth revolution Soyuz 17's orbital parameters were 354 km by 293 km at 51.6°. At this time Salyut 4 was ahead and above the two spacemen in a 350-km circular orbit. Early in the morning of 12 January this gap had been narrowed to only 4 km. At this point the automatic rendezvous system was activated, and with a burn of the propulsion system the closure rate was adjusted to 12 m/sec. When finally at a distance of only 100 meters, Gubarev assumed the controls and completed the docking maneuver manually. If indeed an automatic system malfunction had been responsible for the failure of Soyuz 15, this would not be allowed to happen again. Contact and docking was completed by approximately 0400 hr.[37]

The two cosmonauts confirmed the integrity of the mated Soyuz/Salyut configuration, removed their space suits and entered the orbital laboratory which would be their home for the next month. To their surprise they were greeted by a "Wipe your feet" sign which had been placed on board Salyut 4 before its launch in December 1974 by Salyut launch personnel. All life-support and communication systems were checked and adjusted before Gubarev and Grechko retired at 1300 hr.

The mission of the Soyuz 17 cosmonauts was revealed to be "a normal working flight in the Soyuz program, during which it is planned to test some modifications in the spacecraft control systems, to try out a number of modified life-sustaining systems, as well as to study and partially realize the craft's new resources for a solution of a wider range of scientific and applied tasks in the interests of the national economy." It is amazing that less than 14 years after the world's first manned space flight a 30-day highly scientific earth orbital mission could be called "normal".

Salyut 4 was the second operational station of the second-generation Salyut series. It differed from Salyut 3 primarily only in the experimental apparatus on board (Figure 13). The instruments and equipment available in Salyut 4 have been listed in detail in the previous section of this book. An attempt will now be made to describe briefly some of the major events and results of the 30-day flight of Soyuz 17.

OST-1: Probably the single most valuable instrument on board Salyut 4, the Orbiting Solar Telescope (OST-1) was designed to obtain photographs and spectrographs of the sun in the 800-1300 Å range with a resolution of 1 Å. The first spectrograph lattice boasted of 1200 lines per mm while the second had 2400 lines per mm. The main mirror had a diameter of 25 cm and a focal length of 2.5 m. Apparently the system had first been tested by remote control before the Soyuz 17 cosmonauts arrived. During this time the telescopic orientation system malfunctioned and a difficult repair job had to be carried out by Gubarev and Grechko. On 27 January 34 spectrographs of the sun were taken on cassette film for development after the return to earth. On 1 February in conjunction with earth observatories, the Soyuz 17 team obtained clear pictures of

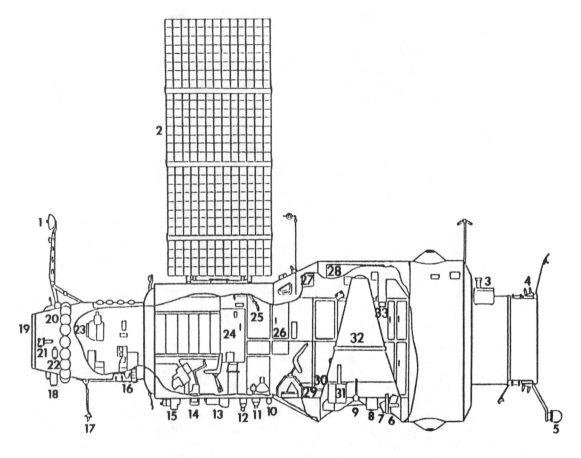

1. Rendezvous antenna
2. Solar panel
3. Filin-2 X-ray spectrometric telescope
4. Attitude control jets
5. Rendezvous transponder
6. RT-4 X-ray telescope
7. KDS-3 diffraction spectrometer
8. KSS-2 solar spectrometer
9. Delta autonomous navigational orbital radioaltimeter
10. Prismatic laser reflector
11. Solar sensor
12. Infrared vertical sensor
13. Television star-direction finder
14. Optical orientor
15. Horizon sensor
16. Spektru apparatus
17. Radiator of the thermal control system

18. Television equipment
19. Soyuz docking port
20. Compressed gas spheres
21. Ion sensor
22. Neytral apparatus
23. Photographic camera
24. Water regeneration system
25. Velergometer (bicycle)
26. Medical and movie camera equipment
27. Silya-4 spectrometer
28. MMK-1 micrometeorite detector
29. Treadmill
30. Chibis medical device
31. ITS-K infrared spectrometric telescope
32. OST-1 orbital solar telescope
33. Freon experiment

Figure 13   The Salyut 4 space station

solar atmospheric flocculi and protuberances. A major experiment during this mission was the resurfacing of the OST-1 mirrors with a special reflective spray. Although the mirrors were located in the conical depression of Salyut 4, some dust collected on the mirror surfaces as the result of micrometeorite collisions with Salyut 4. The results of this experiment were very encouraging for future solar and astronomical space observatories.[38]

Filin-2: This X-ray spectrometric telescope system consisted of four optical sensors (one lunar, one solar, two stellar) and X-ray sensors capable of detecting five energy bands (0-2-0.5 Kev, 0.5-1.8 Kev, 1.8-3.0 Kev, 3.0-6.0 Kev, and 6-10 Kev). The sensors were located on Salyut 4's exterior whereas the remaining controls, power supplies, etc. were placed inside the station. Total receiving area of the X-ray sensors was 500 cm[2] with each individual sensor operating with a 4-by-20-degree window. The lunar and solar sensors acted to turn off the X-ray sensors and stellar photometers when either the earth, moon, or sun entered the viewing region. The Crab Nebula was examined on 18 and 24 January with observations of the constellation Vela on 20 and 25 January. Other celestial X-ray sources were also observed.[39]

ITS-K: Called an infrared spectrometric telescope, the ITS-K was designed to examine radiation from the earth, moon, planets, and stars in the 1-8 micron range. Using a 300-mm diameter mirror, a resolution of 600 lines per mm was possible. One of the principal uses of this instrument was to evaluate atmospheric water vapor and ozone content by measuring the solar radiation passing through the earth's atmosphere during Salyut 4's entrance into sunrise and sunset regions. Such an experiment was carried out on 5 February.[40]

Water Regeneration: A unit was tested which recovered exhausted water vapor from the station atmosphere. This water was then treated and used for drinking, food preparation, and washing. Successful results of this experiment led to the permanent installation of a similar unit on later Salyuts, reducing the enormous amount of water which must otherwise be stored on board the space station and eventually replaced.[41]

Oazis and Other Biological Experiments: Continuation of the earlier Oazis experiments and a variety of other biological testing (Bioterm 2-M, Bioterm 3, Bioterm 4, KM microbe cultivator, FKT celluar division experiment) consumed a large portion of the Soyuz 17 working day. The cosmonauts maintained personal and photographic records of the growing of higher order plants, bacteria, fruit flies, and frog embryos. These studies provided information concerning the long-term effects of adaptation to weightlessness and the feasibility of agricultural undertakings on board large permanent space stations or interplanetary voyages.

Since Soyuz 17 was to become the longest Soviet
manned space flight, great attention was paid to the proper
monitoring of the cosmonauts' health and to rigorous exercise
programs. A new bicycling machine (similar to the one which
had been used on the US Skylab and which had been criticized
by the Soviets) complemented the 90-cm long, 40-cm wide treadmill device which had been installed. Repetition of a four-
day duration physical training program concentrated on different medical aspects each day. Evaluated were cosmonaut pro-
ficiency, maximum capabilities, and endurance. Some of the
additional medical equipment available were the Chibis physical
conditioning suits, the Rezeda-5 pulmonary ventilation recorder,
the Polynon installation, the Amak-3 blood analyzer, the Plotnost bone-tissue density monitor, the Tonus-2 muscular micro-
electric-stimulator and the Levka-3 blood vessel monitor.

A typical day on board Salyut 4 afforded the cosmonauts 4-9 hours for
sleep and 2.5 hours for physical exercise. Four meals were taken each day
from the ship's stores. The variety and quality of space food had changed
dramatically since the early 1960's and now included virtually any foodstuff
available on earth. Whether due to an initial lack of proper rest or to
other factors, both cosmonauts took approximately one week to adjust fully
to the weightless environment of the space station.

One of Salyut 4's major new systems tested by the Soyuz 17 crew was the
Delta autonomous navigation complex. By analyzing readings from the on-
board instruments, including the radio-altimeter, the gyroscopic apparatus,
and the solar and stellar sensors, with the help of a computer Delta was
able to provide the cosmonauts with exact orbit data to fix their location
to schedule communications sessions, and to accomplish orbital corrections.

A second innovation was the installation of the Stroka teletype system.
Routine and personal messages could be sent via this medium without disturb-
ing the cosmonauts from their myriad duties. At a more opportune time the
readouts could be read and appropriate replies sent or actions taken (Figure 14).

By 3 February the cosmonauts were still reporting that their health
and attitudes were good. It was on this day that Gubarev and Grechko surpassed the endurance record of the ill-fated Soyuz 11 cosmonauts. The
Salyut 4 station itself was reported in excellent condition with all life-
support systems operating properly.

On 7 February preparations were begun to temporarily power-down Salyut 4 and allow Gubarev and Grechko to return to earth. During the next

Figure 14   Cosmonauts Gubarev and Grechko during training
in a Salyut mock-up

two days the Soyuz spacecraft systems were tested, experiments completed,
and the descent vehicle loaded with documents and other important materials
Salyut 4 was cleaned and put into proper order for the next group of cosmonauts who were expected to re-man the orbital laboratory in the near
future.

The undocking of Soyuz 17 and Salyut 4 finally came at 0908 hr on 9
February 1975. Approximately three more orbits were completed by the two
cosmonauts before undergoing the fiery reentry. At an altitude of 7 km
the parachute system was deployed. During their descent Gubarev and Grechko
were buffeted by 72 kph winds while the rescue teams also had to contend
with falling snow, a low cloud cover, and a visibility of only 500 meters.
However, touchdown occurred without incident at 1403 hr Moscow time 110 km
NE of Tselinograd. The spacemen were quickly retrieved and given on-the-
spot medical examinations.

Initial and subsequent study of the cosmonauts after their return to
earth indicated no significant medical difficulties encountered as a result of their almost 30-day flight--the third longest to that time. Both

had lost some weight (Gubarev 2.5 kg and Grechko 4.5 kg) but readjustment to a 1 g environment proceeded smoothly. Encouraged by these findings, Soviet planners readied the next Soyuz crew whose goal was to double the Soyuz 17 mark.

SOYUZ 18A

With the safe return of the Soyuz 17 cosmonauts final preparations were made to re-man the still orbiting Salyut 4 laboratory. Chosen for this task were cosmonaut veterans Lazarev and Makarov, who had been paired together in the late 1960s as the back-up crew for the long-duration Soyuz 9 flight. (Recent data indicates that Grechko instead of Makarov may have trained with Lazarev for Soyuz 9.) These two highly trained spacemen had later flown together during the Soyuz 12 mission in September 1973 when they conducted the first manned space flight of the new Soyuz spacecraft following the Soyuz 11 disaster. Many Western observers believe Lazarev and Makarov were originally scheduled to man the ill-fated Kosmos 557 Salyut space station in May 1973, but this attempt was cancelled due to a very early malfunction of Kosmos 557. Now in the spring of 1975 Lazarev and Makarov prepared for the third time, since both had joined the cosmonaut corps in 1966, to make an extended flight in space. Not only would they be thwarted once again in their objective, but also they would come perilously close to perishing in the attempt.

Near the end of March the orbit of Salyut 4 was altered by remote control to set the stage for the launch and docking of the next manned Soyuz mission. This raising maneuver placed Salyut 4 in an orbit 343 km by 356 km and occurred just six weeks after the return of Soyuz 17. Finally, shortly after 1400 hr Moscow time on the 5th of April, Lazarev and Makarov lifted off a launching pad at Baikonur when the standard A-2 launch vehicle atop which they were riding came to life. The launch sequence proceeded on schedule as the two cosmonauts quickly gained altitude and sped downrange (Figure 15). When the fuel in the four strap-on stages had been exhausted, they were discarded without incident as the core engines continued to burn.[42]

During a normal staging sequence between the central core stage and the final stage of the rocket, the final stage ignites first with separation of the spent stage a few seconds later by two sets of pyrotechnic couplings, one set located on and controlled by the core stage, one set located on and controlled by the final stage. According to a report later released by Soviet officials, just prior to the planned separation of the two stages a malfunction in the electrical control system activated half of the upper couplings on one side of the rocket. By breaking a vital electrical connection to the core stage this accident inadvertently disabled the remaining couplings, preventing them from firing on schedule. Hence, when the final stage was ignited the core stage was still attached and would not separate. After a final stage burn of only four seconds the increased weight and the instability of the two loosely connected stages quickly sent the rocket off course, deviating more than the programmed 10-degree attitude limit and automatically triggering an abort of the launch.[43]

Since the abort took place at an altitude of approximately 140 km, the Soyuz emergency escape rocket located at the top of the launch shroud had already been jettisoned (Figure 16). In a nominal flight, the launch shroud and escape rocket are discarded after some two minutes and 40 seconds, whereas the separation between the central core and final stages does not occur until almost two minutes later (approximately 4.5 minutes

Figure 15   Early stage of launch of a Soyuz manned
spacecraft (Courtesy of NASA)

314

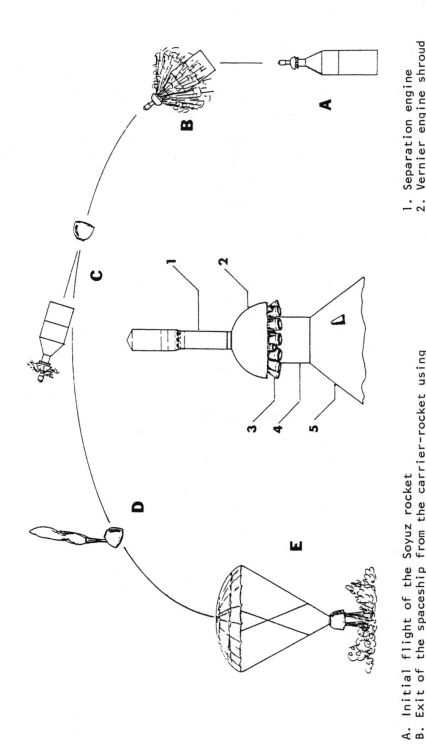

1. Separation engine
2. Vernier engine shroud
3. Vernier engines
4. Main engine
5. Forward launch shroud

A. Initial flight of the Soyuz rocket
B. Exit of the spaceship from the carrier-rocket using
   the main and vernier engines
C. Exit of the main shroud using the separation engine
D. Descent by parachute
E. Soft-landing on earth

Figure 16   Nominal Soyuz abort sequence   (Drawing by R.F. Gibbons)

into the launch). When the Soyuz spacecraft receives a telemetric abort signal at this high altitude, the spacecraft is immediately detached and lifted away from the launch vehicle by the Soyuz propulsion system.

At this point the orbital and propulsion modules are jettisoned, allowing the manned command module to make an emergency reentry following what amounts to a sub-orbital flight. During their abort Lazarev and Makarov could merely sit idly by while these events took place around them since Soyuz does not permit Soviet cosmonauts to participate in the abort process; everything is carried out by automatic systems. One of the reasons for this is the lack of the increased weight and space which instrumentation in the Soyuz command module would require to allow such a capability.[44]

Lazarev and Makarov had no time to think of the disappointment of not being able to man Salyut 4. They had two much bigger goals over which they had virtually no control: (1) to survive the emergency landing and (2) to land on the Soviet side of the Sino-Soviet border. Landfall finally came probably a few minutes later in the rugged terrain of western Siberia SW of Gorno-Altaisk some 1600 km from Baikonur and 320 km north of the Chinese border. While descent had subjected the cosmonauts to almost unbearable loads of 14-15 g's, touchdown was no more hospitable. Although conflicting reports exist, Lazarev and Makarov apparently hit at a higher than normal velocity in mountainous territory. Reports indicate that the two cosmonauts had to wait until the next day before they could be rescued.[45]

Announcement of the launch failure was not made until 7 April when the Soviets acknowledged that the flight attempt failed when "parameters of the carrier rocket's movement deviated from the preset values, and an automatic device produced the command to discontinue the flight program, and detach the spaceship for return to earth." When pressed by US authorities as to the cause of the abort, Soviet spokesmen indicated that the launch vehicle was of an older type than that which was being readied for the upcoming Apollo-Soyuz Test Project and that the staging circuitry had been modified on the newer models to prevent a similar mishap. The standard Soyuz launch vehicle was first used again just nine days after the Soyuz 18A launch abort when a Molniya 3 satellite was successfully orbited.

The next month another attempt was made to rendezvous and dock with Salyut 4. This time the mission was a success, but the designation of the flight as Soyuz 18 came as a surprise. In an attempt to cover up the failure the flight of 5 April 1975 is now officially called the "April 5th Anomaly" by Soviet space reporters. Many specialists, however, use the designations of Soyuz 18A and Soyuz 18B employed by this book.

SOYUZ 18B/SALYUT 4

Following the failure of Soyuz 18A to rendezvous and dock with Salyut 4, the Soviet space station program was on the verge of another costly setback. Of the four known previous Salyuts placed in orbit two (Salyut 2 and Kosmos 557) failed before a crew could reach them and two (Salyut 1 and Salyut 3) had been manned by only one Soyuz team. Salyut, of course, was designed to house two or more Soyuz crews in rotation or (later) simultaneously. The use of a highly expensive Salyut orbiting laboratory by only two or three cosmonauts for less than a month was having a severe effect on the continuing Salyut program.

Salyut 4 had been launched on 26 December 1974 with an estimated lifetime of a little more than six months. Thus with the Soyuz 18A failure in April 1975 and the preparations for ASTP scheduled for July 1975, it appeared that Salyut 4 was going to experience the same fate as her sister space stations. Then on 24 May 1975 word came that another manned Soyuz, Soyuz 18B, had been launched at 1758 hr Moscow time for the purpose of docking with Salyut 4. On board were veteran cosmonauts Klimuk and Sevast'yanov. The former had been commander of the Soyuz 13 reserach flight and the latter had been flight engineer on the record-breaking 18-day flight of Soyuz 9. Both of these missions seem to have been directly related to the Salyut space program.

From an initial orbit of 247 km by 193 km at 51.6°, Soyuz 18B made the usual orbital correction on revolution number 5 which allowed the cosmonauts to close in on Salyut 4. The next day at 2111 hr Moscow time the final docking operation was begun. The automatic rendezvous system quickly brought the two spacecraft to within 100 meters at which point Klimuk took manual control. Soyuz 18B and Salyut 4 were mated in darkness with a relative velocity of only 0.3 m/sec in a textbook maneuver. After a complete check of docking and station systems, the two cosmonauts transferred to

Salyut 4 at 0030 hr on 26 May. They were greeted by a sign reading, "Welcome to our common house", placed there by the departing crew of Soyuz 17 and intended for the Soyuz 18A team.[46]

A number of tasks had already been scheduled for the day when Klimuk and Sevast'yanov boarded Salyut 4. Many systems which had been deactivated since the departure of the Soyuz 17 cosmonauts on 9 February had to be turned on, repaired, or replaced. An orbital correction moved the Soyuz 18B/Salyut 4 combination into an orbit of 356 km by 344 km. Later that night, a laser beam from a Soviet ground station was reflected off a small reflector mounted on the orbiting lab in a successful test of precision satellite tracking.

Although it had been widely reported that the Soyuz 18A flight was to have lasted approximately sixty days, there was disagreement as to whether Soyuz 18B could carry out that plan. The major obstacle was the planned 15 July launch of Soyuz 19, the Soviet half of the ASTP. The ability of the Soviets to conduct two diverse manned space flights simultaneously was hotly debated by US space officials and in the US Congress. In the end, the Soviet Union proved her space expertise by permitting the Soyuz 18B cosmonauts to remain aloft during the entire Soyuz 19 mission and to return after a new Soviet space endurance record of 63 days had been established.

During the two-month stay of Klimuk and Sevast'yanov on board Salyut 4, they conducted a multitude of tests and experiments. To review all these activities adequately would of course require a book in itself. Therefore mention will be made of only some of the more important undertakings. The basic equipment used during Soyuz 18B has already been described in the Salyut 4 and Soyuz 17 sections of this book.

In the first days of their stay on board Salyut 4 the two cosmonauts began a variety of biological experiments. In conjunction with the space gardening tests started by Soyuz 17, onions and peas were planted in the specially constructed plot. The Oazis system was reactivated and studies were made of beetle and fly specimens. Even though several biological experiments were conducted during this mission, they were largely self-regulating and did not occupy a great deal of the cosmonauts' time.

Earth resources experiments were a high priority, including a ten-day program of observations in which 2000 photographs were obtained. Ordinary and multi-spectral photography was widely used over most of the Soviet territory which passed beneath Salyut 4. At the conclusion of their flight, over 8.5 million km^2 of their native land had been recorded on film. Spectrometers were used to detect levels of pollutants in the earth's atmosphere and to aid in crop and mineral-deposit monitoring. Observations were also made of upper atmospheric luminous clouds while extensive photographs and spectrographs captured the beautiful aurora borealis.

Physical studies of near-earth, the sun and outer space consumed most of the cosmonauts' time. The Spektru instrument complex measured the concentration and interaction of Salyut 4 with the tenuous, yet retarding, atmosphere at altitudes of 350 km while the Emissiya apparatus studied the presence of the red line of atomic oxygen between 250 and 270 km above the earth's surface. The temperature of the upper layers of the atmosphere were recorded to be between 700 and 2000° K due to the incidence of solar ultraviolet radiation. Studies of the atmosphere during sunrise and sunset via spectral soundings in the infrared and ultraviolet revealed ozone, water vapor, and nitrogen-ozide concentrations.

Solar investigations centered around the OST-1 solar telescope (Figure 17). By 4 June over 100 spectrograms of the sun had been taken. On 18 June the cosmonauts received a special request from the Crimean Astrophysical Observatory to record a solar disturbance which had just been detected by ground observatories. Before Klimuk and Sevast'yanov departed Salyut 4, they had taken approximately 600 solar photographs.

Astrophysical experiments were largely devoted to X-ray investigations with the RT-4 and Filin telescopes. The former contained a 200-mm diameter parabolic mirror which focused and detected X-rays in a range of 44-60 Å. The constellations of Scorpio, Virgo, Cygnus, and Lyra were examined with the result that Soviet scientists believed they had sufficient data to confirm Cygnus X-1 as the first Black Hole". The Filin instrument's primary mission was to confirm the existence of previously detected X-ray sources and to search for new ones. Its operating range was from 1 to 60 Å.

The day-to-day workings of both men and machines were carefully watched. The cosmonauts underwent frequent and thorough medical examinations in their attempt to double the Soviet space endurance record. Checks of blood pressure, blood circulation, heart rate, and respiration were made while electrocardiograms, kinetocardiograms, and blood samples were taken.

Figure 17   Klimuk and Sevast'yanov while training for
the Soyuz 18B/Salyut 4 mission

Exercises were performed for at least two hours a day with even more rigorous workouts during the final ten days of the flight to prepare them for readjustment to a 1-g environment. The special conditioning suits and treadmill and velergometer were also well used.

The station itself needed regular repairs. While the Soyuz 18B cosmonauts were only half way through their stay, the Salyut 4 laboratory passed its designed six-month lifetime in space. Silya, a light nuclear isotope spectrometer which had failed during the Soyuz 17 mission, was repaired using spare parts brought up in the Soyuz 18B spacecraft. In addition, one of the six gas analyzers and a pump had to be replaced.

Although there is some dispute over the productivity of Salyut crews when compared with those who manned the US Skylab, Klimuk and Sevast'yanov were kept busy. On 23 June they broke the existing Soviet space endurance record of 29½ days set by the first Salyut 4 crew. Two days later the two cosmonauts completed their 500th revolution to be followed on the 4th of July by the marking of Salyut 4's 3000th orbit.

Finally on 15 July Soyuz 19 was launched from the same pad which had seen the lift-off of Soyuz 18B some fifty-two days earlier. During the Soyuz 19/Apollo mission the two cosmonaut crews were able briefly to exchange communications on two occasions. The launch of Soyuz 19 also signaled the beginning of preparations for the return to earth by the Salyut 4 team.

On 21 July the Soyuz 19 spacecraft touched down in Kazakhstan, and three days later as Apollo was making its splashdown in the Pacific, Klimuk and Sevast'yanov fired up Soyuz 18B's propulsion system for five seconds in a test for the trip back to earth. On the next orbit they used the Salyut 4 propulsion system to maneuver the spacecraft into the proper orbit (369 km by 349 km) for reentry. Over the next two days more than 50 kg of scientific materials were packed aboard the Soyuz command module. The last day in space for the courageous crew was 26 July, and at 1356 hr Soyuz 18B with Klimuk and Sevast'yanov on board pulled away from Salyut 4. After a two-orbit check-out of Soyuz systems, the retro-burn was performed and the spacecraft began its searing descent. By 1718 hr Moscow time the two cosmonauts had safely and gently touched down 56 km NE of Arkalyk.

Terrestrial readjustment posed no problems for the two spacemen who now held the record for the second longest manned space flight. Both men refused to be carried from the spacecraft, and within two days they were swimming and playing tennis for short periods. Weight losses of 3.8 kg for Klimuk and 1.9 kg for Sevast'yanov were quickly regained (within one day for Sevast'yanov). The Soviets have given both 6 and 10 days as the time period before complete readjustment was completed.

Without qualification, the entire flight of Soyuz 18B was a tremendous success and a boost for the whole Salyut program. Following the return of the Soyuz 18B crew, the unusual announcement was made that no more manned flights for the next six months were needed. However, it was soon seen that this did not mean that Salyut 4 would remain inactive and alone.

SOYUZ 20/SALYUT 4

The successful flight of Soyuz 18B had proven that the reliability of a Soyuz spacecraft extended at least sixty-three days in a powered-down configuration while attached to a Salyut space station. At this point in the Soviet manned space program, the durability of Soyuz was a limiting factor in determining the mission duration of Salyut operations. Salyut 4 had safely housed cosmonauts after orbiting the earth for seven months, and Salyut 3 had remained aloft for an equal period of time.

For several years before the flight of Soyuz 18B a 60-day Soyuz/Salyut mission was widely believed to be the next Soviet short-term goal. On 30 November 1973 Kosmos 613, an unmanned Soyuz ferry, was launched to test the survivability of Soyuz during two months in space. From an initial orbit of 295 km by 195 km at 51.6°, a week later Kosmos 613 was maneuvered into a higher (396 km by 255 km) orbit which covered those altitudes frequented by both military and civilian Salyut space stations. Most on-board systems were deactivated to simulate their function while docked to a Salyut and to conserve power since Kosmos 613 did not carry solar panels but relied solely on battery energy reserves. Right on schedule 60 days later, Kosmos 613 was deorbited and recovered.

Having successfully passed the 60-day mark for manned space flight with Soyuz 18B, Soviet space planners could now look to the next plateau of 90-100 days. An early manned flight was out of the question. Salyut 4 was too old to support reliably a manned mission, and the Soviets had already acknowledged that no more manned flights would be undertaken for the next six months. An unmanned flight, however, was not ruled out.

In the late afternoon of 17 November 1975 an unmanned Soyuz spacecraft was inserted into an orbit of 263 km by 199 km at an inclination of 51.6°. Designated Soyuz 20, the craft represented only the second time in the nine-year Soyuz program that an unmanned Soyuz had been appropriately labeled. In both cases (Soyuz 2 in 1968 and Soyuz 20 in 1975) the spaceships worked directly with officially recognized elements of the man-in-space program.

For the next two days Soyuz 20 made several precisely programmed orbital corrections which quickly indicated the intention of attempting an automatic docking with the Salyut 4 station. A normal rendezvous and docking procedure involving a manned Soyuz spacecraft and an unmanned Salyut takes slightly more than a day. The extended period given Soyuz 20 permitted careful calculations and analysis of tracking data needed to ensure a successful docking. Finally, in the evening of 19 November under the watchful eyes of Soviet ground controllers, Soyuz 20 gently mated with the eleven month old Salyut 4 in an orbit ranging from 367 km to 343 km.[47]

The significance of this achievement cannot be overstated. Automatic resupply of orbiting laboratories is essential for a longer-term healthy space program. Not only are food, water, and scientific supplies needed by cosmonauts on extended flights, but also vital maneuvering fuel is needed to replenish dwindling reserves. The USSR had completed the world's first automatic dockings in 1967 and 1968 when two pairs of unmanned Soyuz were coupled (Kosmos 186/188 and Kosmos 212/213). But after the Soyuz 15 flight, Soviet spokesmen attributed the failure of that mission to the malfunction of a new automatic rendezvous and docking system. It appears that Soyuz 20 was a retest of this system.[48]

On the day following the Soyuz 20/Salyut 4 docking, Cosmonaut Feoktistov revealed that Soyuz 20 was indeed a part of the larger program to develop automatic cargo tankers for Salyut stations. However, no material or fuel transfer was planned for this mission. With the completion of the automatic docking, Soyuz 20 had two major goals remaining: (1) complete biological experiments on board and (2) conduct a three-month in-flight test of Soyuz systems.

In conjunction with the multi-national biological investigations performed on board Kosmos 782 (22 November - 15 December 1975), Soyuz 20 carried a similar complement of flies, tortoises, vegetable seeds, maize, cacti, and leguminous plants. These tests provided information not only on cosmic-ray and weightless effects on growth and development, but also on design and construction of space farms for permanent and semi-permanent space stations.

The second objective of completing a 90-day mission would pave the way for a later manned flight of equal duration. Although Konstantin Bushuyev, Soviet ASTP Technical Director, shortly after the launch of Soyuz 20 brought up the possibility of another manned mission to Salyut 4, by the return of Soyuz 20 in February 1976 Salyut 4 had functioned for 14 months (eight months longer than its design life) and was slowly showing signs of age.

Finally on 15 February 1976 the Soyuz propulsion system was tested and the Soyuz 20/Salyut 4 combination was maneuvered into a better position for the return of Soyuz 20. Undocking came the next day with a landing on Soviet territory about four hours later.

Soyuz 20 had greatly enlarged the capabilities of the Salyut space program. Cosmonauts could remain aloft with confidence for at least three months. Vital supplies and fuel could automatically be sent to them, and in the event of an emergency an unmanned Soyuz could be delivered to the orbiting spacemen for use as a rescue vessel. Equipped with dual docking ports the next civilian Salyut, Salyut 6, would prove these capabilities and extend them even further.[49]

SOYUZ 21/SALYUT 5

From the return of Soyuz 20 in February 1976 until late June of that same year, the Soviet man-in-space program outwardly appeared dormant. However, behind the scenes, preparations were being completed for a new manned assault on near-earth space. This attack was begun on 22 June 1976 when Salyut 5 was launched into an orbit of 260 km by 219 km at 51.6°.

Salyut 5 represented at least the third attempt to implement the USSR manned military space platform program. (Salyut 2 malfunctioned before being manned and Salyut 3 had accommodated only one Soyuz crew for two weeks). The last of the second-generation Salyuts, Salyut 5 carried an instrument payload quite different from that of the still orbiting civilian Salyut 4.[50]

Throughout the early part of the flight of Salyut 5, Western observers were led to believe that this Salyut had been equipped with dual docking facilities. As a result a number of mission profiles were associated with Salyut 5. Later, Soviet officials acknowledged that Salyut 5 was basically similar to Salyuts 3 and 4 and did not possess an in-flight refueling capability or a second docking port.[51]

Salyut 5 made at least five orbital changes between 23 June and 5 July, the last putting the orbiting platform in a 274-km circular orbit. On the following day at 1509 hr Soyuz 21 with veteran Cosmonaut Boris Volynov (Soyuz 5) and rookie Vitaly Mikhaylovich Zholobov was launched from the

Baikonur Cosmodrome into an initial orbit of 253 km by 193 km. Coupled with the mistaken belief that Salyut 5 had resupply capabilities via a second docking port, speculation was high that Soyuz 21 would attempt the 90-day mission pioneered by Soyuz 20. Although this mission was still feasible even with a second-generation Salyut, subsequent events prevent verification of this mission goal.

By Soyuz 21's fifth orbit the spacecraft orbital parameters had been modified to 280 km by 254 km. During the next twelve hours the cosmonauts rested and prepared for docking with Salyut 5. The gap between the two spaceships had been closed to 500 meters by the afternoon of 7 July, and at 1640 hr Volynov completed a flawless docking with the large Salyut station. A few hours later the two spacemen entered their new home in space and began activating its systems.[52]

The amount of scientific research performed by the Soyuz 21 crew was minimal compared to earlier civilian Salyut teams or US Skylab astronauts. This is not to say that some new and important experiments were not carried out, but a large portion of the cosmonauts' day was devoted to military objectives.

Volynov had only flown in space once before on Soyuz 5 in January 1969, but had been a member of the back-up crew for Vostok 5 and Voskhod 1. This adhered to the pattern of Soviet military flights set forth by Popovich on Soyuz 14 and later followed by Bykovsky on Soyuz 22. Zholobov had been a member of the back-up crew for the military Salyut 3 missions. In addition, he was unusual in the cosmonaut corps with his background as an officer of the Army instead of the Navy or Air Force. This latter background may have been significant in his selection, since one of the objectives of Soyuz 21 was to monitor the conduct of a massive Soviet military maneuver taking place in eastern USSR.[53]

Some of the new experimental apparatus on board Salyut 5 have been described in the previous section. One of the first to be tested was a device named Sfera (sphere) which on 13 July was used to melt an ingot of bismuth, lead, tin, and cadmium and to resolidify in spheres under weightless conditions. The sample was melted at a temperature of 600°C before forming a ball the size of a match head. Experiments of this type have been greatly increased during the missions to the civilian Salyut 6.

The next day an experiment to monitor the growth of crystals in a weightless environment was begun. The crystal seeds were placed in three different vessels containing potash-soda and alum. Their progress was viewed by the cosmonauts, and the samples were returned to earth by the cosmonaut for comparison with earth-grown crystals in an identical apparatus. A second similar procedure was started on 7 August.

On 16 July two more experiments were conducted. The first was with the Potek complex designed to investigate the feasibility of pumping fluids by capillary and surface tension forces without the need for electricity. If successful, the results may find application to future refueling concepts. (The later Progress refueling tankers relied on a pressure feed system.) The second test involved the use of the improved hand-held RSS-2M spectrometer. This instrument was able to scan the earth's atmosphere in search for smoke, dust, and other pollutants.

Meanwhile a series of ongoing experiments with fish were being conducted. On 10 July observations were made of two guppies, one a pregnant female and the other a male, in their adjustment to weightless swimming. Other experiments involving Danio fish and the incubation of fish eggs on board Salyut 5 were all performed with the aim of determining the adaptability and development of their vestibular systems.

Two more materials experiments were carried out during the Soyuz 21 mission. The first, the Diffusia device, was constructed for the production of a homogenous alloy of dibenzyl and tolane. Finally on 28 July experiments in smelting and soldering were begun with the Reaction complex. A follow-on to experiments conducted by the Soyuz 6 crew in 1969, these tests provided for the smelting of high-grade nickel and manganese solder and the soldering of stainless steel tubes. The soldering of the 15-mm diameter stainless steel pipes in a weightless environment was thought to have applications in the much later construction of large space structures.

In their low (compared with civilian Salyuts) earth orbit Volynov and Zholobov were able to carry out extensive earth-resources photography along with their observation work. Emphasis was placed on locating mineral deposits, surveying regions associated with resource development, and observing weather trends.

Of course, tests of new Salyut systems, their own medical examinations, and hours of physical exercises also kept the cosmonauts occupied. Medical equipment on board Salyut 5 included the Levka blood circulation monitor, the Rezeda spirometer for measuring lung capacity, the Impulse apparatus for determining vestibular and brain impulse activity, the Palma stimulus reaction-time tester, and a new massmeter to determine cosmonaut weight while in orbit. An efficiency study was undertaken to determine the best methods to utilize cosmonaut activities. The Stroka teletype which had been first tested on Salyut 4 was operational on Salyut 5 and eased the cosmonaut workload.

Day after day and week after week the two spacemen carried out their tasks. Regular Soviet news reports were fewer than on the previous Salyut 4 missions, but were in accordance with those associated with a militarily oriented flight. On 18 August Volynov and Zholobov completed their 700th orbit on board Salyut 5 and it appeared that they would probably stay for at least 700 more. A remark concerning the cosmonauts' suffering from sensory deprivation was taken to be nothing serious.

Soviet announcements on 20 August and early 24 August suggested that the flight was far from its conclusion. Then, unexpectedly, around noon on 24 August the announcement came that the Soyuz 21 crew were making preparations to land that night. This was totally outside past procedures when ten days before the return to earth the cosmonauts would begin rigorous exercises and different diets. In addition, approximately two days are usually required to pack up the Soyuz command module with a testing of the Soyuz propulsion system a day or two before touchdown. There is no evidence that any of these measures were taken.

With what appeared to be haste, Volynov and Zholobov loaded up Soyuz and exited the Salyut station. At 1812 hr on 24 August Soyuz 21 pulled away from Salyut 5 and two hours and thirty minutes later fired her propulsion engine to initiate reentry. By 2133 hr the two cosmonauts had landed safely in darkness 200 km SW of Kokchetav in what is believed to have been an emergency return to earth.

What precipitated such a quick departure from Salyut 5 and termination of the Soyuz 21 flight? Immediately after the landing most observers held the opinion that the decision to end the mission had been prompted by the crew's psychological condition. The "sensory deprivation" report

327

was cited as evidence. Two months later *Aviation Week and Space Technology* reported that the retreat to the Soyuz spacecraft was caused by an acrid odor emanating from Salyut 5's environmental control system. Unable to find or to correct the problem Volynov and Zholobov had little choice but to leave.[54] This latter view is now widely held as the cause of the end of the Soyuz 21 flight after only 49 days.

What may be an epitaph to the Soyuz 21 flight came just three weeks after its emergency landing when on 15 September 1976 Soyuz 22 was launched on a solo, and not fully explained, mission. (See Soyuz section of this book.) Flown at the unusual inclination of 65° (not used for a manned flight since Voskhod 2 in 1965), this spacecraft was probably devoted to military reconnaissance of a large NATO military maneuver which extended far above 50° N latitude. Although the flight had obviously been planned for some time due to the extensive modifications of the Soyuz orbital module, it seems quite likely that Soyuz 22 had been scheduled to fly while Soyuz 21 was still docked with Salyut 5. Thus double coverage of the Western military exercise could be obtained from different vantage points along with a comparison of the effectiveness of two different surveillance systems. An alternative theory assumes that Soyuz 22 was due to be launched after Soyuz 21 had landed and the NATO exercise was completed, but was moved up when Soyuz 21 was forced down prematurely.

SOYUZ 23/SALYUT 5

With the early return of Soyuz 21 in late August and the eight-day flight of the (military?) Soyuz 22 in mid-September, the next step in the Soviet manned space program was anybody's guess. Was Salyut 5 still habitable? The answer came on 14 October 1976 when Soviet officials announced the 2040-hr launch of Soyuz 23 for the express purpose of continuing "the scientific-technical research and experiments in conjunction with the orbiting scientific station Salyut 5."

Whatever had forced the Soyuz 21 crew down had apparently been corrected or at least pinpointed so that a new crew could make any necessary modifications or repairs. From an initial orbit of 224 km by 188 km at 51.6° Soyuz 23, carrying first-time Cosmonauts Vyacheslav Dmitriyevich Zudov and Valery Ilich Rozhdestvenskiy, performed an orbital correction at 0155 hr, raising its orbit to 275 km by 243 km. Salyut 5 was circling ahead of Soyuz 23 in an orbit of 268 km by 253 km.[55]

According to schedule at 2158 hr the next day, October 15th, the automatic rendezvous system was activated. Soon after, though, the failure of Soyuz 23 to complete the rendezvous and docking with Salyut 5 was apparent. Despair must have engulfed the Soviet space officials who had had only three successes in the nine manned Soyuz/Salyut missions.

The exact nature of the docking failure has not been fully explained by the Soviets. Although a comparison of the Soyuz 15 and Soyuz 23 difficulties are often made, the similarities do not seem complete. Whereas the Soyuz 15 spacecraft was uncontrollable within 30-50 meters of Salyut 3, Soyuz 23 may never have come within the 100-meter distance when manual control was used. If indeed the automatic rendezvous system did malfunction, it is not clear why Zudov did not take over beyond the 100-meter range (assuming this capability exists).

The error was reportedly monitored on board Soyuz 23 and on the ground, and when no correction could be made, the cosmonauts and the Soviet mission control made immediate plans for reentry. In a repeat of the Soyuz 15 situation, Soyuz 23 had only about one more day of power and life support left. Touchdown was now scheduled for 16 October approximately 48 hours after lift-off, near the limit of the battery-powered Soyuz.

Throughout most of 16 October Zudov and Rozhdestvenskiy conserved power and maintained radio silence. At 2002 hr the propulsion engine was ignited, slowing the spacecraft and signaling the start of the reentry sequence. Twenty-three minutes later the command module separated from the orbital module and began the fiery descent. Unfortunately the brave cosmonauts were not safe yet. Weather conditions at the landing site were poor: darkness, high winds, and falling snow. With their bad luck still intact the returning spacemen found their spacecraft being blown into Lake Tengiz 195 km SW of Tselinograd where the first--and thus far only--manned water recovery in the Soviet space program was made at 2046 hr Moscow time.

Rescue teams converged on the scene quickly, but retrieval of the cosmonauts was apparently difficult. Announcement of the safe recovery of Zudov and Rozhdestvenskiy did not come until 0700 hr on 17 October (Figure 18). Fortunately, the crew was said to be in good health. The difficulty of rescuing the cosmonauts was underscored by former Cosmonaut Shatalov when he said,

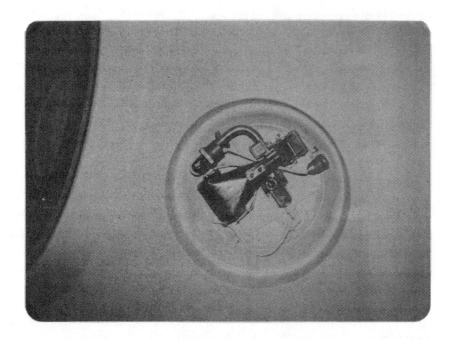

Figure 18   Soyuz descent module recovery beacon
              (Courtesy of R.F. Gibbons)

"All the search and rescue systems were in complete readiness. Everything possible was done to get to the crew quickly. One hardly need say how difficult, and how hard the work was in this situation."

While Zudov and Rozhdestvenskiy were later being made heroes of the Soviet Union, Salyut 5 continued along its lonely vigil circling the earth approximately every ninety minutes, waiting for another Soyuz crew. Two and one-half months later as the year 1976 drew to a close no such crew had been launched.

SOYUZ 24/SALYUT 5

On 3 February 1977 the abandoned civilian Salyut 4 was ordered to destroy itself during reentry after an unprecedented 770 days in space. The world wondered whether the same fate was about to befall Salyut 5. Rumors of a space spectacular in the summer and fall of 1977 to mark the twentieth anniversary of Sputnik 1 were rampant. Possibly the Soviet Union was clearing the skies in order to devote full ground-control resources to the promised extravaganza.

Unexpectedly, in the evening of 7 February Soviet news agencies reported the launch of Soyuz 24 at 1912 hr that day on a mission to the still orbiting Salyut 5. At this time Salyut 5 had been in orbit for almost eight months and had exceeded the previously revealed operational lifetime.

On board Soyuz 24 were Viktor Vasilyevich Gorbatko and Yuri Nikolayevich Glazkov. The presence of these two men, who had been the back-up crew for the unsuccessful Soyuz 23, strongly suggested that an extra-vehicular activity (EVA) would be performed during the mission. Gorbatko, who had joined the cosmonaut corps back in 1960 had been a back-up for Voskhod 2 before being relieved for medical reasons, had been back-up pilot for Soyuz 5, and had finally flown as research engineer on Soyuz 7. Voskhod 2 and Soyuz 5 had indeed involved EVA's (in fact the only Soviet EVA's to that time), and it is suspected that an EVA may have also been planned for Soyuz 7 during the unusual Soyuz 6/7/8 group flight. While Glazkov was on his first space flight he had received his Candidate of Science degree for his thesis on EVA.

The absence of EVA on earlier Soyuz/Salyut flights was puzzling. Before Salyut 3 was launched the USSR revealed that a hatch had been added to the station (and subsequent ones) to permit crew work outside. In addition, in June 1976 Soviet cosmonauts had told Western specialists that EVA's had been planned for earlier Salyut missions, but had later been cancelled due to time restraints.[56]

By 8 February the Soyuz 24 cosmonauts had performed several orbital maneuvers, placing their spaceship in an orbit of 281 km by 218 km. Following the failure of Soyuz 23 to dock with Salyut 5, much care was taken to ensure that this was not going to be a repeat performance. At a distance of 1500 meters from the orbiting laboratory the relative velocity of the two craft had been reduced to 2 m/sec. At 180 meters the velocity had dropped to 69 cm/sec, and finally when the crew took over manual control at a distance of only 80 meters the velocity had been diminished to 30 cm/sec.

Docking occurred at about 2230 hr on 8 February while Salyut 5 was in an orbit of 287 km by 222 km. After ensuring that a firm coupling had been made, Gorbatko and Glazkov retired for a well-deserved rest. At 0846 hr the new Soyuz team entered Salyut 5 for what was to be an uneventful and relatively short stay.[57]

The two cosmonauts quickly reactivated the Salyut systems, many of which had remained dormat since the hasty departure of the Soyuz 21 crew six months earlier. In accordance with the prediction of Chief Cosmonaut Vladimir Shatalov, the activities on board Salyut 5 were routine and were closely following those performed by Soyuz 21.

Further use of the elaborate infrared telescope spectrometer provided new data on the levels of water vapor, ozone, nitrogen oxide, and pollutants in the upper atmosphere. Biological, technological, medical, photographic, and earth-resources investigations were continued along with the military-surveillance objectives.

On 16 February an unexpected release by Soviet news agencies indicated that Soyuz 24's mission had passed the half-way point, implying a return to earth around 25 February after only 18 days in space. Soyuz 24 had apparently been planned as a short-duration mission for specific military purposes or to furnish more information on the status of Salyut 5 itself. By announcing their intention at this point of the flight to return early, speculation of yet another Soyuz-Salyut failure could then be avoided.

One unusual experiment was performed four days prior to landing. On 21 February with a television audience watching, the cosmonauts purged a portion of the space station's atmosphere while releasing new compressed air from stored reserves. The purpose of the experiment was unclear with Soviet officials saying only that the test was "important for prolonged expeditions". A possibly related procedure was conducted in July 1976 by the Soyuz 21 crew when they "depressurized" Salyut 5. Neither event has been fully explained, although a connection with a purification of the station atmosphere or future EVA's is possible.

Preparations to return to earth were begun on 23 February with the routine packing of scientific data into the Soyuz command module and with the retesting of the vital Soyuz systems. The cosmonauts evacuated Salyut 5 two days later and at 0921 hr undocking took place. Retro-fire followed after one more orbit, and touchdown came about noon Moscow time 36 km NE of Arkalyk.

The Soyuz 24 mission had been short, but successful. Although the predicted EVA did not materialize, the reported work level was comparable to that of Soyuz 21.

On the day following the return of Gorbatko and Glazkov the Salyut 5 space station ejected a recovery capsule similar to that released by Salyut 3 in September 1974. It is presumed to have been recovered on Soviet territory. The question has been raised why the module had been jettisoned only one day after Soyuz 24 had departed since the purpose of the module is to bring back high resolution photographs taken while the station is in an automatic regime. Unfortunately, the answer is unknown.

SOYUZ 25/SALYUT 6

From the end of February till late summer of 1977 the Soviet man-in-space program was unusually quiet, like the calm before the storm. Anticipation was high that the Soviet Union was planning a space spectacular worthy of the twentieth anniversary of the space age, the launching of Sputnik 1 on 4 October 1957. The persistent talk of double-ported Salyut stations and unmanned resupply ships opened limitless possibilities for the future exploration of near-earth space.

On 8 August 1977 a radio command sent to the still orbiting Salyut 5 activated the station's propulsion engine and sent it plunging into the earth's atmosphere where it was destroyed. The Soviets appeared to be clearing the way for the long-awaited space offensive. However, seven and one-half more weeks elapsed before the announcement that Salyut 6 had been placed in an orbit of 275 km by 219 km with an inclination of 51.6° for the "purpose of conducting scientific and technical research and experiments for checking on the design of on-board systems of orbital stations."[58]

Since Salyut 5 had been a military space station, it was expected that Salyut 6 would be devoted to scientific civilian projects. That assumption was verified when by 7 October Salyut 6 had been maneuvered into a higher, more circular orbit of 352 km by 336 km. There was as yet no indication as to the design of Salyut 6. Was it indeed a new, more advanced model of Salyut? The disappointing outcome of Soyuz 25 failed to answer the question, but by December and the flight of Soyuz 26, Salyut 6 was confirmed to be the first of the third-generation Salyuts.

Ten days after the launch of Salyut 6, Soyuz 25 rocketed into the skies above Tyuratam carrying rookie Cosmonauts Vladimir Kovalenok and Valery Ryumin. Launched at 0540 hr on 9 October, Soyuz 25 made a standard orbital maneuver on the fifth revolution raising its orbit from 240 km by 194 km to 309 km by 265 km. There was little work to do while the cosmonauts waited for Soyuz 25 to catch up with Salyut 6 and for the delicate docking procedure scheduled for the next day.

As Kovalenok and Ryumin entered their second day in space, the Soyuz 25 spacecraft began its eighteenth orbit (now 352 km by 339 km) and was fast approaching the triple-winged space station. At 0709 hr on 10 October the automatic docking procedure was initiated. Now, from a distance of 120 meters the Soyuz spacecraft edged its way toward Salyut 6. Subsequent reports indicate that Soyuz 25 made contact with the forward docking port of Salyut 6, but could not obtain a hard lock-on. For at least five more orbits Soyuz 25 stayed near Salyut 6 and apparently attempted further dockings before finally being ordered to abort the mission and return to earth.[59]

What had promised to be the beginning of a new era in space exploration had ended in yet another failure. The fact that three of the last eight Soyuz/Salyut missions had failed within 100 meters of the space station was not lost to Western observers. However, the failures of Soyuz 15, 23, and 25, although related to the rendezvous and docking systems, appear to have been caused by three separate malfunctions. Either the design or the actual hardware was in need of a complete overhaul.

Soyuz 25 pulled away from Salyut 6 for the last time and began what was now a "routine" emergency landing. Powered down to save electricity the cosmonauts mulled over what had gone wrong. Ryumin had been described as an "expert on electronic control systems", but he knew he would not have the opportunity to examine the Soyuz docking mechanism since it would be destroyed along with the Soyuz orbital module during reentry.

Touchdown finally came at 0626 hr on 11 October 185 km NW of Tselinograd. Both cosmonauts were reported in good health and were quickly transported back to the Baikonur Cosmodrome for a thorough mission debriefing.

Although Soviet officials were disappointed by the Soyuz 25 failure, they had an even greater worry. If the Salyut 6 forward docking port was responsible for the failure (at this point a 50/50 chance), future plans for Salyut 6 would have to be seriously curtailed. Another Soyuz crew would have to be sent up to investigate.

SOYUZ 26/SALYUT 6/SOYUZ 27/SOYUZ 28

Beginning with the flight of Soyuz 26 in December 1977, the Soviet Union has experienced a series of successes unparalleled in the exploration of space. In the year from December 1977 to December 1978 no fewer than ten flights (6 manned, 4 unmanned) were made to Salyut 6, all outstanding achievements. The Soviet space program after many false starts had finally come of age. Among the many firsts to be made between December 1977 and March 1978 (the duration of the Soyuz 26 mission) were the first dual docking of three spacecraft, the first manned resupply mission, the first unmanned resupply mission, and the longest (96 days) manned space flight.

The record-breaking flight of Soyuz 26 made all this possible. Launched at 0419 hr on 10 December 1977 Cosmonauts Yuri Romanenko and Georgi Grechko rode Soyuz 26 into an initial orbit of 245 km by 205 km inclined at 51.6°. The former had been associated with ASTP, whereas the latter had spent 30 days in space during the Soyuz 17/Salyut 4 mission. By their fifth orbit the orbital parameters had been altered to 329 km by 267 km.

The task given to Romanenko and Grechko was simple: dock with and man Salyut 6. Since the cause of the Soyuz 25 failure had not been definitely pinpointed, Soyuz 26 was targeted to dock with Salyut 6's aft port. If they were successful, an inspection of the forward port could later be made.

Early in the morning of 11 December the final preparations for rendezvous and docking were made. For the first time, a Soyuz spacecraft would approach a civilian Salyut space station from the aft end. This time, though, the rendezvous went off without a hitch, and hard docking was confirmed at 0602 hr Moscow time. Three hours later, the triumphant cosmonauts were congratulating each other inside the Salyut 6 complex (Figure 19).[60]

Cosmonaut Chief Vladimir Shatalov implied that the flight of Soyuz 26 would be a busy one of short duration. In part, he hoped that "the finish of the jubilee year for the Soviet cosmonauts will be with the successful fulfillment of their tasks." The implication was that Soyuz 26 would return to earth by 31 December 1977.

A Soviet press release gave the objectives of the flight as follows:

"Study of physcial processes and phenomena in outer space; exploration of the earth's surface and atmosphere for obtaining data of interest to the national economy; bio-medical investigations, technical experiments, and testing of on-board systems and instruments; in addition checking and testing of docking assembly on the transfer compartment."[61]

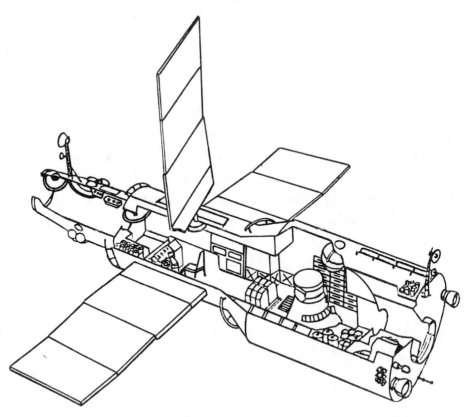

Figure 19   General layout of the Salyut 6 space station

In spite of Shatalov's remarks, thus began the 96-day flight of Romanenko and Grechko. The next week was devoted to activating and checking out Salyut 6's control systems. There had been many modifications and additions since Grechko had spent a month on board Salyut 4. By 18 December the initial "demothballing" of the station was complete.

The next day, 19 December, witnessed the single most important undertaking for the two spacemen. Their objective was to venture outside Salyut 6, to inspect visually and mechanically the forward docking port, and determine the operating status of the port. That evening Grechko and Romanenko donned new, flexible space suits and sealed themselves inside the forward transfer compartment. (There was no need to depressurize the entire station.) Grechko finally opened the Salyut hatch at 0036 hr (20 December) and slipped outside (Figure 20).

The new space suits contained built-in life-support and communications systems, thereby requiring only a simple tether to be attached to the cosmonaut to prevent his floating off. While Romanenko remained in the hatchway to hand tools and cameras to Grechko, the latter eased in front of the forward docking port to look for damage incurred during the Soyuz 25 docking attempt.

Using specially designed tools, Grechko carefully examined the port and found it to be in perfect shape. In fact, he remarked that the mechanism appeared as if it had just been fabricated, and the collision with Soyuz 25 had not left a "single scratch". Reassured that the docking port was in good working order, Grechko reentered Salyut 6 and terminated the exercise. In all, total depressurization had lasted only 88 minutes of which Grechko spent only 20 minutes outside.

With those good words from space Shatalov announced that the full Salyut program could then proceed again. In the days that followed while Western observers awaited another manned or unmanned flight, the Soyuz 26 crew went about their busy schedules.

The basic equipment on board the third-generation space station has already been mentioned in the preceding section. Many of the experimental systems of earlier models were now standard equipment on Salyut 6. One of these was the Delta autonomous navigational system. The purpose of this

Figure 20   Cosmonauts Yu.V. Romanenko and G.M. Grechko undergoing preflight training in the hydrobasin simulator at the Gagarin
Training Center, December 1977   (TASS from Sovfoto)

system was to provide data concerning the station's orbital parameters, position in space, and distance from the earth and to relieve the cosmonauts of the burden of maintaining normal attitude control. The latter function is taken care of automatically by Delta via preprogrammed instructions.[63]

A new experiment named Medusa was aimed at examining the changes which are "caused in elementary living cultures by the entire spectrum of space radiation". To carry this out two sets of vessels were filled with amino acids and similar biopolymers and then separated, one set located outside the station, the other stored inside. Later comparison of the samples would yield results applicable "not only to the practical aspect of space travel, but also to the problems of the origin and tramsmission of life in the universe".

To alleviate problems which had developed on past Salyut missions, the Soyuz 26 crew was allowed to maintain a normal 24-hour day based on Moscow time. Earlier Salyut cosmonauts had followed a shorter "day" to enable maximum use of direct communications while over Soviet territory. The enlarged world-wide Soviet communications and tracking network had greatly reduced some of these restrictions.

Earth observations still held a significant part in the daily schedules. During their first month in space Romanenko and Grechko were credited with detecting forest fires in Africa, an oil slick off that continent's southern coast, another fire near Sidney and a dust storm in another part of Australia, noctiluscent clouds over the North and South Poles, ocean currents off South America, and the melting of glaciers.

Living conditions in Salyut 6 had also been improved since the last Salyut station. In addition to books, music and chess for "off-duty" days, this new orbiting laboratory had a collapsible shower and prerecorded video tapes.

On 29 December the propulsion engine of the Soyuz 26 spacecraft was fired to move the configuration into an orbit of 371 km by 344 km. Since Soyuz 26 was docked at the aft port immediately adjacent to the Salyut main engines, use of these for orbital maneuvers was out of the question. Soyuz 26's presence also prohibited any possible refueling effort. If Romanenko and Grechko were going to remain on board Salyut 6 for an extended period, something would have to be done.

That "something" became clear on 10 January 1978 when, exactly one
month after the launch of Soyuz 26, Soviet officials announced the flight
of Soyuz 27 (lift-off time: 1526 hr) for the purpose of spending five days
on board Salyut 6 with the Soyuz 26 cosmonauts. On board Soyuz 27 were
Vladimir Dzhanibekov and Oleg Makarov. While Dzhanibekov was on his first
mission, Makarov was maintaining his reputation for missing the "big ones".
He may have been a back-up for Soyuz 9, had flown the consolation two-day
Soyuz 12, and had suffered through the Soyuz 18A launch abort. After nine
years of training for extended space flights, he would have to be satis-
fied with a five-day stay on Salyut 6.

From an initial orbit of 223 km by 202 km on 10 January, Soyuz 27
found itself a day later with orbital parameters of 302 km by 257 km and
was soon only 1.5 km away from the Salyut 6/Soyuz 26 combination. Docking came at 1706 hr with ingress into Salyut 6 some three hours later.

Before Soyuz 27 had completed the rendezvous maneuvers Cosmonauts
Romanenko and Grechko withdrew into the Soyuz 26 spacecraft for protection.
In the event of a collision between Soyuz 27 and the station, Soyuz 26
would be able to pull away unharmed. Salyut designers were also concerned
about the peculiar and complicated vehicle dynamics linkage of the three
spacecraft would pose. Tests had already been made on board to evaluate
the simpler Salyut 6/Soyuz 26 configuration. Later similar tests were
conducted during the double docking to assure its stability.

The major reason for the flight of Soyuz 27 soon became apparent.
Although Soyuz 27 became the world's first manned resupply spaceship, its
main task was simple and much more important. In order to clear the rear
docking port, the Soyuz 27 cosmonauts docked with Salyut 6's forward port
and then five days later returned to earth in the Soyuz 26 spacecraft.
The operation would have the Soyuz 26 cosmonauts remain on board Salyut 6
for perhaps two more months with a fresher Soyuz spacecraft at the forward
port and vacant aft port to accommodate unmanned cargo tankers.[64]

The docked configuration of Soyuz 27/Salyut 6/Soyuz 26 represented
the largest space payload ever constructed by the USSR. Thirty meters
long and weighing roughly 32,300 kg, the orbiting platform had a habitable
volume of close to 110 m^3 (Figure 21). This space was divided into six
basic compartment: Two Soyuz command modules, two Soyuz orbital modules,

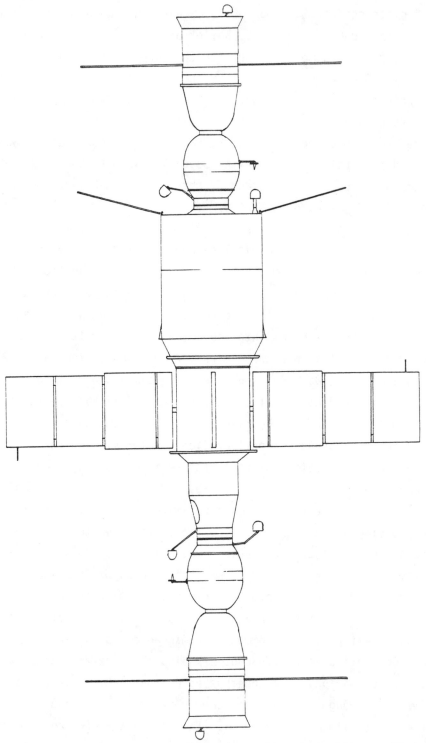

Figure 21   Illustration of the Soyuz 26/Salyut 6/Soyuz 27 docked
configuration   (Drawing by R.F. Gibbons)

the Salyut transfer compartment, and the large Salyut working compartment. In all, there were no less than eight pressure-tight hatches separating these compartments.

Among the many supplies brought to the station complex by the Soyuz 27 cosmonauts were food, film, books, and letters from friends. In addition, a Soviet-French biological experiment called Cytos was transferred to Salyut 6. This device which required the services of all four cosmonauts was designed to observe carefully the influence of weightlessness in the cellular division of Paramecia and Proteidae. By cooling the specimens to 8° C before takeoff, the unicellular organisms were brought to Salyut 6 in a suspended state. The cosmonauts' job was then to raise the temperature of the organisms to 27° C for 12 hours, thereby letting cellular division start again before later reinhibiting growth. This process was repeated eight times with different samples each time. The Soyuz 27 cosmonauts presented the specimens for analysis to Soviet and French scientists upon their return to earth.[65]

The four cosmonauts again collaborated in conducting the Resonance experiment. This test (not to be confused with the electron resonance experiment on Salyut 1) was designed to detect any destructive resonant frequencies which might be set up in the Soyuz/Salyut/Soyuz configuration. Just as bridges have been known to collapse as winds or marching soldiers produce certain frequencies in the structure, so too the delicate coupling of three spacecraft in orbit might be susceptible to a similar occurrence. Upon command from earth the cosmonauts jumped "up" and "down" on the treadmill in Salyut 6 at selected intervals. The resultant effects were closely monitored on the ground, and the structure was subsequently given a clear bill of health.

Before Dzhanibekov and Makarov could leave Salyut 6 in Soyuz 26, their custom-made couch liners had to be transferred from one Soyuz command module to the other. This done, they loaded the Cytos specimens, exposed film, and other scientific data into the Soyuz 26 spacecraft.

On 16 January Dzhanibekov and Makarov donned their space suits, exchanged farewells with Romanenko and Grechko, and boarded Soyuz 26. After undocking, the two cosmonauts completed two to three more revolutions about the earth before landing 310 km W of Tselinograd about 1500 hr Moscow time.

With the departure of their cosmonaut comrades Romanenko and Grechko
again took up the myriad chores associated with running a complex space
laboratory. The 18th and 19th of January were largely devoted to beginning
a series of experiments under the name Raduga. The center of this undertaking was the East German designed MKF-6M multi-spectral camera, an improved model of the MKF-6 flown on Soyuz 22. The primary objective was
to locate and record a variety of natural resources in the USSR and East
Germany on photographic plates which surveyed approximately 33,000 km^2 on
each frame.

On the following day, the Soviet Union ushered in a "new stage in space
exploration" with the launch of the unmanned Progress 1 cargo spacecraft.
A direct descendant of the workhorse Soyuz, Progress was designed to ferry
food, fuel, and scientific supplies economically to orbiting Salyut stations.[66] The spacecraft is not reusable, and once reloaded with refuse
from Salyut it is destroyed during reentry.

Reportedly launched about 1123 hr on 20 January, Progress 1 entered
an orbit of 262 km by 194 km to begin its 50-hour chase of Salyut 6. Unlike the standard 24-hour rendezvous time for Soyuz and Salyut, due to the
automatic nature of Progress and the need constantly to reevaluate orbital
parameters Progress spacecraft are allowed two days to complete the complicated rendezvous and docking maneuvers.

Following correction burns on the 4th, 17th, and 31st orbits, Progress
1 gently docked with the aft port of Salyut 6 at 1312 hr on 22 January
under the watchful eyes of the Soyuz 26 cosmonauts and ground controllers
(Figure 22). During the next nine days Romanenko and Grechko unloaded the
many dry goods stored in the Progress 1 forward compartment. Among these
were mail, food, air and water filters, film, exercises suits, replacement
parts for on-board Salyut 6 systems, and entire new experimental appara-
tuses. By 1 February the cosmonauts had started transferring Salyut 6
waste materials (soiled clothing, sewage, etc.) into Progress 1.[67]

On the last day of January compressed air brought up by Progress 1
was forced into the Salyut 6 environmental control system. Since every
time an airlock was utilized (EVA's, Soyuz and Progress dockings and un-
dockings, waste disposal) some station atmosphere was lost, Salyut 6's
air reserves had to be replenished. With that done, meticulous preparations were begun for the world's first space refueling attempt.

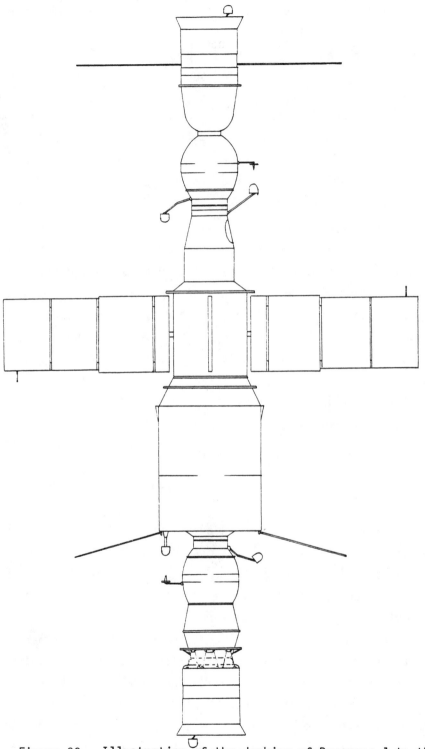

Figure 22   Illustration of the docking of Progress 1 to the
Soyuz 27/Salyut 6 complex (Drawing by R.F. Gibbons)

343

For several days prior to the event Romanenko and Grechko checked the related system components, insured the integrity of propellant lines, and gradually reduced the pressure of the Salyut 6 fuel and oxidizer tanks from 20 to 3 atmospheres. Fuel and oxidizer supplies were finally shifted from Progress 1 to four of the six Salyut 6 holding tanks on 2 and 3 February, respectively. In all, nearly 1000 kg of propellants were transferred during this historic in-orbit refueling operation.[68]

Steps were taken to conclude the Progress 1 visit on 5 February when the transfer lines connecting Salyut 6 and Progress 1 were purged of any remaining propellants. This prevented any possible spacecraft contamination as a result of propellant leakage during undocking of the two space vehicles. That same day the propulsion system of Progress 1 was used to raise the orbit of the entire Soyuz 27/Salyut 6/Progress 1 configuration.

Via radio command from Soviet ground stations at 0853 hr on 6 February Progress 1 undocked from Soyuz 27/Salyut 6 and pulled away to a distance of approximately 15 km. On the next orbit the Progress 1 back-up systems were engaged, and the robot cargo ship retested the automatic rendezvous procedure. Following completion of the maneuver, the orbital laboratory and Progress 1 were allowed to drift apart again. Two days later the Soviets announced the demise of Progress 1 in a fiery reentry over a desolate region of the Pacific Ocean between 0530 and 0600 hr after almost nineteen days in space.

For the week following the death of Progress 1, Romanenko and Grechko returned to a routine similar to that to which they had become accustomed. Several days were spent installing equipment and parts brought by Progress 1 and photographing the earth with the MKF-6M camera.

Between 14 and 17 February the two cosmonauts, who now held the Soviet space-endurance record, devoted a large portion of their time to conducting experiments with the recently delivered Splav 01 (Alloy) installation. Assembled in one of the Salyut 6 airlocks, the purpose of the 23-kg electric furnace was to investigate the feasibility of new welding and soldering techniques and of manufacturing semiconductor alloys in a zero-g vacuum. The melting and crystallization of the dual material samples took place in three separate temperature regions inside Splav 01: 1100° C, 600-700° C, and a region which varied linearly between these two extreme temperature

regions. Samples tested included copper/indium, indium/antimonide, alumi-
num/tungsten, molybdenum/gallium, and aluminum/antimony.[69]

The later part of February saw a renewal of astrophysical experiments,
both in the ultraviolet and infrared ranges. Of major interest was the
operation of the super-cooled (-269° C), infrared BST-1M telescope. Equipped
with a 1.5-m diameter mirror, this instrument not only recorded submilli-
meter radiation from the Galactic center, the Orion Nebula, and interstel-
lar hydrogen clouds, but also made measurements of upper-atmospheric activity.

In the early part of February, rumors surfaced that the first international space crew, a Soviet and a Czech, would be launched around the
27th of that month. An orbital maneuver conducted by Soyuz 27/Salyut 6
on 23 February reinforced these reports. Although 27 February came and
left without incident, only three days later word came of the launch of
Soyuz 28.

The flight of Soyuz 28 marked another milestone in the history of space
exploration. For the first time an international crew was launched into
space, and one of the crew members came from outside the US and USSR. Manning Soyuz 28 were veteran Soviet Cosmonaut Aleksey Gubarev and Czechoslovak
Vladimir Remek. The flight inaugurated the Interkosmos manned space exploration program. (Three more flights have been flown to date.)

Shortly after the 1828-hr lift-off from the Baikonur Cosmodrome on
2 March 1978, Cosmonauts Gubarev and Remek maneuvered their Soyuz 28 spaceship into an earth orbit of 309 km by 269 km. Along with mail, food and
other consumables, the two spacemen carried with them new experiments,
of which two were of Czech origin. Approximately twenty-six hours after
launch (at 2010 hr on 3 March) Soyuz 28 successfully docked at the Salyut
6 aft port, creating for a second time a four-man orbital laboratory.

Three hours after docking Gubarev and Remek joined their fellow cosmonauts inside Salyut 6 and celebrated their feat. About six and one-half
hours later another space record was set when at 0536 hr on 4 March the
Soyuz 26 cosmonauts, Romanenko and Grechko, surpassed the 84-day Skylab 4
endurance record for the longest manned space flight.

Soon after the start of the Soyuz 28 mission, Soviet officials revealed
that the newcomers to space would return on 10 March after a nearly eight-

day flight. Also disclosed was the fact that Romanenko and Grechko would finally be returning to earth soon thereafter, leaving Salyut 6 unmanned until later that year.

The four cosmonauts quickly set about conducting their assigned tasks which included the Czech Morava and Chorella experiments and the joint Soviet-Czech Extinctia and Oxymeter investigations.[70] Morava was a follow-on to the earlier space processing experiments performed with the Splav 01 electric furnace. Samples of lead, silver, and copper chlorides as well as glass and selected metals were melted and crystalized in the search for new alloys suitable for optical electronic applications.

The Chlorella experiment was an extention of several past Soviet attempts to design a long-term system for the production of food and oxygen and the absorption of carbon dioxide on permanent orbiting space stations or protracted interplanetary flights. Extinctia was the program name for the investigation of micrometeoroid dust densities at an altitude of 80-100 km. By careful observations Gubarev and Remek could detect these concentrations by noting change in the apparent brightness of stars as they set behind the earth's horizon. Finally, a Czech-made Oxymeter device determined the levels of oxygen in human tissue in a Czech-Soviet biological experiment.

These and other experiments, including earth photography, kept the four cosmonauts busy until 8 March when they were given an "active day of rest". Next, preparations were begun for the return to earth of the Soyuz 28 cosmonauts. Experimental data acquired since the departure of the Soyuz 27 crew were stowed aboard the Soyuz 28 spacecraft.

Gubarev and Remek gave their farewells to Romanenko and Grechko on 10 March, entered their Soyuz spacecraft, and cast off from the Salyut 6 complex. A little more than three hours later at 1645 hr the first international space crew had successfully landed 310 km west of Tselinograd. Meanwhile space champions Romanenko and Grechko, still orbiting overhead after three months in space, brought their investigations to a close in anticipation of soon joining their comrades back on earth.

Shortly before the Soyuz 28 cosmonauts had departed, Romanenko and Grechko initiated an extensive reconditioning program to better help them endure the sometimes difficult readjustment to a 1-g environment after a prolonged stay in weightlessness. From 9 to 12 March exercises and medical examinations were the order of the day. Not until 13 March did formal mothballing of the Salyut 6 space station begin. Possibly due to the wealth of data already returned, Soviet space program managers had decided to leave Salyut 6 in an unmanned automated state for three months before ferrying a fresh crew to the now famous space station.

The Soyuz 27 spacecraft left by Cosmonauts Dzhanibekov and Makarov two months earlier was now loaded and on 15 March the propulsion engine was fired in a systems test. With Soviet recovery personnel waiting anxiously, the two spacemen pulled away from Salyut 6 at 1100 hr on 16 March after spending some 95 days on board the orbital laboratory. Romanenko and Grechko continued to fly their solo Soyuz spaceship for two more revolutions about the earth before engaging the reentry system.

Landfall came at 1419 hr as the Soyuz command module settled gently onto a snow-clad field 265 km west of Tselinograd, 96 days and 10 hours after lift-off at Baikonur. The cosmonauts were given immediate medical examinations before being whisked away to isolated quarters for recuperation and debriefing.

Readjustment to earth's gravity was gradual. During their first few days back the cosmonauts experienced overall fatigue and muscular pain. Soviet doctors revealed that the two spacemen were "physically" and "mentally" still in space, citing their attempt to "swim" out of their beds in the morning as they had done for the past three months. Even simple chores required effort. Although physical exercises and strolls were daily events, as late as 24 March over a week after his return to earth, Grechko remarked that he was still shaky and felt heavy. By 31 March most preflight conditions (weight, circulations, etc.) had returned to normal, and the two Soviet space heroes were pronounced readapted to a 1-g environment.[71]

The list of accomplishements assembled by the Soyuz 26, 27, and 28 crews was impressive indeed: first dual docking of two spaceships and an orbital space station, first manned resupply mission, first unmanned resupply mission, first in-orbit refueling, first international space crew, largest space station crew size (4), longest space flight (96.42 days).

The achievements, however, were not nearly so important as the demonstrated potential of the versatile Soyuz/Salyut/Progress space systems.

Talk of even longer manned missions and of joining multiple Salyuts in earth orbit was prevalent on both sides of the Iron Curtain. Soviet spokesmen promised renewed flights to Salyut 6 before the end of the year involving further Progress cargo missions and the first Polish and East German cosmonauts. As the Space Age neared its 21st birthday, the Soviet manned space program had indeed come of age.

SOYUZ 29/SALYUT 6/SOYUZ 30/SOYUZ 31

The dictionary defines "routine" as "a customary or regular course of procedure". For those of us who have watched with excitement as man at first tentatively and then more confidently probed space throughout the decades of the '60s and '70s, routine is a word which will never find a place in space exploration. However, for millions of people around the world the marathon mission of Soyuz 29 from June to November 1978 appeared to be just that. With almost predictable regularity Soyuz and Progress spacecraft were flown to the now most frequented space station, Salyut 6. No fewer than three unmanned Progress cargo craft and three manned Soyuz spacecraft visited the orbital laboratory in the span of 140 days.

Soyuz 29 set the ball rolling with a textbook launch at 2317 hr on 15 June 1978, four days after Salyut 6 had been maneuvered into an orbit of 356 km by 340 km. On board were veteran Cosmonaut Vladimir Kovalenok (commander of the aborted Soyuz 25 mission) and rookie Alexander Ivanchenkov who had trained for the 1975 ASTP.

Twenty-five hours and forty-one minutes after lift-off Soyuz 29 nudged its docking probe into the docking receptacle of the Salyut 6 forward port and completed the day-long chase and rendezvous maneuvers. Kovalenok became the first man to revisit the same Salyut space station; through this time he would be eminently more successful.

The objectives of the Soyuz 29 mission were broadly to continue the experiments begun by their predecessors on board Salyut 6. In general, this included earth-resources, astrophysical, biological, instrumentation, and manufacturing investigations.[72] The first few days on board Salyut 6 were devoted to activating many of the necessary man-related systems. A defective ventilator on the Splav 01 furnace was replaced and repairs to the Salyut airlock were accomplished.

For the first time, Kovalenok and Ivanchenkov followed a standard earth work-week schedule. Most experiments were conducted between 0900 and 1700 hr, Monday through Friday, with Saturday and Sunday set aside for personal, housekeeping, and administrative chores. From 24 to 26 June the space duo conducted extensive materials experiments using the Splav 01 furnace. To prevent even the smallest introduction of forces on the materials during the crystallization process, Salyut 6 was placed in a gravity gradient stabilization regime so that the station attitude-control thrusters would not fire and disturb the zero-g environment.

On the day following the completion of these experiments and only 12 days after the launch of Soyuz 29, Soviet news agencies announced the launch at 1827 hr on 27 June of Soyuz 30. Carrying veteran Soviet Cosmonaut Pyotr Klimuk and a rookie Polish Cosmonaut Miroslaw Hermaszewski, Soyuz 30 was scheduled to dock with the aft port of Salyut 6 the next day for a stay of seven days (Figures 23 and 24).

Docking and completion of the Soyuz 29/Salyut 6/Soyuz 30 complex came at 2008 hr on 28 June. Klimuk and Hermaszewski joined Kovalenok and Ivanchenkov to form the third four-man Salyut space-station crew. Among the new experiments delivered to the station was a Soviet-Polish venture in materials processing called Sirena. Using the Splav 01 electric furnace, this undertaking envisioned the formation of semiconductors of cadmium-mercury-telluride.[73]

Another experiment conducted by Klimuk and Hermaszewski involved comparing personal estimates of heat-exchange phenomena with instrument recordings. The day of 3 July was a busy one which saw additional Splav 01 tests, completion of a psychological investigation called Relaks, and earth-resources photography. The latter employed the MKF-6M multi-spectral camera to photograph areas in the USSR and Poland. Some photographic sessions were timed to coincide with aerial photography of the same region from aircraft and helicopters. In order to better train the Salyut 6 cosmonauts for this type of observation work many preflight hours were spent in high-altitude aircraft. Prior familiarization of the territory from altitudes of 9 km aided the cosmonauts in locating designated sites and detecting other interesting targets.

Also on board Salyut 6 for topographical studies was a KATE-140 camera. One photographic plate scanned a region approximately 450 km by 450 km

Figure 23   Soviet Cosmonaut Klimuk and Polish Cosmonaut Hermaszewski
during training for the Soyuz 30 mission to Salyut 6

(compared with a 200 km by 165 km picture taken with the MKF-6M), enabling
an area of over 200,000 km^2 to be captured on film at a time. Within five
minutes a territory could be mapped which would have required almost two
years work by conventional means.[74]

The fourth of July 1978 marked the winding down of the short Soyuz 30
mission. On 5 July Klimuk and Hermaszewski reboarded their Soyuz 30 spacecraft and at 1315 hr undocked from Salyut 6. Recovery came at about 1631
hr some 300 km west of Tselinograd.

The Soyuz 30 crew had barely begun debriefing when it was announced that at 1426 hr on 7 July Progress 2 had been launched from Baikonur into an orbit of 262 km by 193 km on a resupply mission to Soyuz 29/Salyut 6. Thus, at 1559 hr on 9 July only four days after Soyuz 30 vacated the Salyut 6 aft docking port, Progress successfully mated with the orbital laboratory. On board Progress 2 were life-support equipment (water ~200 liters, foodstuffs 235 kg), a new processing kiln named Kristall, other experiments, replacement parts, mail, and 600 kg of fuel and oxidizer for transfer to the Salyut 6 propulsion system.[75]

Progress 2 delivered materials necessary to continue the Splav 01 experiments with samples of aluminum, tin, and molybdenum. Pure crystals of gallium arsenide were also the object of manufacture since this compound is widely used in diodes (laser and electroluminescent) and solar batteries. Optical material processing was also now possible for the first time. A containerless system permitted melting and resolidification to take place in weightless conditions without physical contact with the apparatus. This procedure has promise in the making of fine lenses and mirrors.

Figure 24   Klimuk and Hermaszewski inside a Salyut trainer

The refueling of Salyut 6 by Progress 2 was conducted differently from the similar operation with Progress 1. This time the transfer was made under the guidance and control of ground-support personnel, leaving Kovalenok and Ivanchenkov free to perform other duties. The procedure also suggested the possibility of automatically refueling an unmanned Salyut station should the need ever arise. By 21 July this operation, too, had been completed.

For the next week the Soyuz 29 crew divided their time between continued melting and manufacturing experiments and earth-resources work. Vast regions of the southern USSR were photographed for agricultural and mineral purposes. In particular, the experimental Salsky agricultural center north of Moscow was observed to test space-borne detection capabilities.

On 29 July Kovalenok and Ivanchenkov undertook the task of conducting the Soviet Union's fourth EVA. The purpose of the excursion was to retrieve several experiments which had been in operation since the launch of Salyut 6 in late September 1977. These included a micrometeorite sensor, a radiation sensor, several new materials being evaluated for exposure to space environments (plastics, rubbers, etc.), and the external component of the Medusa experiment involving radiational effects on biopolymers.

Kovalenok and Ivanchenkov donned the same space suits worn by the Soyuz 26 crew on their EVA seven months before. After depressurizing Salyut 6's transfer and forward docking compartment, the two cosmonauts opened the side EVA hatch at 0655 hr Moscow time as they passed over Korea in daylight. Using handrails, Ivanchenkov carefully made his way to the experiment packages as Kovalenok monitored his actions and sent color TV images to ground controllers. About thirty minutes into the EVA the orbital complex entered the earth's shadow where spotlights enabled the space walkers to continue their chores. In addition to retrieving the desired equipment, a new radiation sensor was placed on Salyut 6's exterior and a general inspection of the space station was made.

By 0900 hr Kovalenok and Ivanchenkov had reentered Salyut 6, completing an EVA lasting two hours and five minutes. After the access hatch had been closed, the airlock was repressurized, and the cosmonauts shed their space suits and transferred back into the main Salyut 6 compartment.

Now the reason for the prolonged stay of Progress 2 was apparent. During the EVA and with each use of the Splav 01 furnace precious atmosphere is irretrievably lost. Progress vehicles, however, carry replenishments for the space station's atmospheric system. By keeping Progress 2 until after the EVA, that cargo ship was able to again fill Salyut 6's air reserves.

At 0757 hr on 2 August four days after the space walks Progress 2, loaded with waste, separated from the Soyuz 29/Salyut 6 complex. For two more days the unmanned transport ship was maneuvered in space and many of its systems were tested before self-destructing over the Pacific Ocean upon radio commands from Soviet mission control.

On the following day (5 August) the Soyuz 29 cosmonauts were hard at work again with the Kristall apparatus with which monocrystals of germanium and indium antimonide were produced. That same day the orbital parameters of the Soyuz 29/Salyut 6 complex were modified to accommodate the imminent launch of yet another resupply vehicle, Progress 3.

Launched at 0131 hr on 8 August into an orbit of 249 km by 195 km, Progress 3 docked with Salyut 6's aft port at 0300 hr on 10 August. The extremely short period between Progress 2 and Progress 3 was seen as indicating a prolonged stay for the Soyuz 29 crew. Although no fuel was off-loaded from Progress 3, the transport craft did carry a full load of other supplies, including 280 kg of foodstuffs, 450 kg of atmospheric gases, 190 liters of water, and a host of experiment materials. Much to Ivanchenkov's delight he also found that his custom-made guitar had been shipped to him by friends.[76]

For the next eleven days Kovalenok and Ivanchenkov returned to their normal routine of exercises, medical examinations, astrophysical investigations and materials research. The fresh supplies in Progress 3 were eventually removed and replaced with Salyut 6 refuse. By 21 August the Soyuz 29 crew had spent 65 days on board Salyut 6 with no indication of a return to earth in the near future. In fact, Soviet spokesmen had already announced that a new Soyuz flight was being prepared to visit the two cosmonauts in late August or early September and that a member of the new flight would be an East German (Figure 25). That same day, 21 August, Progress 3 was finally undocked and moved away from Salyut 6 after a stay of only 11 days. Progress 3 remained in space a day longer that the pattern established by Progress 1 and 2 with reentry over the Pacific Ocean occurring on 24 August.

Figure 25   Preparation for the launch of a Soyuz manned spacecraft.
The rocket and spacecraft are being erected on the launch
pad.   (Courtesy of NASA)

Just two days later at 1751 hr on 26 August, Soyuz 31, carrying Vostok
and Soyuz veteran Valery Bykovsky and Sigmund Jaehn of the German Democrat-
ic Republic, was launched. The Soyuz 29/Salyut 6/Soyuz 31 configuration
was completed with docking at 1938 hr on 27 August. Beginning with the
docking of Soyuz 30 with Salyut 6 on 28 June the aft docking port of the
orbital laboratory had scarcely been vacant with the flights of Progress
2, Progress 3, and Soyuz 31 following in quick succession. The tremendous
amount of resources dedicated to Salyut and Soyuz 29 revealed the Soviet
desire for a permanent presence in space.

One of the major activities of the new four-man Salyut crew was an
earth-resources and photography program, code named Syomka, utilizing the
MKF-6M multi-spectral camera. The prototype of the camera was flown by
Bykovsky on Soyuz 22 in 1976 and was built in East Germany. Four biological experiments examining growth of bacteria and microorganisms were performed by Jaehn. Other joint Soviet-East German experiments included:[77]

Audio - an investigation of human auditory limits in space. This
experiment was prompted by reports from previous cosmonauts of undesirable noise levels in Salyut 6.

Berolina- another attempt at creating pure semiconductor crystals

Reporter - photographic exercise inside Salyut involving several types of film and a Praktica EE2 camera

Vremya - testing of cosmonaut reaction time in a space environment.

Soon after the arrival of Soyuz 31, the intention of returning the Soyuz 31 cosmonauts in the Soyuz 29 spacecraft was revealed. This maneuver had been expected and was thought to have been the reason behind the closely spaced flights of Progress 2 and Progress 3, since such a procedure would leave the Soyuz 31 spacecraft at the aft Salyut 6 docking port, blocking further Progress flights. However, such was not to be the case.

The Soyuz 31 mission concluded on 3 September. Prior to this time the specially fitted couches in the Soyuz 29 and 31 spacecraft were exchanged. Bykovsky and Jaehn bade Kovalenok and Ivanchenkov farewell, undocked the Soyuz 29 spaceship at 1153 hr, and sailed to a soft landing at 1440 hr some 140 km SE of Dzhezkazgan (Figure 26).

An entirely new venture was begun on 5 and 6 September when the Soyuz 29 cosmonauts spent two days stowing loose items inside the Salyut 6 space station. Their goal: undock the Soyuz 31 spacecraft from the aft docking port and redock at the forward docking port. If successful, this would free the rear port for a further Progress mission. The maneuver was complicated by the desire to rotate the Salyut space station 180 degrees in orbit to accomplish the feat instead of flying Soyuz 31 around to the front of the station.

On 7 September Kovalenok and Ivanchenkov retreated to Soyuz 31, undocked, and pulled away from Salyut 6 to a distance of 100 to 200 meters (Figure 27). Ground controllers then guided Salyut 6 through the turn-around maneuver so that the forward docking port was now facing Soyuz 31. The total operation was completed within one orbit when Soyuz 31 received confirmation of a hard docking at the forward site.[78]

The Soyuz 29 cosmonauts were now ready to continue their epic space flight. With a fresh Soyuz spacecraft and the possibility of further visits by Progress vehicles, the length of their mission was open-ended. As the days passed, more and more time was spent conducting medical tests and evaluating the condition of the crew. At 0197 hr on 20 September Kovalenok and Ivanchenkov surpassed the Soyuz 26 crew's endurance record

Figure 26   A picture representative of the Soyuz 29/Salyut 6/
            Soyuz 31 configuration   (TASS from Sovfoto)

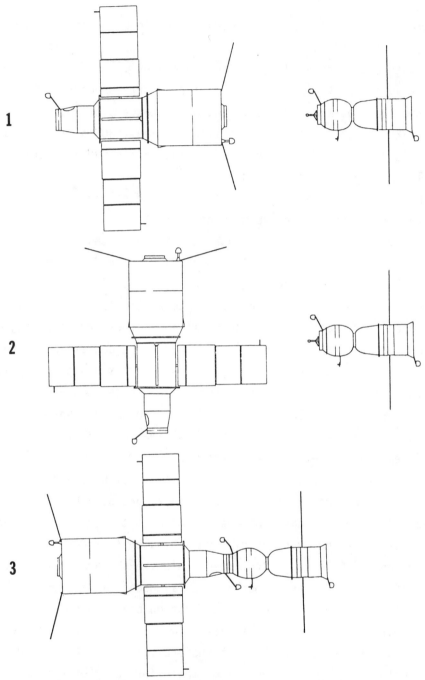

1. Undocking of the Soyuz 31 spacecraft from the
   aft port of Salyut 6
2. 180 degree rotation of Salyut 6
3. Redocking of Soyuz 31 with the Salyut 6 forward
   port

Figure 27   Turn-around maneuver performed by the Soyuz 29 cosmonauts to
reposition the Soyuz 31 spacecraft (Drawing by R.F. Gibbons)

and became the new world record holders of continuous time in space. At
the time, Soviet officials directly related extended earth-orbital missions
with the future goal of sending men to the planets.[79]

More than two weeks passed with regular reports concerning the activities of the two spacemen. By early October in excess of 18,000 photographs
had been taken of the earth. In addition, at least 30 materials had been
processed in the Splav 01 and Kristall installations. New experiments with
the BST-1M telescope were also undertaken.[80]

On the twenty-first anniversary of the launching of Sputnik 1, Progress
4 lifted off to become the eleventh mission to Salyut 6 in less than a year.
Launched at 0209 hr Moscow time, Progress 4 followed the standard rendezvous maneuvers and docked with Salyut 6 at 0400 hr on 6 October. Along
with propellants, fresh water, and various food supplies, Progress 4 delivered new Penguin muscular stress suits to replace the deteriorating
original ones, fur boots to keep the cosmonauts' feet from becoming cold
due to reduced blood circulation, lithium hydroxide canisters for the air
purification system, and partitions to allow each cosmonaut more privacy.[81]

The cosmonauts took a break in unloading Progress 4 on 7 October in
order to observe a total lunar eclipse from their unique vantage point in
space. New manufacturing experiments, this time involving the crystallization of lead telluride, also were resumed.

While Progress 4 was being relieved of its precious cargo, Soviet
spokesmen gave the first indication that the flight of Soyuz 29 was coming
to an end. Allowing ten days for operations with the latest unmanned supply ship, Kovalenok and Ivanchenkov were scheduled to return to earth
"toward the end of October". Prolonged medical examinations and exercise
sessions lasting as long as three hours a day became more frequent as the
crew completed four months of weightlessness on board Salyut 6.[82]

As October came to a close the pace of activity on board the year-old
space station heightened. Bit by bit the orbital laboratory was deactivated and mothballed for the several months before another crew was expected
to arrive. Progress 4's propulsion system was used to place the Soyuz 31/
Salyut 6/Progress 4 combination in the proper orbit for the reentry attempt. Following this action, the spent cargo ferry was released at 1607
hr on 24 October and finally was destroyed during reentry two days later.

The last processing experiments were performed with the results that samples of cadmium sulfide and a cadmium-mercury-tellurium semiconductor were created.[83]

On 2 November 1978 after 140 days in space the heroic cosmonauts ate their last meal in Salyut 6. The Soyuz 31 spacecraft had been loaded and its main engine had already been tested to ensure proper operation after the undocking maneuver. Having donned their space suits for the last time, Kovalenok and Ivanchenkov entered the Soyuz orbital module, closed the docking hatches, and then floated to their seats in the command module.

Soyuz 31 withdrew from the now deserted Salyut 6. When the operation of all vital systems on board Soyuz 31 had been verified, the final countdown for reentry was initiated. The blast of the Soyuz 417-kg-thrust hypergolic primary engine slammed the two space veterans into their custom-made couches. With the exception of small orbital maneuvers performed by the Salyut 6 complex, this was the cosmonauts' first taste of "weight" after 140 days in a gravity-free environment. In order to minimize the shock of 1 g to their space-accustomed bodies, both men drank quantities of a saline solution to maintain blood pressure.

Under the watchful eyes of the Soviet recovery forces, the Soyuz 31 command module descended gently to a 1405-hr landing 180 km SE of Dzhezkazgan. An anxious medical team rushed to the capsule and examined Kovalenok and Ivanchenkov on the spot. Although the cosmonauts experienced disorientation and a "heavy" feeling, the preliminary inspection showed the duo were able to be flown to Tyuratam some 514 km away.[84]

For the next several weeks Kovalenok and Ivanchenkov were the objects of extensive medical and psychological tests. The Soyuz 26 cosmonauts had required longer than expected to readjust to earth's gravity after their 96-day mission. If the Soyuz 29 cosmonauts could not readapt in the anticipated time frame, the prospect for future, even longer flights would be in jeopardy.

In January 1979 Soviet doctors released the initial results of their evaluation of the Soyuz 29 crew's readaptation to 1 g. For several days the men were plagued with a tired feeling, and their work performance also suffered. Although their body weights, red blood cells, and hemoglobin were all below preflight levels, the changes were not as severe as had been anticipated. The two men took a short walk on their second day back on earth, and by the sixth day the first level of readjustment had been completed. At this point the major body systems had returned to normal levels. Certain muscular systems did not regain their preflight abilities until after 27 November, twenty-five days after touchdown. Overall, however, the progress of Kovalenok and Ivanchenkov was viewed to be excellent. Flights in space of at least six months were now seen as reasonable.[85]

Soyuz 29 mission proved much more than merely man's ability to withstand the rigors of a weightless environment for 140 days. Scores of experiments had been performed with the Splav 01 and Kristall furnaces. Thousands of photographs had been taken of the earth and space. Biological investigations involving a wide variety of simple and complex organisms were conducted.

SOYUZ 32/SALYUT 6/SOYUZ 33/SOYUZ 34

Three months had elapsed between the first and second expeditions (as the Soviets referred to the Soyuz 26 et al. and the Soyuz 29 et al. missions) to the Salyut 6 space station. A similar period of almost 4 months passed before the third expedition was begun. The goal for this latest space marathon was to achieve that long-desired milestone of six months in space. Like the 140 day mission before it, this third expedition was to involve three Soyuz ferries and three Progress cargo ships. Hence by late summer 1979 no fewer than 17 spacecraft (10 Soyuz and 7 Progress) had visited or attempted to visit the Salyut 6 station.

At 1454 hr on 25 February 1979 the great experiment began with the launching of Soyuz 32 from the Tyuratam complex. On board were rookie Commander Vladimir Lyakhov and veteran Flight Engineer Valery Ryumin. Ryumin was the second member of the unfortunate Soyuz 25 team to be given another chance to man Salyut 6. His commander on that October 1977 flight, Vladimir Kovalenok, had of course commanded the Soyuz 29 second expedition to Salyut 6.

Twenty-five hours after launch the two cosmonauts were quickly closing in on their target. Docking came at 1630 hr on 26 February in an orbit of 309 km by 296 km. These low orbital parameters along with two unusual aspects of the initial Soyuz 32 mission pointed to possible problems with Salyut 6. Following a burn by the Progress 4 spacecraft on 20 October 1978 (two weeks before the departure of the Soyuz 29 crew) raising Salyut to

360

an average 370 km altitude, Salyut 6 had steadily decayed. While this procedure for an unmanned space station is not in itself unusual, the failure to maneuver Salyut 6 prior to the launch of Soyuz 32 was a departure from established procedures. Another historical deviation came when the Soyuz 32 propulsion engine was used to raise the orbit of the Soyuz 32/ Salyut 6 complex to an orbit of 338 km by 308 km shortly after docking.[86] The severity of the problem was revealed later during the following month.

The day following their boarding of Salyut 6 the Soyuz 32 cosmonauts were already hard at work. Of immediate priority was the shutting down of their Soyuz ferry systems and the demothballing of the orbital laboratory. Salyut 6 had now been in orbit 17 months, longer than any other manned spacecraft. Concern was obviously high that all vital Salyut systems should be thoroughly inspected and repaired or replaced if necessary. Even repairs to non-modularized equipment could be performed with a specially designed soldering iron capable of effecting reliable electrical connections in a weightless environment. In a lighter vein, Lyakhov and Ryumin found themselves not immune from the historical fight between man and household pests when a container of experimental flies being transferred from Soyuz 32 to Salyut 6 was opened, letting loose several specimens into the space station.[87]

During the two weeks following their arrival on Salyut 6, the two cosmonauts continued the extensive checkout of their new home in space. One object of their examinations was verification of the functioning of all airlock systems necessary for future dockings and EVA's. Daily reports to mission control kept Soviet space planners abreast of their progress and enabled ground personnel to make ready replacements for those parts and instruments found defective. These items along with new experiments and consumables (food, water, propellants, etc.) were quietly being loaded into the first robot resupply ship of this latest space mission.

At 0847 hr on 12 March 1979, Progress 5 was launched from Tyuratam into an orbit of 256 km by 195 km. Following the now standard two-day rendezvous maneuvers, Progress 5 now under control of Lyakhov and Ryumin successfully docked with the aft port of Salyut 6 at 1020 hr on 14 March 1979. The cosmonauts quickly set about unloading the cargo which included an improved version of the Kristall furnace and a gamma-ray telescope named Yelena. The original Kristall furnace was dismantled and stowed.

Amid reports that after a year and a half of exposure to the harsh space environment Salyut 6's solar arrays were deteriorating, Progress 5 brought a new chemical storage battery for connection into the station electrical system. A television receiver was delivered to enable the cosmonauts to receive TV transmissions from the ground.[88]

Soon after the arrival of Progress 5, the extent of the Salyut propulsion system problem was disclosed. Apparently, toward the end of the Soyuz 29 mission that crew noted deviations in the performance of calculated burns. During the four month interval between the Soyuz 29 and Soyuz 32 flights, Soviet engineers evaluated the readings and pinpointed the probable discrepancy. The results of this investigation indicated that one of the fuel tank internal membranes separating the high-pressure nitrogen and the unsymmetrical dimethylydrazine had leaked some fuel into the nitrogen side. Although Salyut 6 held two other fuel tanks which could be used, contamination could have spread throughout the entire propulsion system if the situation deteriorated further.[89]

To alleviate the troublesome fuel tank problems Lyakhov and Ryumin carefully followed a multi-day procedure already tested on ground mock-ups. First, the Soyuz/Salyut/Progress complex was placed in a slow rotation attitude for the purpose of creating a small artificial gravity field designed to separate the fuel/nitrogren mixture on the nitrogen side of the tank membrane. The fuel remaining in the tank was then channeled to other tanks on board Salyut 6 and Progress 5. Finally, the suspect tank was purged with nitrogen and vented into space.

The success of this repair operation has not yet been publicly determined. Virtually all orbital maneuvers carried out during the Soyuz 32 mission were performed by the engines of either Soyuz or Progress spacecraft. However, the attitude-control system of Salyut 6 which feeds on the same propellant tanks of the propulsion system appears to have continued functioning properly. A further question of the reliability of this portion of the Salyut main engine system came in April 1979 when the Soviets revealed Lyakhov and Ryumin engaged in work with a set of standby fuel tanks.[90]

The remainder of March and the first part of April were devoted to medical and experimental tasks. The new Kristall furnace was assembled with the first diffusion experiments employing French supplied samples of tin/lead and aluminum/copper. The Yelena gamma-ray telescope was also unpacked and tested. Plant growth experiments were initiated using a new portable centrifuge which created gravitational-like forces in the otherwise weightless environment. The medical condition of the Soyuz 32 cosmonauts was carefully monitored with an eye to determing the most efficient means for quick acclimation to zero-g conditions on board Salyut 6.[91]

With the stay of Progress 5 rapidly nearing its end, the automated transport raised the orbit of the orbital station on 30 March and 2 April. Then, at 1910 hr on 3 April with its mission completed, Progress 5 undocked and pulled away from Soyuz 32 and Salyut 6. Two days later a radio command sent Progress 5 to its destruction in the atmosphere over the Pacific Ocean. The aft Salyut 6 docking port was now vacant, implying the first Interkosmos crew to visit the Soyuz 32 cosmonauts was close at hand. On 6 April the Soyuz 32 propulsion engine was fired to set the stage for this event.

Final preparations for the flight of Soyuz 33 were completed on 10 April, followed by a launch at 2034 hr that evening (Figure 28). On board were Cosmonaut Nikolay Rukavishnikov (now on his third space mission) and his Bulgarian crew member Georgi Ivanov. This flight held special meaning for Rukavishnikov since almost exactly eight years earlier he had flown on the world's first (and unsuccessful) mission to an orbiting space station on Soyuz 10. A day later, Rukavishnikov seemed destined never to serve on board a Salyut station.

Lift-off of the manned spacecraft appeared flawless, and Soyuz 33 soon began the set of maneuvers designed to bring it to Salyut 6 the following day. Having entered an orbit of 330 km by 273 km by revolution 13, the Interkosmos crew started the final approach maneuvers at 2154 hr Moscow time on 11 April. On the 17th revolution as Soyuz 33 pulled to within 3 km of Salyut the automatic rendezvous system was engaged. However, the two cosmonauts noticed that the engine was not functioning "normally"--a fact immediately confirmed by ground controllers. A quick diagnosis of the problem was unable to reveal the cause of the malfunction, but the seriousness of the situation called for an abort of the rendezvous and for a return to earth as soon as possible.[92]

Figure 28   Soyuz rocket being prepared for launch (Courtesy of NASA)

The following report was issued from Soviet mission control at 0605 hr Moscow time:

In accordance with the program of the flight of the international crew, on 11 April at 2154 hr Moscow time the approach of the spacecraft Soyuz 33 to the orbital complex Salyut 6/Soyuz 32 was commenced. During the process of approach there occurred deviations from the regular mode of

operation of the approach correcting propulsion unit of the Soyuz 33
spacecraft and the docking of the craft with the Salyut 6 station was
aborted. The Cosmonauts, Nikolay Rukavishnikov and Georgi Ivanov, be
ban preparations for the return to earth.

Later, Soviet officials revealed that the combustion chamber pressures were
lower than normal during the final engine burn. Although a 6-second burn
was planned, the engine ignited irratically and shut down after only 3
seconds.

Reentry was scheduled for the first opportunity to land in the standard
Soyuz recovery zone the next evening. To avoid stressing the questionable
propulsion engine system no further burns were planned until reentry when
the back-up engine was to be fired. As a result of the low quality of re-
dundancy between the main and back-up engines, the reliability of the emergency engine was also suspect. This dictated that Soyuz 33 would have to
undergo a long, crushing ballistic reentry from their present altitude
rather than a more gentle, guided return from a lower, intermediate altitude. At about 1847 hr on 12 April Rukavishnikov fired the back-up engine
for a period of 213 seconds as the spacecraft passed over the South Atlantic.

As the spacecraft entered the denser layers of the atmosphere the noise
and vibration inside Soyuz 33 rose sharply. The two cosmonauts were pinned
to their couches under the unusual 10-g loads. Touchdown came at 1934 hr
some 320 km SE of Dzhezkazgan. The weary, but happy, cosmonauts climbed
out of their overturned capsule to greet the rescue team.

Meanwhile, the Soyuz 32 cosmonauts still on Salyut 6 had been monitoring the situation. Although elated with the safe return to earth of their
comrades, the failure of Soyuz 33 had ramifications on their own mission.
Following the completion of the planned 7-day stay of Soyuz 33, the Interkosmos crew may have been scheduled to return to earth in the older Soyuz
32 spacecraft, leaving behind their fresher vehicle. With Soyuz spacecraft man-rated for only 90 days, the possibility of a curtailed Soyuz 32
flight now presented itself since an investigation into the Soyuz 33 failure was sure to take longer than a month.

Temporarily unsure of their future, Lyakhov and Ryumin continued with
their experiment-packed flight plan. For the next month the two Soviets
concentrated on a wide variety of undertakings. Photographic sessions
involving land, water, and cloud coverage were held along with further
astrophysical investigations using the BST-1M telescope. Processing of

new compounds in weightless, vacuum environments was continued under a joint Soviet-French experiment. The Yelena gamma-ray telescope was also put to work again from the orbital module of Soyuz 32.

A month and a day after the return of the Soyuz 33 cosmonauts, Progress 6 was launched on yet another unmanned resupply mission to the record-breaking Salyut 6 station. From a 0717 hr Moscow time launch on 13 May, the cargo transport encountered no difficulties before its 0919 hr docking with Salyut 6 two days later. On board Progress 6 were food, mail, new scientific experiments, more replacement parts, and propellants for the Salyut 6 propulsion system.

Cosmonauts Lyakhov and Ryumin maintained their level of activity throughout the rest of the month of May, paying particular attention to their own physical fitness, as Soviet planners decided how to recoup from the Soyuz 33 failure. On 27 May the Soyuz 32 spacecraft marked 91 days in space, the limit of safe operation established by the unmanned Soyuz 20 in 1975-1976. Two days later the orbit of the Soyuz 32/Salyut 6/Progress 6 complex was circularized in a maneuver reminiscent of pre-launch activities prior to a Soyuz launch.

However, on 2 June 1979 Soviet reports hinted that a Soyuz 34 Interkosmos mission involving a Soviet and a Hungarian had been called off. The purpose of the flight was to trade spacecraft with the veteran Soyuz 32 cosmonauts to permit them to complete their 6-month mission. The age of the Soyuz 32 spacecraft and the possibility it might suffer a failure similar to that of Soyuz 33 now made such an effort impossible.[93] At this same time reports were also circulating that Salyut 6, too, was showing signs of its age, and might not continue to support cosmonaut crews much longer.

Cancelling the Interkosmos mission, of course, did not solve the problem of Soyuz 32 itself. If Soyuz 32 was not reliable enough for the Soyuz 34 cosmonauts, it certainly could not be used by Lyakhov and Ryumin either. Thus the two cosmonauts were at least temporarily "stranded" in orbit. The only solution was to send an unmanned Soyuz to Salyut 6 for use by the Soyuz 32 cosmonauts on their return to earth. At the time of the cancellation of the Soyuz 34 Interkosmos mission, an unmanned Soyuz was being prepared (Figures 29 and 30).

Figures 29 and 30   Transport of the Soyuz rocket to the launch pad
(Courtesy of NASA)

The rescue spacecraft was finally launched at 2113 hr Moscow time on 6 June. With the designation of Soyuz 34 it became only the third Soyuz spacecraft to be launched unmanned with a Soyuz program number. From an initial orbit of 270 km by 198 km, Soyuz 34 began the 48-hour trek to the waiting cosmonauts.

When Soyuz 34 was launched, the Progress 6 transport was still attached to Salyut 6. Hence at 1100 hr on 8 June, just twelve hours before the arrival of Soyuz 34, Progress 6 was undocked from the space station's aft port and maneuvered to a standby position nearby. Lyakhov and Ryumin then guided Soyuz 34 through the final rendezvous maneuvers and achieved a successful docking at 2302 hr that day. The now unneeded Progress 6 was brought down from orbit two days later.

The question now was when would the Soyuz 32 cosmonauts return to earth. Since a fresh spacecraft was presently docked at Salyut's aft port, the urgency of their return was greatly diminished. Had they been forced to use the Soyuz 32 spacecraft, an early return was inevitable. Five days after the arrival of Soyuz 34, the unmanned Soyuz 32 spacecraft was undocked from the forward port of Salyut 6 at 1251 hr and guided to a successful recovery on Soviet territory approximately 295 km NW of Dzhezhazgan at 1918 hr Moscow time on 13 June. The safe return of the Soyuz 32 descent module after 108 days in space may now be regarded as the "man-rated" lifetime of future Soyuz spacecraft.

The departure of the Soyuz 32 spacecraft left only one vehicle docked with Salyut 6: Soyuz 34 at the aft port. If Lyakhov and Ryumin were planning to finish out their six-month mission (two more months to go), at least one other Progress mission was likely to be needed. Since propellants can be off-loaded only at the aft port, a switching maneuver similar to that performed by the Soyuz 29 cosmonauts was now necessary.

Thus, on 14 June the Soyuz 32 cosmonauts entered Soyuz 34, secured all the hatches, temporarily undocked from Salyut 6 at 1918 hr and pulled away to a distance of 100 meters. Ground controllers then turned the large space station through 180 degrees so that its forward end was now facing the Soyuz 34 ship. The operation was completed with a firm docking at the Salyut forward port.

After a week of intensive activity the two cosmonauts now settled back into a daily routine of experiments, exercise, and sleep. Two weeks later the final mission to this third Salyut 6 expedition was begun, and with it came another major innovation in space research. At 1225 on 28 June Progress 7 rocketed away from the Baikonur Cosmodrome on its way to Salyut 6. Fifty hours later (at 1418 hr on 30 June) the probe of Progress 7 nudged into the aft port of Salyut 6. For the eleventh time in eighteen months both docking ports on Salyut 6 were occupied.

Progress 7 carried the usual assortment of mail, food, experiments, propellants. Over the next several days the two cosmonauts carefully transferred this special cargo into their home, while trying to maintain their already large list of ongoing experiments and duties. On 8 July in what may be a prelude to a long unmanned period to come, the main engine of Progress 7 was fired to raise the orbit of Salyut 6 to a record 411 km by 399 km. At this altitude several months will pass before additional maneuvers are required as a result of atmospheric drag.

One of the new experiments delivered by Progress 7 was named Isparitel (Vaporizer). This device consisted of an electron beam gun designed to coat mirror surfaces in space. A similar but different mechanism had been tested earlier on Salyut 4. In fact Isparitel was conceived and constructed after Salyut 6 had already been placed in orbit. Placed in a depressurized chamber, Isparitel vaporized a silver sample and then deposited the vapors on a titanium substrate. Thickness from one micron to tenths of a micron are possible by varying the exposure time. A future operational model may weigh only 1.5 kg including its power supply.[94]

Less than a week later Lyakhov and Ryumin became the world's longest space travelers when on 14 July they surpassed the 139 day 14 hour and 48 minute mark set by Kovalenok and Ivanchenkov during the Soyuz 29 flight. No time was allowed for extended celebrations as the cosmonauts labored to prepare the last of their great experiments.

Progress 7 had delivered to the cosmonauts the KRT-10 radio-telescope apparatus. Stowed within the compact forward compartment of Progress 7, the heart of this device was a parabolic, mesh antenna which when deployed would stretch to a maximum diameter of 10 meters--the largest such structure ever erected in space. For several days Lyakhov and Ryumin unpacked the experimental package which consisted of a highly-directional mesh antenna, five radiometers, a time recording device, apparatus for converting and recording received information, a control console, and mechanisms for

erecting and positioning the antenna. Inside Salyut 6 the antenna assembly
resembled a folded umbrella with a diameter of only one-half meter. The
light weight mesh itself (1 m^2 weighed only 0.5 kg) was a tricot fabric of
metal threads only 50 microns in diameter coated with a thin metalic layer.[95]

Finally, with the KRT-10 complex positioned in the aft Salyut docking
port, Progress 7 was slowly pulled away. The latter maneuver came at 0605
hr on 18 July. The spent cargo ship set up station keeping with Salyut 6
in order that its TV camera could be focused on Salyut's aft port during
the deployment operation.[96] Carefully the two Soviet spacemen edged the
antenna beyond the end of the station and proceeded to activate the unfurl-
ing mechanism as ground controllers monitored their efforts via the Progress
7 camera (Figure 31).

The next several days were devoted to calibrating and testing the KRT-10
equipment. At their unique vantage point some 400 km above the earth, typical terrestrial radio interference is minimized. Objects of study included
solar radio emissions, electromagnetic radiation from Cassopeia A, and even
the earth itself. In addition, by using special interferometry techniques

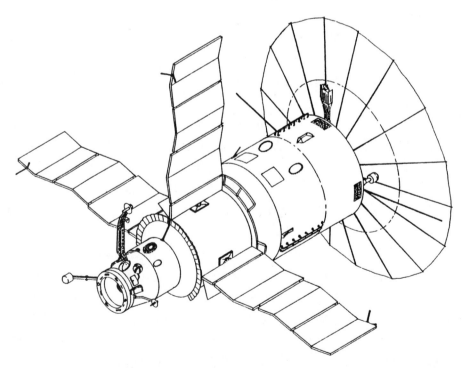

Figure 31   Salyut 6 with the 10-meter KRT-10 radio telescope deployed
             (Drawing by R.F. Gibbons)

in conjunction with the 70 m diameter structure at the Soviet Center for Long Distance Space Communications in the Crimea, an effective very long baseline receiver was established.

As the Soyuz 32 cosmonauts were evaluating the potential of the new radio telescope, they were also making plans for their long awaited return to earth. Exercise periods were extended to at least two hours a day. Medical examinations were becoming more frequent and thorough. Meanwhile, the rest of the experiments still operating on Salyut 6 were being brought to a close. Progress 7 had been destroyed during reentry two days after the KRT-10 deployment.

By 9 August the short experimental program with the ten-meter diameter antenna had been concluded. Since the antenna now blocked the aft docking port no further missions could utilize that area unless the large array was discarded. An attempt on this day to eject the mechanism failed when the fine wire mesh of the antenna became entangled with projections of the Salyut 6 space station itself. The Soviets were now faced with a dilemna. Not only was the aft docking port now useless (perhaps a severe handicap to future missions), but also there was the possibility that the antenna could become even more entangled with the station, curtailing its effectiveness.[97]

Rumors appearing before 9 August indicated that Lyakhov and Ryumin were due to leave Salyut 6 in a matter of days, although Phillip Clark has shown that the Soyuz 32 cosmonauts eventually landed at the first opportunity. The problem with the radio antenna now apparently postponed that return. After great persuasion by the cosmonauts themselves, Soviet mission planners decided to let the two spacemen conduct an EVA in an attempt to free the unwanted structure. In a manner reminiscent of the US attempt to rescue Skylab after its launch, Soviet cosmonauts and engineers worked out the tools and procedures deemed necessary to safely cut the antenna away.

At 1716 hr on 15 August the Soyuz 32 cosmonauts exited Salyut 6 from the EVA hatch at the forward end of the station. Installing special hand holds as they went, the two men carefully made their way to the problem area. Using a pair of wire cutters, Lyakhov and Ryumin were soon able to free the antenna and toss it off into space. While outside the station the two also dismounted portions of structural, optical, polymer, and heat-protective samples and retrieved a section of the micrometeor detector. Within 83 minutes of the start of the EVA, the two heroes were safely back inside Salyut 6.[98]

Having salvaged Salyut 6 for future manned and unmanned missions, Lyakhov and Ryumin finally prepared for their return to earth in earnest. Since the decision had been made to postpone any further flights to Salyut 6 for at least a few months, many of the station's systems had to be deactivated and mothballed. Four days after their space walk both cosmonauts were at least ready to leave their orbiting home.

On 19 August Lyakhov and Ryumin climbed into their Soyuz spacecraft for the last time. A brief maneuver performed while the Soyuz 34 spacecraft was still attached to Salyut 6 had slightly altered the proposed landing site to avoid a region of ditches and ravines. Bidding farewell to the now deserted space station, the two tired spacemen pulled slowly away and began preparations for their retro-burn. By 1730 that day Lyakhov and Ryumin had soft-landed some 170 km SE of Dzhezkazgan after 175 days in space.

Members of the rescue party quickly converged on the Soyuz 34 command module to assist the cosmonauts. As had been the case with the return of the Soyuz 26 and Soyuz 29 cosmonauts, Lyakhov and Ryumin were temporarily incapacitated by the seemingly oppressive force of gravity. The cosmonauts were helped out of their spacecraft and carried to special chairs to lessen the effect of 1 g on vital body systems.

Preliminary evaluations of the readaptation of the Soyuz 32 cosmonauts indicate that conscientious maintenance of regular exercises (two or more hours per day) prevents serious degradation of bodily functions upon return to earth after six months in a zero-g environment. With this valuable information and the now-demonstrated utility of manned orbital stations, the stage has been set for the beginning of continuous manned Salyut operations. In-flight handovers of control of Salyut at six month intervals are now possible, permitting full exploitation of the potential of Salyut space stations.

Over a span of two years Salyut 6 time and again had proved that the same Soviet space technology which had excited the world with the first artificial satellite, the first man in space, and the first soft landing on the moon and on another planet now was capable of instituting continuous manned observations from space. Salyut 6 itself continued to circle the globe every hour and a half, waiting for another crew to house. In training in the Soviet Union are prospective cosmonauts from Cuba and Vietnam with natives of France and India expected soon.

Meanwhile, the thoughts of Soviet space planners and Western specialists shifted to manned space systems of the future.

Publication Note

*In the present state of Soviet manned space flight every volume is out-
dated in part before it is published. While this manuscript was being
set, the USSR initiated the fourth Salyut 6 expedition. The unmanned
Soyuz T-1 was returned to earth on 25 March 1980 after 95 days docked to
Salyut 6. Two days later, Progress 8 was launched, followed on 9 April
with the launch of Soyuz 35 carrying Soviet Cosmonauts Leonid Popov and
Valery Ryumin. Progress 8 was separated from Salyut 6 on 25 April to be
replaced with Progress 9 which docked on 29 April. Progress 9 in turn
was detached on 20 May and was replaced on 27 May by the Soyuz 36 Interkosmos spacecraft carrying Soviet Valeriy Kubasov and Hungarian Bertalan
Farkas. After conducting a number of earth resources experiments, the
Soyuz 36 crew returned to earth on 3 June in the Soyuz 35 spacecraft.
The next day the Soyuz 35 cosmonauts undocked the Soyuz 36 spacecraft
from the Salyut 6 aft port and redocked with the forward port. On 5 June
the first manned flight of the newly modified Soyuz spacecraft was begun
with the launch of Soyuz T-2 carrying Soviet Cosmonauts Yuri Malyshev
and Vladimir Aksenov. After a flight of only four days Soyuz T-2 returned
to earth with its original crew. A recent announcement also indicated
that a Soviet space shuttle project has been abandoned. Cosmonaut Shatalov
indicated that effort has been shifted toward improvements of the Soyuz
spacecraft, e.g., Soyuz T.*

Chapter 15

FUTURE OPERATIONS
OF SOYUZ-SALYUT

The Salyut space stations are the Soviet Union's first attempts to
fulfill the prophecies of K. E. Tsiolkovskiy for the creation of permanent
manned orbital outposts forever circling the earth. Tsiolkovskiy began
descriptions of such space platforms in earnest in 1911 with the publication of *Investigation of Outer Space by Rocket Devices*.

In a 1926 treatise this founder of Soviet rocketry detailed the conquest of interplanetary space in what must now be viewed as a truly pro-
phetic work. His sixteen-point plan included:

1. A rocket airplane with wings and the usual parts of steering is
   arranged. But the petrol engine is changed by an explosion pipe,
   where the explosive substances are pumped in by a weak engine.
   There is no air-screw. There is the reserve of explosive materials
   and space is left for the pilot covered with something transparent
   for protection from the coming wind, since the velocity of such a
   machine is more than that of an airplane. The device, due to the
   reactive action of explosion will roll down on the slides on the
   lubricated rails. After that it is lifted on the air, attains
   the maximum of velocity, loses all the reserve of explosive substances and having become lighter begins to glide similarly to
   the usual or motorless airplane, so as to land on dry land safely.

   The quantity of the explosive substances for the force of explosion
   should be increased bit by bit, as also the maximum velocity, re-
   moteness, and mainly the altitude of flight. In view of the per-
   meability for air the human seat in the airplane in height, of
   course, cannot be more than the known record height: 5 km is sufficient. The aim of these experiments is the skill to steer the
   airplane (at a considerable velocity), by explosion pipe and gliding.

2. The wings of the latest airplanes should be reduced a little, the
   force of the engine and its velocity should be increased. We shall
   have to resort to acquiring preliminary pre-explosion velocity with
   the help of the means mentioned earlier.

3. The body of future airplanes will have to be made gas proof and filled with oxygen, and with devices, absorbing carbon dioxide gas, ammonia and other products of human excretion. The aim is to achieve the desired rarefaction of air. The altitude may exceed much more than 12 km. By reason of high speed, for purposes of safe landing, landing may be made on water. Proofing of the body will not allow the rocket to sink.

4. The rudders mentioned by me and functioning excellently in the vacuum and in very rarefield air, where the rocket flies are used. A wingless airplane duplex or triplex, inflated by oxygen, hermetically sealed, well-gliding is set in motion. For ascent into the air it requires huge initial velocity and, consequently, improvement in fitting for the take-off run. The additional velocity will provide it the possibility to ascend higher and higher. The centrifugal force will make its effect manifest and will decrease the work of motion.

5. The velocity reaches 8 km/sec, the centrifugal force fully neutralizes gravity and the rocket in the beginning goes beyond the limits of the atmosphere. Having flown the distance for which oxygen and food suffice, it returns towards the earth, its path being in the form of a spiral, retarded by air and gliding without explosion.

6. After that it is permissible to employ a simple, undoubled body. Flights beyond the atmosphere are repeated. The reactive devices recede farther and farther from the air jacket of the earth and remain in the ether longer and longer. All the same, they return, since they have a limited supply of food and oxygen.

7. Attempts are made to get rid of carbon dioxide gas and other human excretions with the help of selected well-grown plants, providing at the same time edible substance. Many people are already working on this project though slowly, yet some success is being achieved.

8. Ethereal diving helmets (dresses) are arranged for safe emergence from the rocket into the ether.

9. For getting oxygen and food and cleaning of the rocket air, special space for plants is devised. All this is carried off into the ether by the rockets in complicated form and there it is spread and joined together. Human beings achieved a large measure of independence from the earth, since they will strive for the means of livelihood independently.

10. Extensive settlements are established around the earth.

11. Solar energy will be made use of not only for nourishment and comforts of life, but also for travel in the whole solar system.

12. Colonies will be founded in the girdle of asteroids and other places of the solar system where there are small celestial bodies only.

13. Industry will develop and colonies will multiply unimaginably.

14. Individual (personality of individual human being) and social (socialistic) perfection will be achieved.

15. The population of the solar system will become one hundred thousand million times more than the contemporary earth's population. Limit will be achieved after which new settling in the entire Milky Way will become unavoidable.

16. Extinction of the sun will begin. The remaining population of the solar system will recede from it to other suns, towards the earlier flown-off brethren.[99]

The development of the first jet planes and early manned space flights can be seen in the above scenario. EVA's and the first orbital habitations are described along with the problems of reentry. Even the contruction of still larger orbital platforms is predicted.

Three years later in his *Aims of Astronautics* Tsiolkovskiy expanded his ideas just how such space dwellings might be built. He postulated that future space stations might be cylindrical in nature with a diameter of 3 m and a length as great as 3 km orbiting at an altitude of 1000-2000 km. A station of this type was seen to consist of 300 segments separated by air-tight doors. Each compartment was 10 m long with a volume of 70 m^3. When Salyut 1 finally flew some 42 years later, its living/working compartment would be almost exactly this size.[100]

Strongly influenced by Tsiolkovskiy, the Soviet space program's ideological objective is to colonize eventually the entire solar system. Since the early 1950s when rocket technology suggested that these dreams were indeed possible, Soviet scientists have concentrated on the task of constructing permanent earth orbiting stations from which to mount their assault on outer space. Hundreds of Soviet papers have been published on this subject.[101] In general space stations which will appear during the rest of this century will fall into one of two categories: ground assembly and orbital assembly.

The Salyut space stations have, of course, been of the former classification. Completely outfitted on the ground, these laboratories are launched unmanned into space in one piece. Soyuz and Progress spacecraft are then flown to the waiting Salyuts to complete individual programs. The present size of Salyut limits the number of crew members to about four cosmonauts. An enlarged 25-ton Salyut (as discussed in the previous section) might increase this capacity to 6 to 8 cosmonauts.

Orbital assembly of space platforms represents the next step in the USSR man-in-space program. Initially these complexes can be assumed to consist of one or more Salyut stations arranged in various configurations. Some of the suggested forms include:

1. <u>One Salyut vehicle and multi-docking module</u>. With the multiple docking compartment attached to the forward end of Salyut, up to five Soyuz spacecraft could rendezvous and dock with the station. Each of the five Soyuz orbital modules could be specially designed to carry out different experiments. In all, a crew of ten cosmonauts could work together (albeit crowdedly) in the 12 interconnected compartments. Perhaps a more logical development would be a process whereby each succeeding Soyuz mission (up to 4) would leave behind its orbital module. Thus a three or four man station with several specialized research compartments could be constructed in a relatively short period of time (Figure 32).

2. <u>Two Salyut space stations</u>. These may be mated directly front to front or there may be a docking adapter joined between them to allow for Soyuz dockings in the center of the complex (see diagram of previous section). If the former concept is adopted two Soyuz or a Soyuz and a Progress could dock at the aft end of the stations. Such a configuration would weigh over 51,000 kg and stretch 46 meters in length. With a central docking adapter, up to six Soyuz-type spacecraft could be accommodated, bringing the total habitable volume of the outpost to 236 m^3.

3. <u>Three Salyut stations and one central docking module</u>. In the first attempt to construct a roughly wheel-like space structure, three Salyut space stations could be docked like spokes at 120-degree intervals to a large central hub (Figure 33). The complex would closely approximate a 36-m diameter circular assemblage. Three docking ports at the aft end of the stations plus one or more at the hub could accommodate a fleet of manned and unmanned spacecraft. This type of system may also include solar panels stretched from the aft end of each Salyut to the other two Salyuts, giving an even greater illusion of a wheel. An assembled space station of this type (excluding ferry spacecraft) might weigh over 60,000 kg and furnish more than 300 m^3 for living and working.

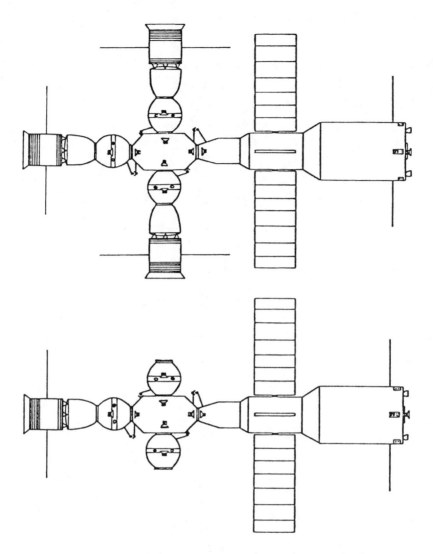

Figure 32   Three Soyuz spacecraft docked to Salyut 6--type space station
equipped with special multiple docking adapter (upper). After
crews of two Soyuz spacecraft have returned to earth the discarded orbital modules are left behind to serve as additional
experimental compartments.

Eventually, a true toroidal space station will probably be constructed.
Most of the volume of the station will lie on the periphery of the wheel
and not along the spokes as in case (3) above. A station of this type will
require extensive in-space construction and will take years to complete.
One Soviet design foresees a 12- to 16-sided rim connected to the station
hub by 6 to 8 spokes. The rim compartments would be used for control of
the complex, eating, and resting. Artificial gravity could be created in

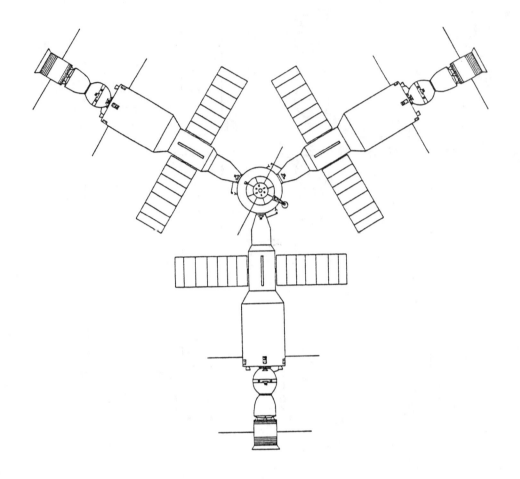

Figure 33   Speculative drawing of three Salyut space stations
             joined to a central hub

this region by rotating the entire station about the hub. The spoke areas
would house the life-support equipment, scientific instruments, experiments,
and maneuvering fuel. The hub would serve as the docking and transfer module of the station for visiting cargo and personnel spacecraft.

    In order to efficiently utilize any space station a reusable earth-to-
orbit-to-earth vehicle must be implemented for the transfer of crews and
cargos. For many years the Soviets have discussed the need and advantages
of such a "spaceplane", but until recently there has never been a verification that a reusable shuttle was in fact under development in the USSR.[102]

    In a 1974 Soviet publication the significance of the problem was pointed
out by noting that, "development of orbital space laboratories is closely

connected with the task of creating multiple-use transport systems".[103]
Since that time, Soviet scientists have discussed the existence of a Soviet
shuttle more openly until finally in 1978 several reports verified the development of such a vehicle for operation in the 1980s.

Several designs for a Soviet shuttle have appeared over the past several
years. Most are based on a two-stage delta-winged totally reusable vehicle.
The first stage will carry the orbiter to a high altitude (~30 km) and then
return to earth while the second stage continues on into space. An interim
system using an upper stage reusable orbiter and a throw-away rocket launcher
may be inaugurated while testing continues with the TU-144 style fly-back
launcher.

An integral part of a complete Salyut/Shuttle system is a space tug
capable of moving large modules into position during the creation of a
permanent space station (Figure 34). Whether the task is to move the
components first to a high earth orbit or merely to nudge them together
for mating, a cosmic taxi, either manned or unmanned, would prove invaluable.

What physical evidence, then, is there that the USSR is currently pur-
suing a space program of this magnitude? In December 1976 and again in
1978 and 1979 the Soviet Union conducted what is believed by many to be
the first flight tests of shuttle hardware. On these occasions a Proton
launch vehicle inserted dual probes (Kosmos 881/882, Kosmos 997/998, and
Kosmos 1101/1102) into a single revolution about the earth before reentry
and recovery were completed. In the latest test the second probe may have
completed two revolutions before returning to earth. These missions may
be related to separation and recovery tests of a two-stage reusable shuttle vehicle.[104]

Finally in July 1977 came the puzzling Kosmos 929. The Proton-launched
spacecraft maneuvered extensively in space and exhibited characteristics
which have led many to believe that this was a test of a space-tug system.
On the other hand, the satellite appeared to be a dual-natured vehicle and
hence may be related to Kosmos 881/882, 997/998, and 1101/1102. These four
missions were all launched into relatively low earth orbits inclined at
about 51.6 degrees to the equator--a further indication of their man-related nature.[105]

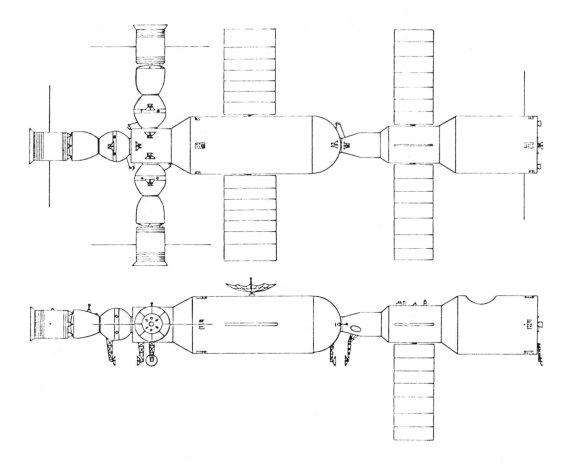

Figure 34   Possible future configuration of a Salyut space station
with specialized working module and multiple docking ports

There have also been a number of Soyuz-class vehicles flown since 1974
whose missions have yet to be determined.   These include Kosmos 670, 772,
869, 1001, and 1074.   The suggestion has been made that one or more of
these spacecraft were directly related to the new shuttle/space station
programs.   Perhaps one or more involved the long-awaited redesign of Soyuz
again to accommodate a three-man crew.

Due to the lack of solid evidence surrounding these programs this section has only been able to touch briefly on the possible future road of
the Soviet man-in-space program.   Although time lines are very fragile
depending as they do on thousands of technological achievements, the eventual role which the USSR will play in space is in no doubt.   The Soviets
have made it well-known that the space stations will be built and from
there cosmonauts will travel to the moon and beyond.

REFERENCES AND NOTES - SECTION V

1. Bumshtein, S.I., *Salyut Space Station in Orbit,* p. 38; Boriesenko, I.G., *Space Launches and Finishes,* p. 48.

2. Bumshtein, S.I., *ibid.,* Borisenko, I.G., *op. cit.,* p. 49.

3. Bumshtein, S.I., *op. cit.,* p. 39.

4. Borisenko, I.G., *op. cit.,* p. 48.

5. Bumshtein, S.I., *op. cit.,* p. 27; *Russian Report to COSPAR (15th) Session Held in Madrid Spain in 1971,* p. 69.

6. *Journal of the British Astronomical Association,* Dec. 1975, pp. 57-59 and Dec. 1973, pp. 34-35. See also his latest methods in *Spaceflight,* June 1979, pp. 259-263.

7. *Spaceflight,* Sep.-Oct. 1978, p. 358.

8. *Space World,* May 1974, pp. 12-13.

9. See the following for a sample of the continuing debate of the Soyuz 11 crew composition: *Space World,* Feb. 1978, p. 42; *Spaceflight,* June 1976, p. 236; Nov. 1976, p. 414; Dec. 1976, pp. 450, 452; Jan. 1978, p. 40; Feb. 1978, pp. 79-80; July 1978, p. 229; Sep.-Oct. 1978, p. 358.

10. A third possibility is that the Soyuz 11 crew were originally trained as back-ups for Soyuz 11, but assumed the prime status when one of the primary crew became ill.

11. Bumshtein, S.I., *op. cit.,* pp. 101-102.

12. Bumshtein, S.I., *op. cit.,* pp. 102-104.

13. Bumshtein, S.I., *op. cit.,* pp. 39, 104; Borisenko, I.G., *op. cit.,* p. 51.

14. Bumshtein, S.I., *op. cit.,* pp. 105-107.

15. See *Soviet Space Programs, 1971-1975,* pp. 192-193 and Bumshtein, S.I., *op. cit.,* pp. 105-144 for day by day accounts of cosmonaut activities Also see Dmitriyev, A.Yu., *From Spaceships to Orbiting Stations,* pp. 97-100; Borisenko, I.G., *op. cit.,* pp. 52-53; *Russian Report to COSPAR (15th) Session Held in Madrid, Spain in 1971,* pp. 66-87.

16. Bumshtein, S.I., *op. cit.,* pp. 143-144; Borisenko, I.G., *op. cit.,* p. 53.

17. *Spaceflight,* Jan. 1976, pp. 38-39; *Soviet Space Programs, 1971-1975* p. 194.

18. The utter failures of Salyut 2 and Kosmos 557 in April and May of 1973 had undoubtably postponed the Soyuz 12 mission. See previous section.

19. *Pravda,* 6 July 1974; Sagdeyev, R.Z., ed., *The Conquest of Outer Space in the USSR 1974,* pp. 128-140; Borisenko, I.G., *op. cit.,* p. 60.

20. See preceding section.

21. Borisenko, I.G., *ibid.*

22. *Space Research Conducted in the USSR in 1974, COSPAR Report,* p. 78.

23. Sagdeyev, R.Z., ed., *op. cit.,* pp. 128-223.

24. *Jane's All the World's Aircraft, 1975-1976,* p. 676; Sagdeyev, R.Z., ed., *op. cit.,* pp. 149-151; Borisenko, I.G., *op. cit.,* pp. 59-63; *Space Research Conducted in the USSR in 1974,* pp. 74-78, 81-83; *Aviation Week and Space Technology,* 15 July 1974, pp. 292-293 and 22 July 1974, p. 15.

25. Sagdeyev, R.Z., ed., *op. cit.,* pp. 164, 168, 179-180.

26. *Aviation Week and Space Technology,* 29 July 1974, p. 11.

27. Sagdeyev, R.Z., ed., *op. cit.,* pp. 223-227.

28. Sagdeyev, R.Z., ed., *op. cit.,* p. 231.

29. Sagdeyev, R.Z., ed., *op. cit.,* pp. 232-234.

30. Sagdeyev, R.Z., ed., *op. cit.,* pp. 231-234.

31. Gatland, Kenneth, *Manned Spacecraft,* pp. 242-243; Turnill, Reginald, *The Observer's Spaceflight Directory,* pp. 303-304; *Soviet Space Programs, 1971-1975,* p. 204.

32. See also *Aviation Week and Space Technology,* 2 Sep. 1974, 16 Sep. 1974, and 24 Nov. 1975; *Jane's All the World's Aircraft, 1975-1976* p. 676.

33. It is interesting to note that Sarafanov was one of the youngest cosmonauts to fly. To have been named commander of a Soyuz mission would indicate a bright future. A precedent for a return to space after a failure has been recently set by both members of the Soyuz 25 crew. Kovalenok and Ryumin failed in their attempt to be the first cosmonauts

aboard Salyut 6 in 1977, but a year later Kovalenok returned to command the record breaking Soyuz 29 flight and in 1979 Ryumin flew again on Soyuz 32. The difference may lie in their responsibilities for their respective Soyuz failures.

34. See the subsequent failures of Soyuz 23 and 25.

35. See the previous section.

36. It has been suggested *(Astronauts and Cosmonauts Biographical and Statistical Data,* 1977 and *Spaceview)* that Gubarev and Grechko were the back-up crew for Soyuz 12. If this is true, it would support the notion that Kosmos 557 was originally scheduled to be a civilian Salyut visited by Soyuz 12 cosmonauts Lazarev and Makarov.

37. Details of Soyuz 17/Salyut 4 can be found in *Soviet Space Programs, 1971-1975,* pp. 208-211; Turnill, Reginald, *op. cit.,* pp. 305-307; Gatland, Kenneth, *op. cit.,* pp. 244-246; *Aviation Week and Space Technology,* 27 Jan. 1975, pp. 18-19 and 3 Feb. 1975, pp. 19-20; *Spaceflight,* Apr. and June 1975; *Space World,* Nov. 1976.

38. Feoktistov, K.P., *The Salyut-4 Space Laboratory,* pp. 10-11; *Spaceflight,* June 1975, pp. 223-225; *Aviation Week and Space Technology,* 30 June 1975, pp. 22-23; Turnill, Reginald, *op. cit.,* pp. 306-307; *Soviet Space Programs, 1971-1975,* pp. 210-211.

39. Feoktistov, K.P., *op. cit.,* pp. 13-14; *Spaceflight,* June 1975, pp. 222-223; *Soviet Space Programs, 1971-1975,* p. 210.

40. Feoktistov, K.P., *op. cit.,* p. 6; *Spaceflight,* June 1975, p. 225; *Soviet Space Programs, 1971-1975,* pp. 209-210.

41. *Spaceflight,* June 1975, p. 225; Turnill, Reginald, *op. cit.,* p. 306.

42. *Spaceflight,* June 1975, p. 201.

43. *Aviation Week and Space Technology,* 2 June 1975, pp. 25-26.

44. Ponomarev, A.N., *The Years of the Space Era,* p. 43.

45. Turnill, Reginald, *op. cit.,* pp. 307-308; *Aviation Week and Space Technology,* 14 Apr. 1975, pp. 14-15 and 12 May 1975, p. 21; *Space World,* Nov. 1976, pp. 22-24; *Spaceflight,* July 1975, pp. 252-254.

46. For a description of the entire Soyuz 18B mission see: *Soviet Space Programs, 1971-1975,* pp. 212-213; *Spaceflight,* Jan. 1976, pp. 13-18; *Space World,* Nov. 1976, pp. 24-29; Turnill, Reginald, *op. cit.,* pp. 308-310; *Aviation Week and Space Technology,* 5 July 1976, pp. 49-54 along with several articles appearing during the flight.

47. *Spaceflight,* Feb. 1977, pp. 64, 80 and Mar. 1976, pp. 95, 98; *Aviation Week and Space Technology,* 24 Nov. 1975, p. 21.

48. Kosmos 772 is sometimes thought to have been involved in the testing of these systems (*Space World,* Nov. 1976, p. 28; *Spaceflight,* Mar. 1976, p. 95).

49. An interesting yet questionable scenario for similar operations involving the second-generation, single-ported Salyuts can be found in *Spaceflight,* Mar. 1976, pp. 98, 115-116.

50. See the Salyut section of this book.

51. *Aviation Week and Space Technology,* 21 June 1976, pp. 23-24 and 25 Oct. 1976, p. 9; *Science News,* 17 July 1976, p. 39.

52. See *Spaceflight,* Jan. 1977, pp. 5-6 and Apr. 1977, pp. 138-144 and Turnill, Reginald, *op. cit.,* pp. 311-313, for a summary of Soyuz 21 operations. See also *Aviation Week and Space Technology* 1976 issues: 12 July, 19 July, 26 July, 9 Aug., 23 Aug., 30 Aug., and 18 Oct.

53. *Aviation Week and Space Technology,* 19 July 1976; Turnill, Reginald, *op. cit.,* p. 313.

54. *Science News,* 28 Aug. 1976, p. 134 and 19 Feb. 1977, p. 117; *Aviation Week and Space Technology,* 18 Oct. 1976, p. 13 and 25 Oct. 1976, p. 23.

55. The following provide adequate summaries of the flight of Soyuz 23: *Spaceflight,* Apr. 1977, pp. 144-145; Turnill, Reginald, *op. cit.,* p. 314; *Aviation Week and Space Technology,* 25 Oct. 1976, pp. 23-24.

56. *Aviation Week and Space Technology,* 21 June 1976, p. 23.

57. See *Spaceflight,* May 1977, pp. 161, 196, 198 and July-Aug. 1977, pp. 266-268; *Aviation Week and Space Technology,* 14 Feb. 1977 and 7 Mar. 1977.

58. The Salyut 6 space station is described elsewhere in this book.

59. *Spaceflight,* Dec. 1977, p. 418; Feb. 1978, p. 52; Mar. 1978, pp. 118-120; *Aviation Week and Space Technology,* 17 Oct. 1977, pp. 25-26.

60. *Spaceflight,* Feb. 1978, p. 49; *Aviation Week and Space Technology,* 19 Dec. 1977.

61. *Flight International,* 31 Dec. 1977, p. 1900; *Science News,* 17 Dec. 1977, p. 406; *Aviation Week and Space Technology,* 19 Dec. 1977.

62. *Flight International, ibid; Spaceflight,* Mar. 1978, pp. 108-109; *Aviation Week and Space Technology,* 2 Jan. 1978, pp. 20-21.

63. For more on this and other new systems see: *Spaceflight,* June 1978, pp. 229-233; Mar. 1979, pp. 110-112; Apr. 1979, pp. 178-183;

Space World, May 1978, pp. 29-30; *Flight International,* 7 Jan. 1978, p. 16; *L-5 News,* Apr. 1978, pp. 9-11; *Aviation Week and Space Technology,* 16 Jan. 1978, pp. 20-23, 9 Jan. 1978, p. 25. See also succeeding references.

64. An alternate maneuver (and a simpler one) would have been for Soyuz 26 to undock with the aft port and redock with the forward port. This type of procedure was carried out during the Soyuz 29/Soyuz 31 mission.

65. *Flight International,* 21 Jan. 1978, p. 196 and 28 Jan. 1978, p. 255; *Aviation Week and Space Technology,* 16 Jan. 1978, pp. 20-21 and 23 Jan. 1978, p. 19.

66. Construction of the Progress vehicle is described in the preceding section.

67. *Flight International,* 4 Feb. 1978, p. 289 and 11 Mar. 1978, p. 715; *Spaceflight,* Nov. 1978, pp. 373-376.

68. *Flight International,* 8 Apr. 1978, pp. 996-997; *Spaceflight,* Nov. 1978, pp. 376-378; *Aviation Week and Space Technology,* 6 Feb. 1978. 13 Feb. 1978, and 20 Feb. 1978.

69. *Spaceflight,* May 1978, p. 186 and Feb. 1979, pp. 56-57; *Aviation Week and Space Technology,* 27 Feb. 1978, p. 21.

70. *Spaceflight,* May 1978, p. 191 and Dec. 1978, pp. 430-434; *Aviation Week and Space Technology,* 20 Mar. 1978, p. 15.

71. *Spaceflight,* Aug. 1978, pp. 294-295.

72. See *Aviation Week and Space Technology,* 26 June 1978, p. 24; *Spaceflight,* Sep.-Oct. 1978, pp. 321, 339; Dec. 1978, pp. 421-422; Mar. 1979, pp. 127-133; May 1979, pp. 216-222; July 1979, pp. 318-324; Aug.-Sep. 1979, pp. 359-363.

73. *Spaceflight,* Sep.-Oct. 1978, p. 339; *Aviation Week and Space Technology,* 3 July 1978, p. 25 and 10 July 1978, p. 17.

74. *Space World,* Oct. 1978, p. 31; *Aviation Week and Space Technology,* 17 July 1978, p. 19.

75. *Spaceflight,* Nov. 1978, pp. 361-362; *Aviation Week and Space Technology,* 17 July 1978, p. 19; 31 July 1978, p. 23; 7 Aug. 1978, p. 21.

76. *Flight International,* 26 Aug. 1978, pp. 643-644; *Spaceflight,* Nov. 1978, p. 395; *Aviation Week and Space Technology,* 14 Aug. 1978, p. 21 and 21 Aug. 1978, p. 18.

77. *Spaceflight,* Dec. 1978, pp. 401-402; *Aviation Week and Space Technology,* 4 Sep. 1978, p. 27 and 18 Sep. 1978.

78. *Aviation Week and Space Technology,* 18 Sep. 1978.

79. *Aviation Week and Space Technology,* 25 Sep. 1978, pp. 13-14.

80. *Spaceflight,* Dec. 1978, p. 402; *Aviation Week and Space Technology,* 25 Sep. 1978, p. 14 and 9 Oct. 1978, p. 55.

81. *Aviation Week and Space Technology,* 16 Oct. 1978, p. 22.

82. *Aviation Week and Space Technology,* 16 Oct. 1978, p. 22 and 23 Oct. 1978, p. 18.

83. *Aviation Week and Space Technology,* 30 Oct. 1978, p. 19.

84. *Aviation Week and Space Technology,* 6 Nov. 1978, p. 21 and 13 Nov. 1978, p. 21.

85. *Aviation Week and Space Technology,* 22 Jan. 1979, p. 17.

86. *Aviation Week and Space Technolgoy,* 12 Mar 1979, p. 211.

87. *Aviation Week and Space Technology,* 12 Mar. 1979, p. 213 and 19 Mar. 1979, p. 33.

88. *Spaceflight,* June 1979, p. 242; *Aviation Week and Space Technology,* 19 Mar. 1979, p. 33; 26 Mar. 1979, p. 20; 2 Apr. 1979, p. 20.

89. *Spaceflight,* July 1979, p. 289; *Aviation Week and Space Technology,* 26 Mar. 1979, p. 20.

90. *Aviation Week and Space Technology,* 16 Apr. 1979, p. 20.

91. *Spaceflight,* July 1979, p. 290; *Aviation Week and Space Technology,* 2 Apr. 1979, pp. 19-20 and 9 Apr. 1979, p. 21.

92. *Aviation Week and Space Technology,* 16 Apr. 1979, p. 20; 23 Apr. 1979, pp. 22-23; 13 Aug. 1979, p. 21.

93. *Spaceflight,* Oct. 1979, p. 386; *Aviation Week and Space Technology,* 11 June 1979, p. 41.

94. *Sotsialisticheskaya industriya,* 3 Aug. 1979, p. 1.

95. *Pravda,* 11 Aug. 1979, p. 3.

96. *Aviation Week and Space Technology,* 13 Aug. 1979, pp. 21, 54-55.

97. *Soviet Aerospace,* 20 Aug. 1979, pp. 126-127, 128; *Aviation Week and Space Technology,* 20 Aug. 1979, p. 20 and 27 Aug. 1979, pp. 21-22.

98. *Sovetskaya Rossiya,* 16 Aug. 1979, p. 1.

99. Tsiolkovskiy, K.E., *Study of Outer Space by Reaction Devices*, pp. 433-437.

100. Tsiolkovskiy, K.E., *op. cit.*, pp. 551-557.

101. See Wukelic, G.E., ed., *Handbook of Soviet Space-Science Research*, pp. 473-486; Sykes, M.W., *Selected Bibliography on Manned Orbital Space Stations;* Dmitriyev, A.Yu., *op. cit.*, pp. 105-118; *Spaceflight*, Aug. 1969, p. 264 and Aug. 1978, p. 295; Sagdeyev, R.Z., ed., *op. cit.*, pp. 118-126; *Soviet Space Programs, 1966-1970*, pp. 319-321, 359-384; *Soviet Space Programs, 1971-1975*, pp. 501-502, 525-552; *Aviation Week and Space Technology*, 9 Oct. 1978, p. 55; *Soviet Aerospace*, 1 Nov. 1976, p. 5.

102. *Flug Revue*, Jan. 1977, pp. 17-19, *Air Press*, 9 Oct. 1976, p. 1053; *Flight International*, 4 June 1977, p. 1667; *Spaceflight*, June 1977, p. 211; Aug. 1978, p. 320; Sept.-Oct. 1978, pp. 322-326; *Aviation Week and Space Technology*, 20 Mar. 1978, pp. 14-15; 16 Oct. 1978, p. 25; 6 Nov. 1978, p. 19; 9 Apr. 1979, p. 21.

     The above represent recent reports. For older predictions see: James, Peter N., *Soviet Conquest from Space*, pp. 125-153; Ponomarev, A.N., *op. cit.*, pp. 351-387; *Spaceflight*, Feb. 1972, p. 67; *Aviation Week and Space Technology*, 22 Apr. 1974, pp. 20-21; *Soviet Space Programs, 1966-1970*, p. 364; *Soviet Space Programs, 1971-1975*, pp. 486, 527, 542, 546.

103. Ponomarev, A.N., *op. cit.*, p. 258.

104. *L-5 News*, May 1978, pp. 7-8; *Spaceflight*, Jan. 1978, p. 38 and May 1978, pp. 197-198; *Soviet Aerospace*, 28 May 1979, p. 30.

105. *L-5 News*, Mar. 1978, p. 12; *Spaceflight*, Feb. 1978, p. 77; May 1978, p. 197; July 1978, p. 280; Sep.Oct. 1978, pp. 353-55; Jan. 1979, p. 2.

Appendix I

SOVIET SPACE LAUNCH VEHICLES

Appendix I

SOVIET SPACE LAUNCH VEHICLES

Since the launch of the simple Sputnik 1 atop a Soviet ICBM in 1957, a wide variety of rockets has been employed for the many diverse missions of the Soviet civilian and military space programs. Until 1965, all Soviet spacecraft were launched by military missile derivatives, prompting the USSR to withhold details concerning the configuration and performance statistics of the launchers. This led to several speculative drawings of the vehicles by Western analysts relying largely on the experience of the United States orbital programs. When the Sputnik booster was finally unveiled in 1967, the futility of this exercise was readily apparent. Soviet rocket designs differed radically from the track followed by Western nations. Details of the older launch vehicles have slowly been made public, although a full photograph of the largest Soviet booster (in use since 1965) did not appear until the end of 1984 (Fig. 1).

Due to the sparsity of information in the early years of the Space Age, different classification systems arose to describe the capabilities of these launch vehicles as evidenced by their satellite payloads and military potential. Finally, in 1968 Dr. Charles S. Sheldon II published an identification system for Soviet launchers in an article for the 1968-1969 Winter TRW Space Log.[1] This system is now widely recognized and utilized by many Western civilian analysts. Unfortunately, the unknown nature of the later Soviet launch vehicles and differentiation between payload and rocket stages have resulted in minor variations of the Sheldon system by its users. A simplified version used throughout this volume is outlined here.[2]

Sheldon assigned letter designators (A, B, C, etc.) to the different basic launch vehicles while reserving numbers (1, 2, etc.) for the upper orbital stages. Lower case letters could also be added to indicate final stages of specialized purposes, e.g., Earth escape capabilities (e),

393

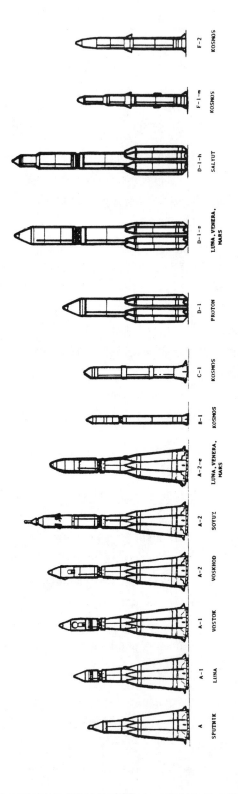

Figure 1   The arsenal of Soviet space launch vehicles

maneuverability (m), or reentry (r). The following sections review the major Soviet space launch vehicle variants which flew between 1957 and 1980.

A-CLASS VEHICLE

The oldest and still most widely used Soviet space rocket, the A-class launch vehicles were successfully used on over 800 orbital missions by the end of 1980. These missions spanned the entire spectrum of Earth orbital and deep space objectives, including the first artificial Earth satellite, the first lunar, Mars, and Venus robot explorers, and every manned Soviet space flight as well as communications, weather, reconnaissance, and scientific satellites.

The specifications of the A-class vehicle (and subsequent Soviet launchers) can be found in Tables I and II of this Appendix. This basic first generation ICBM was drafted into service in 1957 and 1958 to orbit Sputniks 1-3. However, the A launcher (as this configuration was subsequently designated) merely represented a preliminary attempt to investigate the problems and consequences of orbital space flight. Additional upper stages were already under development to increase the payload capability and versatility of the A-class family to include sophisticated unmanned Earth satellites, manned spacecraft, and interplanetary explorers. By January 1959 the first A-class upper stage was completed and had successfully propelled Luna 1 on its historic voyage to the moon and beyond.

The direct ascent trajectories followed by Lunas 1-3 to the moon were limited and did not fully utilize the potential lifting ability of the A-class launcher. The technique used to launch all Soviet lunar and planetary probes since Luna 3 has involved the placing of the automated spacecraft in orbit about the Earth still attached to a special escape stage. Then after a partial revolution about the Earth, the escape stage fires, hurling the automated probe to its destination. Unfortunately, some developmental problems arose with this final escape stage, resulting in the stranding of many of the early planetary and lunar probes in Earth orbit. Here they faced an early death when their "temporary" orbits soon decayed, destroying the spacecraft upon reentry into the Earth's atmosphere.

Table IA SOVIET ROCKET ENGINES (1957-1980)

Name	Propellants	Configuration	Thrust (tons)	I_{sp} (m/s)	Chamber Pressure (atm)	Launch Vehicle Usage
RO-7	Kerosene/LOX	1 main nozzle 4 vernier nozzles	5.6	3195	?	A-class upper stage (Vostok)
RD-107	Kerosene/LOX	4 main nozzles 2 vernier nozzles	102	3077	60	A-class 1st stage strap-on
RD-108	Kerosene/LOX	4 main nozzles 4 vernier nozzles	96	3087	52	A-class 1st stage core
RD-461	Kerosene/LOX	4 main nozzles	30	3234	?	A-class upper stage (Soyuz)
RD-111	Kerosene/LOX	4 main nozzles (gimballed)	166	3107	80	1st stage of unknown booster
RD-119	UDMH/LOX	1 main nozzle 4 vernier nozzles	11	3450	80	B-class 2nd stage
RD-214	Kerosene/ Nitric Acid	4 main nozzles	74	2587	45	B-class 1st stage
RD-216	UDMH/Nitric Acid	2 main nozzles	176	2860	74	C-class 1st stage
RD-219	UDMH/Nitric Acid	2 main nozzles	90	2871	75	F-class 2nd stage
RD-253	UDMH/N_2O_4	1 main nozzle	167	3100	150	D-class 1st stage
--	Kerosene/LOX	1 main nozzle	8.7	3430	?	D-class escape stage

LOX: Liquid Oxygen

UDMH: Unsymmetrical Dimethylhydrazine

Table IB SOVIET MANNED SPACECRAFT PROPULSION SYSTEMS (1957-1980)

Spacecraft	Year Introduced	Thrust (kg)	I_{sp} (m/s)	Propellants	Chamber Pressure (atm)	Type of Propellant Feed	Engine Starts	Number of Nozzles
Vostok/Voskhod	1960	1614	2610	Amine-based/ Nitrous Oxide	57	Pump	1 ?	1
Soyuz/Salyut (civilian)	1966	417 (main) 411 (backup)	2770	UDMH/Nitric Acid	40	Pump	Multiple	1 (main) 2 (backup)
Salyut 6	1977	600	?	UDMH/N_2O_4	?	Pressure	Multiple	2
Soyuz T	1978	300	?	UDMH/N_2O_4	?	Pressure	Multiple	1 ?

Table II SOVIET SPACE LAUNCHERS (1957-1980)

Designator	Launch Facilities	Payload Capacity (kg)	First Year in Operation	Major Payloads Carried
A-Class Vehicles (Based on SS-6, Sapwood ICBM)				
A	TT	1500 to Earth orbit	1957	Sputniks 1-3
A-1	TT, PL	5000 to Earth orbit 400 to Moon	1959	Vostok, 1st generations Lunas, Meteor (weather), Kosmos (reconnaissance, elint)
A-2	TT, PL	7500 to Earth orbit	1963	Voskhod, Soyuz, Progress, Kosmos (reconnaissance)
A-2-e	TT, PL	7500 to Earth orbit 1800 to Moon 1200 to Venus, Mars	1961	2nd generation Lunas, 1st generation planetary probes, Molniya (communications), Kosmos (early warning, communications)
B-Class Vehicles (Based on SS-4, Sandal IRBM)				
B-1	PL, KY	450 to Earth orbit	1962	Kosmos (weather, military), Interkosmos (scientific)
C-Class Vehicles (Based on SS-5, Skean LRBM)				
C-1	TT, PL, KY	1700 to Earth orbit	1964	Kosmos (scientific, navigation, communications, elint, satellite killer targets)
D-Class Vehicles (Not related to operational military missile)				
D-1	TT	12200 to Earth orbit	1965	Proton 1-3
D-1-e	TT	21000 to Earth orbit 6000 to Moon 5000 to Venus, Mars	1967	Zond 4-8, 3rd generation Lunas, 2nd generation planetary probes, geosynchronous satellites
D-1-h	TT	21000 to Earth orbit	1968	Salyut, Kosmos (space station module)
F-Class Vehicles (Based on SS-9, Scarp ICBM)				
F-1-m/r	TT	4000 to Earth orbit	1966	Kosmos (ocean surveillance, anti-satellites, fractional orbit bombardment system — FOBS)
F-2	PL	5500 to Earth orbit	1977	Kosmos (elint, oceanographic)
G-Class Vehicles (never flown successfully; non-military derivative)				
G-1	TT	100,000 - 135,000 to Earth orbit	-	Space station components
G-1-e	TT	100,000 - 135,000 to Earth orbit 45,000 to Moon	-	Manned lunar spacecraft

TT: Tyuratam   PL: Plesetsk   KY: Kapustin Yar

397

While the new deep-space escape stage was undergoing development in the late 1950's and very early 1960's, a new improved upper stage was also being designed to replace the smaller, less powerful stage used by Luna 1-3 and the Vostok spacecraft. Whereas the older A-1 launcher could orbit a 5000 kg payload, the new A-2 launcher was able to lift 7500 kg into a low Earth orbit. This latter launch vehicle has been used by all the manned Voskhod and Soyuz flights as well as a multitude of civilian and military unmanned satellites.

After service careers of nearly 30 years, the A-1, A-2, and the A-2-e are still the mainstay of the Soviet space program and account for more than half of all annual space flights from the USSR.

B-CLASS VEHICLE

The Soviet Union's second launch vehicle did not make its debut until 1962. The introduction of the B-1 launcher not only signaled a growing flexibility of the Soviet space program, but its first flight inaugurated the Kapustin Yar launch complex and the multi-faceted Kosmos series. The endurance of the A-class launch vehicle for orbiting payloads in the 2000-7000 kg range attests to its efficiency both economically and functionally. However, many scientific and militarily oriented spacecraft in the 1960's weighed much less than 2000 kg. Thus, a smaller and more economical rocket was needed to accommodate the requirements of these payloads.

This simple two-stage rocket was successful in 144 orbital launches during its 16-year service life (1962-1977) with payloads of up to 450 kg. Initially flown only from the launch facilities at Kapustin Yar, the B-1 appeared at Plesetsk a year after this new cosmodrome was opened. After 1973, all B-1 launches were exclusively from Plesetsk.

In its early days the B-1 launcher was largely devoted to scientific spacecraft in the Kosmos series. Later, when the international Interkosmos program was begun, the B-1 was responsible for orbiting seven of the first nine of these probes. Although the B-1 supported some military spacecraft from Kapustin Yar, after the move to Plesetsk the duties of this rocket were almost solely of a military nature.

No variation of the B-class vehicle from the original B-1 design was flown. Although not a heavily used rocket (in only four years were there more than a dozen flights), the B-1 appears to have found favor in its simplicity, reliability, and expense. The last flight of the B-1 in 1977 marked the first (and as of 1988 only) retirement of any Soviet launch vehicle class since the Space Age began.

C-CLASS VEHICLE

The third Soviet space launcher was designed to fill the void between the small-capacity B-class vehicle and the much larger A-class vehicle. About the same height as the B-1, the C-1 launcher was roughly twice the diameter and could lift spacecraft weighing up to 1700 kg into low Earth orbit. In accordance with the philosophies of the A- and the B-class launchers, the design of the C-1 was based on an existing, nuclear-tipped military missile, the SS-5 Skean LRBM.

The C-class space rocket is the second most used launch vehicle and is the only launch vehicle to have been flown from all three Soviet cosmodromes. A wide variety of payloads has been carried by the C-1, including civilian scientific spacecraft (Kosmos and Interkosmos), navigational satellites, electronic intelligence (elint) gathering satellites, and on occasion target vehicles for the testing of the Soviet satellite killer system.

Like the B-class launcher, the C-class launcher is a simple two-stage rocket and has only been seen in the C-1 configuration. The C-1 is widely known for its frequently demonstrated ability to orbit eight different satellites (each about 40 kg) at one time. In 1979 the C-1 launcher orbited its 200th payload, followed just five years later by the 300th C-class space mission.

D-CLASS VEHICLE

The 7500 kg capacity of the A-class vehicle was obviously inadequate to fulfill the needs of the larger spacecraft which the Soviet Union would have to manufacture in order to maintain her prestige in space exploration. Although advanced lunar and planetary explorers and geosynchronous satellites launched by the USSR to date have been less than 6000 kg, their trajectories and orbital requirements place demands on the launch vehicle far in excess of the capabilities of the A-class launchers. In addition, even small manned space stations or space station modules weigh in the tens of thousands of kilograms -- again beyond the capabilities of the A-class rocket.

Therefore, by the early 1960's plans for a new space rocket with a lifting ability three times that of the A-2 (then the rocket with the largest payload capacity) were finalized. In 1965 this rocket made its maiden voyage, placing the 12,200 kg Proton 1 satellite into Earth orbit. Since that time, this launch vehicle has been named the Proton launch system by the Soviets and is often referred to simply as the Proton rocket (regardless of its upper-stage configuration).

Until the 1980's the D-class was unique in the Soviet space rocket arsenal in that it was not directly related to any operational military missile. Although occasional reference has been made linking the D-class vehicle with a Khruschev-era ICBM capable of delivering a 100-megaton "city buster" hydrogen bomb, there is no direct evidence of this, and any such military project was surely abandoned at an early state.

The Soviet reluctance to discuss the specifications of the D-class launchers for nearly 20 years led to several postulated variants. We now know that only three basic versions were ever flown. A simple two-stage configuration (D-1) confirmed the essential design during the Proton 1-3 missions. A three-stage version, called D-1-h in this volume for historical reasons, increased the payload capacity from 12.2 metric tons to 21 metric tons. For lunar and interplanetary missions a fourth stage (escape stage) was added and is herein designated the D-1-e even though it also makes use of the "h" third stage.

D-class vehicle payloads fall into three broad categories: heavy low-Earth orbit spacecraft, geosynchronous satellites, and lunar/planetary explorers. The first category includes the original namesake scientific satellites Protons 1-4 and the man-related Salyut space stations, now orbited exclusively by the D-1-h. Geosynchronous satellites and lunar/planetary explorers are orbited by the D-1-e variation. In the case of the former payloads, the "escape" stage is employed in the complicated maneuvers required to place a satellite launched from within the USSR into a stationary orbit over the equator. The D-1-e variant has sent spacecraft weighing 6000 kg to the moon, 5000 kg to Mars and Venus, and 2100 kg to geostationary locations.

Facilities to launch D-class vehicles are located only at Tyuratam. By the end of 1980, 66 spacecraft had been placed into initial low Earth orbits by this massive rocket with a frequency of about five per year. In 1983 the flight rate was increased, leading to a record 13 missions in 1984.

F-CLASS VEHICLES

Debuting a year after the Proton, F-class launch vehicles, based on the SS-9 ICBM, were for many years devoted to high value military payloads: the Satellite Interceptor (sic, killer) System (SIS), the Fractional Orbit Bombardment System (FOBS), and the Ocean Surveillance System (OSS). The SIS and OSS programs are regarded as employing the F-1-m launcher due to the orbital maneuvers demonstrated by both these systems. However, the design of the upper "m" stage is likely to be slightly different for the SIS and OSS programs as a result of different maneuver requirements Meanwhile, the short-lived FOBS program utilized a F-1-r launch vehicle since its primary mission was to send nuclear warheads through reentry and back to Earth after completing less than one full revolution about the Earth.

The F-1-m appeared in 1966 with a payload capability of about 4000 kg and was followed within a year by the F-1-r. Today the FOBS program is believed to have been cancelled with no confirmed flight of the F-1-r since 1971. (The SALT II Treaty recognized the existence of this system and called for its abolishment.) Although the SIS is an on-again, off-again project, the F-1-m vehicle continues to find regular use in the Soviet ocean surveillance system.

In 1977 a third stage was added to the F-1, resulting in a new designator of F-2. This vehicle with its greater payload capacity of 5500 kg has assumed responsibility for many of the payloads originally flown by the

A-1 and the C-1, including meteorological, elint, and communications satellites. After entering operational service in 1979-1980, the usage of this variant increased to about 12 flights per year in the mid-1980's.

Soviet launch vehicle activity (1957-1980) for A-F class vehicles is presented in Table III and Figure 2.

G-CLASS VEHICLE

Although this vehicle was never successfully test-flown, its existence has been the topic of wide-spread debate for more than two decades, warranting a brief discussion here. As powerful as the D-class launcher was, US analysts were quick to point out that it was incapable of supporting manned lunar missions unless costly, and perhaps difficult, Earth orbital assembly was undertaken. Since the world assumed (and all evidence supports) that the Soviets were indeed involved in a race to land men on the moon, some large launch vehicle must necessarily have been under development for use in the late 1960's.

Affectionately referred to as "Webb's Giant" after the former NASA Administrator James Webb's mention in the mid-1960's of an imminent Soviet Saturn V-class launcher, the G-class launch vehicle is widely reported to have undergone at least three launch attempts--all of which supposedly ended in spectacular failure. A complete review of the reports, predictions, and ramifications of the G-class vehicle is beyond the scope of this short appendix, but its probable general characteristics will be outlined.[3]

The debate conducted in the United States to decide the method of landing and returning Apollo astronauts during their lunar expeditions was a heated one. Ultimately, the Lunar Orbital Rendezvous (LOR) method won out, but only after the Earth Orbital Rendezvous (EOR) and direct ascent trajectories had been proven beyond the capabilities of a single Saturn V. The same physical laws, of course, applied to the Soviet Union's efforts. Whether the Soviets also chose the LOR technique has not been confirmed, but to permit an analysis for the G-class launch vehicle, a performance roughly equal to that of the US Saturn V has been assumed.

402

Table III

SOVIET LAUNCH VEHICLE ACTIVITY
(1957-1980)

(Successful launches per year by launch vehicle class)

	A	B	C	D	F
1957	2				
1958	1				
1959	3				
1960	3				
1961	6				
1962	13	7			
1963	13	4			
1964	22	7	1		
1965	33	7	6	2	
1966	34	7	0	1	2
1967	36	13	4	2	11
1968	41	16	6	4	7
1969	43	14	6	4	3
1970	43	18	10	4	6
1971	40	12	19	6	6
1972	47	12	13	1	1
1973	53	10	15	7	1
1974	49	6	17	6	3
1975	58	5	18	4	4
1976	54	4	28	5	8
1977	54	2	28	4	10
1978	59	0	21	5	3
1979	60	0	18	6	3
1980	63	0	16	5	5
	830	144	226	66	73

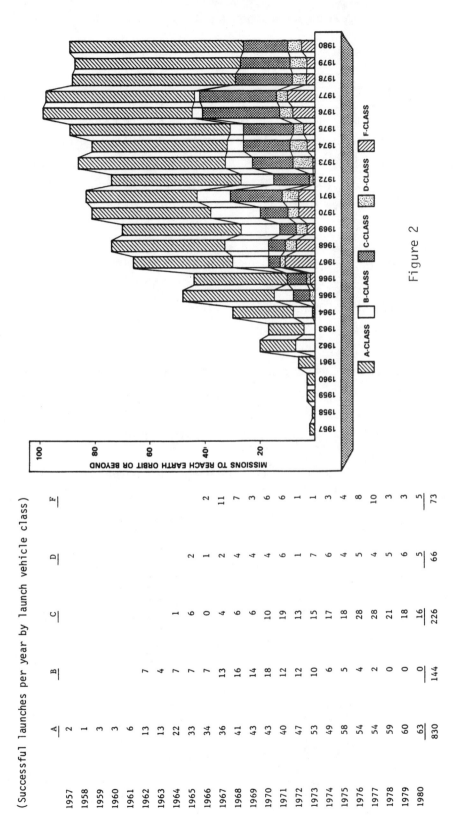

Figure 2

403

During the 1969-1972 period when the US Apollo missions were flown to the moon, the total weight of the Apollo/Lunar Module combination ranged from 44.5 to 47 metric tons. This represents nearly the minimum weight for any manned spacecraft launched by a single rocket and designed to land on the moon and return to Earth. Therefore, a G-1-e ("e" indicating Earth-orbital escape capability) launch vehicle is presumed to have had a 45-50 metric ton payload after translunar injection. Similarly, a G-1 type launch vehicle should have been capable of sending 100-135 metric tons into a low Earth orbit.

The reputed history of the G-class vehicle was inglorious indeed. After repeated delays, the first attempted launching is said to have occurred in June-July 1969, but ended in disaster when the rocket exploded while still on the ground, demolishing not only the rocket itself, but also the launching complex. The next attempt reportedly came in the summer of 1971. This try, however, proved little better -- the rocket exploding in flight while still under power of the first stage. The last G-class launching is said to have come on 24 November 1972 when the rocket was once again destroyed during the initial portion of its flight.

Soviet military launchers (1957-1980) are presented in Table IV.

Table IV   SOVIET MILITARY LAUNCHERS   (1957-1980)

Designator	Code-name	Est. Year Operational	Type	Propellants	Maximum Range (km)	Comment
SS-1	Scunner	1947	MRBM	Liquid	350	
SS-1B	Scud A	1957	MRBM	UDMH/IRFNA	130	
SS-1C	Scud B	1957	MRBM	UDMH/IRFNA	280	
SS-2	Sibling	1948	MRBM	?	?	Very few deployed
SS-3	Shyster	1955	MRBM	Kerosene/LOX	900	
SS-4	Sandal	1959	IRBM	Kerosene/nitric acid	2,000	
SS-5	Skean	1961	LRBM	UDMH/nitric acid	3,500	
SS-6	Sapwood	1957	ICBM	Kerosene/LOX	8,500	First generation ICBM
SS-7	Saddler	1961	ICBM	Liquid	10,500	
SS-8	Sasin	1963	ICBM	Liquid	11,000	
SS-9	Scarp	1965	ICBM	Storable liquid	12,000	Second generation ICBM
SS-10	Scrag	1965	ICBM	Kerosene/LOX	12,000	Not deployed
SS-11	Sego	1966	ICBM	Storable liquid	10,500	
SS-12	Scaleboard	1968	MRBM	Solid	800	First solid fuel ballistic missile
SS-13	Savage	1968	ICBM	Solid	9,400	
SS-14	Scapegoat	1968	LRBM	Solid	4,000	Upper two stages of SS-13
SS-15	Scrooge	1969	LRBM	Solid	5,600	Modified SS-13
SS-16	Spinner	1977	ICBM	Solid	9,500	Very few deployed; mobile
SS-17	Spanker	1975	ICBM	Storable liquid	11,000	SS-11 replacement
SS-18	Satan	1976	ICBM	Storable liquid	16,000	SS-9 replacement
SS-19	Stiletto	1975	ICBM	Storable liquid	10,000	SS-11 replacement
SS-20	Saber	1976	LRBM	Solid	5,000	Lower stages of SS-16
SS-21	Scarab	1979	SRBM	Solid	100	Replacement for FROG short range tactical surface to surface
SS-22	Scaleboard	1979	MRBM	Solid	900	Modified SS-12

REFERENCES AND NOTES

1. Mr. Sheldon, then acting Chief of the Science Policy Research Division, Legislative Reference Service of the Library of Congress, is now Chief of the Science Policy Research Division, Congressional Research Service of the Library of Congress and is considered one of the foremost US experts on the Soviet space program.

2. See the following for variations of the Sheldon system:

   TRW Space Log, Winter 1968-1969, pp. 8-19; *Soviet Space Programs, 1971-1975,* pp. 39-64; Turnill, R., *The Observer's Spaceflight Directory,* pp. 336-337; *Spaceflight,* Feb. 1977, pp. 54-60, 80

3. Several very good attempts have been made to examine the "history" of this fascinating launch vehicle. See:

   Clark, P.S., *The Proton and Type-G Launch Vehicles, A Review, Spaceflight,* Dec. 1973, pp. 457-471 and Mar. 1974, pp. 94-104. *Soviet Space Programs, 1971-1975,* pp. 61-64, 218-221, 502-515

   For related reports see:

   Aviation Week and Space Technology, 10 Mar. 1969, 17 Nov. 1969, 6 July 1970, 17 Mar. 1975; *Spaceflight,* July-Aug. 1976, p. 237; Baker, D., *The Rocket,* p. 225

Appendix II

SOVIET SPACE LAUNCH FACILITIES

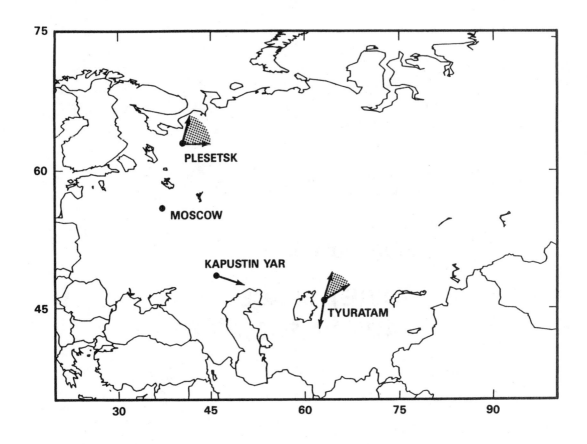

Figure 1   The location of the three Soviet launch facilities

Appendix II

SOVIET SPACE LAUNCH FACILITIES

For more than two decades the Soviet Union has utilized three different
launching complexes for orbital spacecraft and deep-space probes (Fig. 1).
In the early years, the strictest secrecy surrounded these sites as evidenced by the use of misleading geographical names, improper coordinates,
and the nighttime arrivals and departures of US officials during the
Apollo-Soyuz Test Project (ASTP) preparations. In part this was due to
the military as well as civilian activities which took place at the space
centers. Although other testing bases exist for evaluating military
rockets (ICBM's, LRBM's, etc.) and smaller weapon systems, classified
military orbital payloads are launched from the same three locations as
all civilian spacecraft. Two of the facilities, including the world's
busiest spaceport, were not officially acknowledged until 1983.

TYURATAM

The launch of Sputnik 1 in October of 1957 provided additional evidence
for the location of the launch facilities which had also tested the world's
first ICBM two months earlier. The exact location of the launchings could
not be pinpointed from Sputnik 1 alone, but its presence could be narrowed
down to lying somewhere along the initial groundtrack of that satellite.
After Yuri Gagarin's flight in 1961, the Soviet Union attempted to mis-
lead Western specialists by christening the launch complex the Baikonur
Cosmodrome. Not by coincidence, the railroad town of Baikonur did in
fact lie down range on the Sputnik 1 and Vostok 1 missions. However,
subsequent launches fixed the launching site some 370 km SW of Baikonur,
near the town of Tyuratam in Kazakhstan.

United States' Earth survey satellites have been able to place the Baikonur
Cosmodrome (or Tyuratam complex as the launching facilities are often

interchangeably called) at 45.6° N, 63.4° E. Near the Aral Sea this complex is located in the southern portion of Soviet Central Asia to ease launch vehicle requirements for placing payloads in low inclination orbits. Unfortunately, this site is still much further north than comparable US launching facilities, resulting in substantial penalties for orbiting such spacecraft as communications and early warning satellites in geostationary orbits. Almost all payloads from Tyuratam are initially launched to the northeast into 50-72° inclination orbits, although a very few have been launched to the southwest to enter 97-98° retrograde orbits.

Tyuratam is roughly analagous to the facilities of the Kennedy Space Center/Eastern Test Range at Cape Canaveral, Florida. All manned and lunar/planetary missions originate there. In addition, a wide range of scientific and military satellites are launched every year at Tyuratam. Tyuratam has launched every class of orbital carrier rocket with the exception of the small (450 kg payload) B-1 launcher.

Mating of the payload and launcher for the A-class and D-class vehicles is done horizontally in assembly buildings at the cosmodrome. In the case of Soyuz (and Vostok and Voskhod before it) this takes place in the MIK (Montazhno Ispytatel'nyy Korpus) some 1.6 km from the launching pad. After preliminary checkouts have been completed, the entire launcher with payload is transported again horizontally by rail to the launch site. Erection of the rocket and final preparations then ensue.

KAPUSTIN YAR

In March 1962 the broad Kosmos program was inaugurated with the launch of Kosmos 1 by a new space rocket (B-1) from a new space launching facility. Located north and to the west of the Baikonur Cosmodrome, the new launching grounds at Kapustin Yar (48.4° N, 45.8° E) is the smallest of the three Soviet complexes. From a maximum of eight launches in 1968, Kapustin Yar has orbited only 1 or 2 payloads per year throughout most of the 1970's and 1980's. Only the two smallest Soviet space rockets, the B-1 and C-1, have been launched from the site. Payload types include Soviet and Interkosmos scientific spacecraft and small military satellites.

Kapustin Yar dates back to pre-Sputnik days as a rocket test center and was the site of the first Soviet ballistic missile launch in 1947. This site is also used to send up high altitude geophysical probes and to evaluate space-related military systems. Satellites from Kapustin Yar are placed into orbits with inclinations between 48.9° and 50.6°.

PLESETSK

The newest launching facility and now the world's most productive launch site, Plesetsk, is located still further north, near the Arctic Circle at 62.8° N, 40.1° E. Devoted primarily to orbiting militarily oriented satellites, such as photo reconnaissance, meteorological, navigation, and electronic intelligence, Plesetsk is also the site from which many of the Molniya, Interkosmos, and Biosatellites originate.

Since its first orbital launching in 1966, Plesetsk had launched 755 space rockets successfully by the end of 1980 and completed its 1000th mission in 1986. After only three years of operation, Plesetsk was launching more rockets than Tyuratam and Kapustin Yar combined. During the ten year period, 1971-1980, launch control personnel averaged placing a space vehicle in orbit once every 6 days. From Plesetsk's location close to the Arctic Circle, spacecraft are placed into Earth orbits with high inclinations with respect to the equator; ranging from 62.8° to 83°. With the retirement of the B-class launch vehicles, Plesetsk now maintains facilities for only A-class, C-class, and F-class rockets.

Table I presents Soviet space launches to Earth orbit and Figure 1 shows the number of launches to Earth orbit 1957-1980.

Table I

SOVIET SPACE LAUNCHES TO EARTH ORBIT
(1957-1985)

	Tyuratam	Kapustin Yar	Plesetsk
1957	2		
1958	1		
1959	3		
1960	3		
1961	6		
1962	13	7	
1963	13	4	
1964	23	7	
1965	41	7	
1966	31	7	6
1967	33	7	26
1968	36	8	30
1969	29	4	37
1970	28	5	48
1971	29	1	53
1972	20	2	52
1973	23	2	61
1974	25	1	55
1975	26	1	62
1976	34	1	64
1977	27	2	69
1978	25	1	62
1979	19	2	66
1980	24	1	64
	514	70	755

TOTAL LAUNCHINGS: 1339

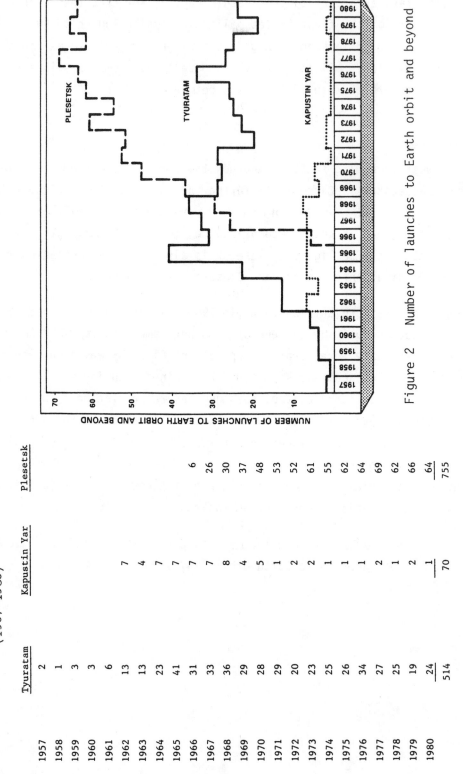

Figure 2   Number of launches to Earth orbit and beyond

412

Appendix III

SOVIET MANNED
SPACE MISSIONS

This appendix presents a summary of Soviet manned space flight through 1985 (Table I), status and activities of Soviet cosmonauts through 1985 (Table IIA) and of intercosmos and international cosmonauts (Table IIB). It includes a tabulation of major manned space firsts (Table III), a graph of Soviet man-hours in space vs. space missions (Figure 1) and a comparison of the configuration of Soviet manned spacecraft (Figure 2).

Table I
SUMMARY OF SOVIET MANNED SPACE FLIGHT

DESIGNATOR	DATE LAUNCHED	MISSION DURATION (DAYS)	CREW	ACHIEVEMENTS
VOSTOK 1	12 APR 1961	0.075	GAGARIN	FIRST MANNED SPACEFLIGHT
VOSTOK 2	6 AUG 1961	1.05	TITOV	FIRST DAY LONG MANNED SPACEFLIGHT
VOSTOK 3	11 AUG 1962	3.93	NIKOLAYEV	RENDEZVOUS WITH VOSTOK 4
VOSTOK 4	12 AUG 1962	2.96	POPOVICH	RENDEZVOUS WITH VOSTOK 3
VOSTOK 5	14 JUN 1963	4.96	BYKOVSKY	NEW SPACEFLIGHT ENDURANCE RECORD (NOT BROKEN BY USSR UNTIL SOYUZ 9); RENDEZVOUS WITH VOSTOK 6
VOSTOK 6	16 JUN 1963	2.95	TERESHKOVA	FIRST WOMAN IN SPACE; RENDEZVOUS WITH VOSTOK 5; ENDED VOSTOK PROGRAM
VOSKHOD 1	12 OCT 1964	1.01	KOMAROV YEGAROV FEOKTISTOV	FIRST MULTI-MAN SPACEFLIGHT
VOSKHOD 2	18 MAR 1965	1.08	BELYAYEV LEONOV	FIRST SPACE WALK; ENDED VOSKHOD PROGRAM
SOYUZ 1	23 APR 1967	1.11	KOMAROV	FIRST MANNED FLIGHT OF SOYUZ; FIRST SPACE FATALITY
SOYUZ 2	25 OCT 1968	2.95	NONE	UNMANNED RENDEZVOUS TARGET FOR SOYUZ 3
SOYUZ 3	26 OCT 1968	3.95	BEREGOVOI	RENDEZVOUS WITH SOYUZ 2
SOYUZ 4	14 JAN 1969	2.97	SHATALOV	DOCKED WITH SOYUZ 5
SOYUZ 5	15 JAN 1969	3.04	VOLYNOV KHRUNOV YELISEYEV	DOCKED WITH SOYUZ 4; KHRUNOV AND YELISEYEV COMPLETED FIRST IN ORBIT CREW EXCHANGE
SOYUZ 6	11 OCT 1969	4.95	SHONIN KUBASOV	FIRST MANNED SPACE WELDING EX – PERIMENTS; MEMBER OF SOYUZ 6/7/8 TRIPLE RENDEZVOUS
SOYUZ 7	12 OCT 1969	4.95	FILIPCHENKO VOLKOV GORBATKO	MEMBER OF SOYUZ 6/7/8 TRIPLE RENDEZVOUS
SOYUZ 8	13 OCT 1969	4.95	SHATALOV YELISEYEV	MEMBER OF SOYUZ 6/7/8 TRIPLE RENDEZVOUS
SOYUZ 9	1 JUN 1970	17.71	NIKOLAYEV SEVASTYANOV	SET NEW SPACE ENDURANCE RECORD
SOYUZ 10	22 APR 1971	1.99	SHATALOV YELISEYEV RUKAVISHNIKOV	FIRST DOCKING WITH AN EARTH OR- BITAL LABORATORY; FAILED TO ENTER SALYUT 1
SOYUZ 11	6 JUN 1971	23.77	DOBROVOLSKY PATSAYEV VOLKOV	FIRST MANNED OCCUPATION OF SPACE STATION; CREW DIED DURING REENTRY
SOYUZ 12	27 SEP 1973	1.97	LAZAREV MAKAROV	FIRST MANNED FLIGHT OF REDE- SIGNED SOYUZ
SOYUZ 13	18 DEC 1973	7.87	KLIMUK LEBEDEV	PERFORMED BIOMEDICAL AND ASTROPHYSICAL EXPERIMENTS
SOYUZ 14	3 JUL 1974	15.73	POPOVICH ARTYUKHIN	FIRST CREW TO MAN THE MILITARY SALYUT 3
SOYUZ 15	26 AUG 1974	2.01	SARAFANOV DEMIN	FAILED TO DOCK WITH SALYUT 3
SOYUZ 16	2 DEC 1974	5.93	FILIPCHENKO RUKAVISHNIKOV	ASTP REHEARSAL FLIGHT
SOYUZ 17	11 JAN 1975	29.56	GRECHKO GUBAREV	FIRST CREW TO MAN THE CIVILIAN SALYUT 4

Table I (Continued)

DESIGNATOR	DATE LAUNCHED	MISSION DURATION (DAYS)	CREW	ACHIEVEMENTS
SOYUZ 18A	5 APR 1975	0.014	LAZAREV MAKAROV	FIRST MANNED LAUNCH ABORT
SOYUZ 18B	24 MAY 1975	62.97	KLIMUK SEVASTYANOV	SET NEW SOVIET SPACE ENDURANCE RECORD ON BOARD SALYUT 4
SOYUZ 19	15 JUL 1975	5.94	LEONOV KUBASOV	ASTP MISSION; FIRST INTERNATIONAL MANNED SPACEFLIGHT
SOYUZ 20	17 NOV 1975	91.00	NONE	UNMANNED DOCKING WITH SALYUT 4 IN LONG DURATION TEST OF SOYUZ RELIABILITY
SOYUZ 21	6 JUL 1976	49.27	VOLYNOV ZHOLOBOV	FIRST CREW TO MAN MILITARY SALYUT 5
SOYUZ 22	15 SEP 1976	7.91	BYKOVSKY AKSENOV	PERFORMED EARTH RESOURCES EXPERIMENTS; ONLY SOYUZ FLOWN AT 65° INCLINATION
SOYUZ 23	14 OCT 1976	2.00	ZUDOV ROZHDESTVENSKY	FAILED TO DOCK WITH SALYUT 5
SOYUZ 24	7 FEB 1977	17.72	GORBATKO GLAZKOV	SECOND CREW TO MAN SALYUT 5
SOYUZ 25	9 OCT 1977	1.99	KOVALENOK RYUMIN	FAILED TO DOCK WITH THE CIVILIAN SALYUT 6
SOYUZ 26	10 DEC 1977	96.42	ROMANENKO GRECHKO	FIRST CREW TO MAN SALYUT 6; SET NEW WORLD SPACE RECORD; PERFORMED FIRST IN-SPACE REFUELING
SOYUZ 27	10 JAN 1978	5.98	DZHANIBEKOV MAKAROV	PERFORMED FIRST MANNED DOUBLE DOCKING AND RESUPPLY WITH SALYUT 6
SOYUZ 28	2 MAR 1978	7.94	GUBAREV REMEK (CZECHOSLOVAKIA)	FIRST INTERNATIONAL SOYUZ CREW; VISITED AND RESUPPLIED SOYUZ 26 COSMONAUTS ON BOARD SALYUT 6
SOYUZ 29	15 JUN 1978	139.62	KOVALENOK IVANCHENKOV	SET NEW WORLD SPACE ENDURANCE RECORD ON BOARD SALYUT 6; VISITED BY 2 MANNED AND 3 UNMANNED RESUPPLY SHIPS
SOYUZ 30	27 JUN 1978	7.92	KLIMUK HERMASZEWSKI (POLAND)	SECOND INTERNATIONAL SOYUZ CREW; VISITED SOYUZ 29 COSMONAUTS ON BOARD SALYUT 6
SOYUZ 31	26 AUG 1978	7.87	BYKOVSKY JAHN (EAST GERMANY)	THIRD INTERNATIONAL SOYUZ CREW; VISITED SOYUZ 29 COSMONAUTS ON BOARD SALYUT 6
SOYUZ 32	25 FEB 1979	175.03	RYUMIN LYAKHOV	SET NEW SPACE ENDURANCE RECORD OF 175 DAYS ON BOARD SALYUT 6; VISITED BY 1 UNMANNED SOYUZ AND 3 UNMANNED RESUPPLY SHIPS
SOYUZ 33	10 APR 1979	1.96	RUKAVISHNIKOV IVANOV (BULGARIA)	FOURTH INTERNATIONAL SOYUZ MISSION; FAILED TO DOCK WITH SALYUT 6
SOYUZ 34	6 JUN 1979	73.76	NONE	UNMANNED SOYUZ FERRIED TO SALYUT 6 FOR USE BY THE SOYUZ 32 COSMONAUTS FOR THEIR RETURN TO EARTH IN AUGUST 1979
SOYUZ T-1	16 DEC 1979	100.39	NONE	FIRST TEST OF SOYUZ T SPACESHIP; DOCKED WITH SALYUT 6 FOR 95 DAYS
SOYUZ 35	9 APR 1980	184.84	POPOV RYUMIN	SET NEW SPACE ENDURANCE RECORD; VISITED BY 4 MANNED AND 4 UNMANNED RESUPPLY SHIPS
SOYUZ 36	26 MAY 1980	7.87	KUBASOV FARKAS (HUNGARY)	FIFTH INTERNATIONAL MISSION; VISITED SOYUZ 35 ON BOARD SALYUT 6

Table I (Continued)

DESIGNATOR	DATE LAUNCHED	MISSION DURATION (DAYS)	CREW	ACHIEVEMENTS
SOYUZ T-2	5 JUN 1980	3.95	MALYSHEV AKSENOV	FIRST MANNED FLIGHT OF SOYUZ T SPACECRAFT; VISITED SOYUZ 35 ON BOARD SALYUT 6
SOYUZ 37	23 JUL 1980	7.86	GORBATKO PHAM TUAN (VIET NAM)	SIXTH INTERNATIONAL MISSION; VISITED SOYUZ 35 ON BOARD SALYUT 6
SOYUZ 38	18 SEP 1980	7.86	ROMANENKO TAMAYO MENDEZ (CUBA)	SEVENTH INTERNATIONAL MISSION; VISITED SOYUZ 35 ON BOARD SALYUT 6
SOYUZ T-3	27 NOV 1980	12.80	KIZIM MAKAROV STREKALOV	FIRST FLIGHT OF 3-MAN SOYUZ T, BRIEFLY MANNED SALYUT 6
SOYUZ T-4	12 MAR 1981	74.78	KOVALENOK SAVINYKH	LAST EXPEDITION TO SALYUT 6; VISITED BY 2 MANNED AND 1 UN-MANNED RESUPPLY SHIPS
SOYUZ 39	22 MAR 1981	7.87	DZHANIBEKOV GURRAGCHA (MONGOLIA)	EIGHTH INTERNATIONAL MISSION; VISTIED SOYUZ T-4 ON BOARD SALYUT 6
SOYUZ 40	14 MAY 1981	7.86	POPOV PRUNARIU (ROMANIA)	NINTH INTERNATIONAL MISSION; VISTIED SOYUZ T-4 ON BOARD SALYUT 6; LAST FLIGHT OF SOYUZ SPACECRAFT
SOYUZ T-5	13 MAY 1982	211.38	BEREZOVOY LEBEDEV	FIRST EXPEDITION TO SALYUT 7; SET NEW SPACE ENDURANCE RECORD; VISITED BY 2 MANNED AND 4 UN-MANNED RESUPPLY SHIPS
SOYUZ T-6	24 JUN 1982	7.91	DZHANIBEKOV IVANCHENKOV CHRETIEN (FRANCE)	TENTH INTERNATIONAL MISSION; VISITED SOYUZ T-5 ON BOARD SALYUT 7
SOYUZ T-7	19 AUG 1982	7.91	POPOV SEREBROV SAVITSKAYA	FIRST FLIGHT OF FEMALE COSMONAUT SINCE VOSTOK 6; VISITED SOYUZ T-5 ON BOARD SALYUT 7
SOYUZ T-8	20 APR 1983	2.01	TITOV STREKALOV SEREBROV	PLANNED TO START SECOND EXPEDI-TION TO SALYUT 7; FAILED TO DOCK
SOYUZ T-9	27 JUN 1983	149.45	LYAKHOV ALEKSANDROV	SECOND EXPEDITION TO SALYUT 7; VISITED BY 3 UNMANNED RESUPPLY SHIPS INCLUDING THE LARGE KOSMOS 1443
SOYUZ T-10A	26 SEP 1983	0.00	TITOV STREKALOV	LAUNCH FAILURE; CREW EJECTED FROM ROCKET ON PAD; INTENDED TO DOCK WITH SALYUT 7
SOYUZ T-10B	8 FEB 1984	236.96	KIZIM SOLOVYOV ATKOV	THIRD EXPEDITION TO SALYUT 7; FIRST 3-MAN SPACE STATION RESIDENT CREW SINCE 1971; VISITED BY 2 MANNED AND 5 UNMANNED RESUPPLY SHIPS; SET NEW SPACE ENDURANCE RECORD
SOYUZ T-11	3 APR 1984	7.90	STREKALOV MALYSHEV SHARMA (INDIA)	ELEVENTH INTERNATIONAL MISSION; VISITED SOYUZ T-10B ON BOARD SALYUT 7
SOYUZ T-12	17 JUL 1984	11.80	DZHANIBEKOV SAVITSKAYA VOLK	ALL SOVIET CREW; VISITED SOYUZ T-10B ON BOARD SALYUT 7; SAVITSKAYA BECAME THE FIRST WOMAN TO FLY TWO SPACE MISSIONS AND FIRST WOMAN TO WALK IN SPACE
SOYUZ T-13	6 JUN 1985	112.13	DZHANIBEKOV SAVINYKH	FOURTH EXPEDITION TO SALYUT 7; REVIVED DEAD SPACE STATION; visited by 2 UNMANNED RESUPPLY SHIPS
SOYUZ T-14	17 SEP 1985	64.91	VASYUTIN GRECHKO VOLKOV	RELIEF CREW FOR SALYUT 7; VASYUTIN AND VOLKOV REMAINED ON BOARD SALYUT 7 WITH SAVINYKH WHILE GRECHKO AND DZHANIBEKOV RETURNED IN SOYUZ T-13; VISITED BY LARGE KOSMOS MODULE

APPENDIX B.   THE SOVIET COSMONAUT TEAM by Rex Hall

The Soviet cosmonauts join the training programme in distinct groups in a very similar way as the Americans do, but they also recruit individuals to the team probably to provide particular expertise within the team. Ordinarily cosmonauts become known only when they make a flight. The exceptions to this rule were the Apollo-Soyuz project when five rookies were identified and the French mission when one was named. The exact size of the cosmonaut team is unknown though recent indications put the size of the team as about the same as that in the U.S.A. Military cosmonauts live and work at Star Town, just outside Moscow after their selection. Civilian trainees only come to Star Town when they are assigned to a particular training cycle. Currently they have 50 cosmonauts including three women in direct mission training.

Information on the cosmonauts is difficult to obtain but the accompanying table is based on the latest material from Soviet sources. For the purpose of this listing, active indicates a cosmonaut who is still available for future crew assignments. Inactive indicates a cosmonaut who is still associated with the cosmonaut programme but is not available for future space missions. Resigned indicates a cosmonaut who has left the program. The Soviets do not publish information concerning flight status but this table is based on the best available material.

THE INTERKOSMOS PROGRAM

The Interkosmos organization agreed in September, 1976, to join a joint program that would put a citizen from each country into space. All the cosmonauts were selected in pairs from each country to fly a single man with one acting as prime pilot and the other as a back-up. After the program the crew members stood down, returning to their normal duties including a heavy public relations schedule. The program was headed by Major General A. Leonov and Colonel V. Lazarev.

THE INTERNATIONAL PROGRAM

This was an extension of the Interkosmos program and enabled citizens from France, India, and Syria to train for missions on the same basis as the Interkosmos crews.

Table IIA
SOVIET COSMONAUTS

NAME	YEAR OF SELECTION	YEAR OF 1ST FLIGHT	NO. OF MISSIONS	STATUS	CURRENT ASSIGNMENT	RANK
AKSENOV, V.	1973	1976	2	INACTIVE	WORKING AT TsPK	CIVILIAN
ALEKSANDROV, A.	1978	1983	1	ACTIVE	COSMONAUT	CIVILIAN
ANDREYEV, B.	1970			RESIGNED	WORKING AT TsPK	CIVILIAN
ANIKEYEV, I.	1960			DISMISSED	LEFT TEAM 1961 RETIRED AF	AF OFFICER
ANOKHIN, S.	1966			DECEASED	DIED APRIL 1986 AFTER ILLNESS	COLONEL AF
ARTYUKHIN, YU.	1963	1974	1	INACTIVE	UNKNOWN	COLONEL ENGINEER AF
ATKOV, O.	1977	1984	1	ACTIVE	COSMONAUT	CIVILIAN
BELYAYEV, P.	1960	1965	1	DECEASED	DIED JAN 1970 SURGERY	COLONEL AF
BEREGOVOI, G.	1964	1968	1	INACTIVE	COMMANDER TsPK	LT. GENERAL AF
BEREZOVOI, A.	1970	1982	1	ACTIVE	COSMONAUT	COLONEL AF
BONDARENKO, V.	1960			DECEASED	DIED MARCH 1961 IN FIRE	SUR. LT. AF
BYKOVSKY, V.	1960	1963	3	ACTIVE?	TRAINING MANAGER TsPK	COLONEL AF
DEMIN, L.	1963	1974	1	RESIGNED	RETIRED	COLONEL ENGINEER AF
DOBROVOLSKY, G.	1963	1971	1	DECEASED	DIED SOYUZ 11 JUN 1971	LT. COLONEL AF
DZHANIBEKOV, V.	1970	1978	5	ACTIVE	WORKING TsPK	MAJOR GENERAL AF
FEOKTISTOV, K.	1964	1964	1	INACTIVE	LEADING DESIGNER SPACECRAFT	CIVILIAN
FILATYEV, V.	1960			DISMISSED	LEFT TEAM 1961 RETIRED AF	AF OFFICER
FILIPCHENKO, A.	1963	1969	2	INACTIVE	WORKING AT TsPK	MAJOR GENERAL AF
GAGARIN, YU.	1960	1961	1	DECEASED	JET CRASH MARCH 1968	COLONEL AF
GLAZKOV, YU.	1965	1977	1	ACTIVE	COSMONAUT	COLONEL ENGINEER, AF
GORBATKO, V.	1960	1969	3	INACTIVE	TRAINING MANAGER WORKING AT TsPK	MAJOR GENERAL AF
GRECHKO, G.	1966	1975	3	INACTIVE	DESIGN BUREAU	CIVILIAN
GUBAREV, A.	1963	1975	2	INACTIVE	TRAINING MANAGER WORKING AT TsPK	MAJOR GENERAL AF
ILLARIONOV, V.	1970			ACTIVE?	UNKNOWN	AF OFFICER
IVANCHENKOV, A.	1970	1978	2	ACTIVE	COSMONAUT	CIVILIAN
KARTASHOV, A.	1960			RESIGNED	LEFT TEAM 1960 RETIRED AF	AF OFFICER
KHRUNOV, YE.	1960	1969	1	INACTIVE	TRAINING MANAGER TsPK	COLONEL ENGINEER AF
KIZIM, L.	1965	1980	3	ACTIVE	COSMONAUT	COLONEL AF
KLIMUK, P.	1965	1973	3	INACTIVE	POLITICAL DEPT. TsPK	MAJOR GENERAL AF
KOMAROV, V.	1960	1964	2	DECEASED	DIED SOYUZ 1 APRIL 1967	COLONEL ENGINEER AF

NAME	YEAR OF SELECTION	YEAR OF 1ST FLIGHT	NO. OF MISSIONS	STATUS	CURRENT ASSIGNMENT	RANK
KOVOLYONOK, V.	1967	1977	3	ACTIVE	COSMONAUT	COLONEL AF
KUBASOV, V.	1966	1969	3	INACTIVE	DESIGN BUREAU	CIVILIAN
LAZAREV, V.[1][2]	1964/66	1973	2	INACTIVE	TRAINING MANAGER TsPK	COLONEL AF
LEBEDEV, V.	1972	1973	2	ACTIVE	COSMONAUT	CIVILIAN
LEONOV, A.	1960	1965	2	INACTIVE	1ST DEPUTY COMMANDER TsPK	MAJOR GENERAL AF
LYAKHOV, V.	1967	1979	2	ACTIVE	COSMONAUT	COLONEL AF
MAKAROV, O.[2]	1966	1973	4	INACTIVE	DESIGN BUREAU	CIVILIAN
MALYSHEV, YU.	1967	1980	2	ACTIVE	COSMONAUT	COLONEL AF
NELYUBOV, G.	1960			DECEASED	DISMISSED TEAM 1961 KILLED FEB 1966	AF OFFICER
NIKOLAYEV, A.	1960	1962	2	INACTIVE	DEPUTY COMMANDER TsPK	MAJOR GENERAL AF
PATSAYEV, V.	1969	1971	1	DECEASED	DIED SOYUZ 11 JUN 1971	CIVILIAN
POPOV, L.	1970	1980	3	ACTIVE	COSMONAUT	COLONEL AF
POPOVICH, P.	1960	1962	2	INACTIVE	DEPUTY COMMANDER TsPK	MAJOR GENERAL AF
RAFIKOV, M.	1960			RESIGNED	LEFT TEAM 1962 RETIRED AF	OFFICER AF
ROMANENKO, YU.	1970	1977	2	ACTIVE?	COSMONAUT DEPUTY CAPCOM SALYUT 7	COLONEL AF
ROZHDESTVENSKY, V.	1965	1976	1	ACTIVE?	COSMONAUT	COLONEL ENGINEER AF
RUKAVISHNIKOV, N.	1967	1971	3	INACTIVE	HEAD FEDERATION OF COSMONAUTICS	CIVILIAN
RYUMIN, V.	1973	1977	3	INACTIVE	FLIGHT DIRECTOR SALYUT 7/MIR	CIVILIAN
SARAFANOV, G.	1965	1974	1	ACTIVE	TRAINING MANAGER TsPK	COLONEL AF
SAVINYKH, V.	1978	1981	2	ACTIVE	COSMONAUT	CIVILIAN
SAVITSKAYA, S.	1980	1982	2	ACTIVE	COSMONAUT	CIVILIAN
SEREBROV, A.	1978	1982	2	ACTIVE	COSMONAUT	CIVILIAN
SEVASTYANOV, V.	1967	1970	2	INACTIVE	DESIGN BUREAU	CIVILIAN
SHATALOV, V.	1963	1969	3	INACTIVE	CHIEF COSMONAUT TRAINING	LT GENERAL AF
SHONIN, G.	1960	1969	1	INACTIVE	UNKNOWN DUTIES	LT GENERAL AF
SOLOYVOV, V.	1978	1984	2	ACTIVE	COSMONAUT	CIVILIAN
STREKALOV, G.[3]	1973	1980	3	ACTIVE	COSMONAUT	CIVILIAN
TERESHKOVA, V.	1962	1963	1	RESIGNED	PRESIDIUM OF SUPREME SOVIET	COLONEL ENG AF, CIVILIAN
TITOV, G.	1960	1961	1	RESIGNED	UNKNOWN DUTIES	LT GENERAL AF
TITOV, V.[3]	1976	1983	1	ACTIVE	COSMONAUT	COLONEL AF
VARLAMOV, V.	1960			RESIGNED	LEFT TEAM 1960 DIED OCT 1980 BRAIN HEMORRHAGE	AF OFFICER
VASYUTIN, V.	1976	1985	1	ACTIVE	COSMONAUT	LT. COLONEL AF

NAME	YEAR OF SELECTION	YEAR OF 1ST FLIGHT	NO. OF MISSIONS	STATUS	CURRENT ASSIGNMENT	RANK
VOLK, I.	1978	1984	1	ACTIVE	COSMONAUT	CIVILIAN
VOLKOV, A.	1976	1985	1	ACTIVE	COSMONAUT	LT. COLONEL AF
VOLKOV, V.	1966	1969	2	DECEASED	DIED SOYUZ 11 JUN 1971	CIVILIAN
VOLYNOV, B.	1960	1969	2	ACTIVE	COMMANDER COSMONAUT GROUP	COLONEL AF
YEGAROV, B.	1964	1964	1	RESIGNED	HEAD MEDICAL LABORATORY	CIVILIAN
YELISEYEV, A.	1966	1966	3	INACTIVE	RECTOR BAUMAN HIGHER TECHNICAL SCHOOL	CIVILIAN
ZAIKIN, D.	1960			RESIGNED 1968	RETIRED AF	AF OFFICER
ZHOLOBOV, V.	1963	1976	1	RESIGNED	UNKNOWN	COLONEL ENGINEER AF
ZUDOV, V.	1965	1976	1	ACTIVE	WORKING AT TsPK	COLONEL AF

[1] LAZAREV SELECTED IN 1964 THEN STOOD DOWN AND RESELECTED in 1966.

[2] LAZAREV/MAKAROV WERE INVOLVED IN A LAUNCH ABORT APRIL 1975.

[3] V. TITOV AND STREKALOV SUFFERED A LAUNCH ABORT IN SEPTEMBER 1983.

TsPK IS THE COSMONAUT TRAINING CENTER NAMED FOR YU. GAGARIN. THIS IS LOCATED IN STAR TOWN OUTSIDE MOSCOW.

Table IIB
INTERKOSMOS AND INTERNATIONAL COSMONAUTS

NAME	COUNTRY	FLIGHT AND DATE	CURRENT STATUS
SELECTION DECEMBER 1976			
PELCEK, O.	CZECHOSLOVAKIA	NONE	RETURNED DUTIES CZECHOSLOVAKIA AF
REMEK, V.	CZECHOSLOVAKIA	SOYUZ 28, 1978	RETURNED DUTIES CZECHOSLOVAKIA AF COLONEL
HERMESZEWSKI, M.	POLAND	SOYUZ 30, 1978	RETURNED DUTIES POLISH AF COLONEL
JANKOWSKI, Z.	POLAND	NONE	RETURNED DUTIES POLISH AF
JAHN, S.	D.D.R.	SOYUZ 31, 1978	RETURNED DUTIES D.D.R. AF COLONEL
KOLLNER, E.	D.D.R.	NONE	RETURNED DUTIES D.D.R. AF
SELECTION MARCH 1978			
ALEKSANDROV, A.	BULGARIA	NONE	RETURNED DUTIES BULGARIAN AF
IVANOV, G.	BULGARIA	SOYUZ 33, 1979	RETURNED DUTIES BULGARIAN AF COLONEL ENGINEER
FARKAS, B.	HUNGARY	SOYUZ 36, 1980	RETURNED DUTIES HUNGARIAN AF COLONEL
MAGYARI, B.	HUNGARY	NONE	RETURNED DUTIES HUNGARIAN AF
FALCON, J.A.	CUBA	NONE	RETURNED DUTIES CUBAN AF
MENDEZ, A.	CUBA	SOYUZ 38, 1980	RETURNED DUTIES CUBAN AF COLONEL
GANZORIG, M.	MONGOLIA	NONE	RETURNED DUTIES MONGOLIAN AF
GURRAGCHA, J.	MONGOLIA	SOYUZ 39, 1981	RETURNED DUTIES MONGOLIAN AF MAJOR GENERAL
DEDIU, D.	ROMANIA	NONE	RETURNED DUTIES ROMANIAN AF
PRUNARIU, D.	ROMANIA	SOYUZ 40, 1981	RETURNED DUTIES ROMANIAN AF MAJOR AF
SELECTION APRIL 1979			
BUI THANH LIEM	VIETNAM	NONE	RETURNED DUTIES VIETNAMESE AF, DIED AIR CRASH
PHAM TUAN	VIETNAM	SOYUZ 37, 1980	RETURNED DUTIES VIETNAMESE AF
SELECTION SEPTEMBER 1980			
BAUDRY, P.	FRANCE	NONE	RETURNED CNES, FLEW U.S. SHUTTLE MISSION, ASSIGNED HERMES PROGRAM
CHRETIEN, J-L.	FRANCE	SOYUZ T-6, 1982	RETURNED CNES, ASSIGNED TO NEW TRAINING GROUP 1986
SELECTION SEPTEMBER 1982			
MALHOTRA, R.	INDIA	NONE	RETURNED DUTIES INDIAN AF
SHARMA, R.	INDIA	SOYUZ T-11, 1984	RETURNED DUTIES INDIAN AF
SELECTION SEPTEMBER 1985			
MOHAMMED FARIS	SYRIA	NONE, FLIGHT DUE 1987	ACTIVE SYRIAN AF
MUNIR HABIB	SYRIA	NONE, FLIGHT DUE 1987	ACTIVE SYRIAN AF

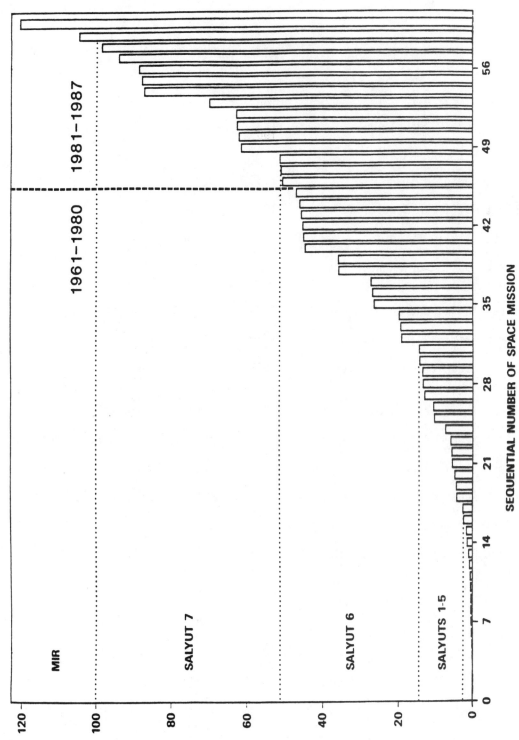

Figure 1

423

Table III

MAJOR MANNED SPACE FIRSTS

Event	Year	Mission
First Man in Space	1961	Vostok 1
First Dual Spacecraft Mission	1962	Vostok 3 and Vostok 4
First Woman in Space	1963	Vostok 6
First Multi-man Spacecraft	1964	Voskhod 1
First Walk in Space	1965	Voskhod 2
First Docking of Manned Space-craft	1969	Soyuz 4 and Soyuz 5
First In-space Crew Transfer	1969	Soyuz 4 and Soyuz 5
First Triple Spacecraft Mission	1969	Soyuz 6, Soyuz 7, Soyuz 8
First Occupation of a Space Station	1971	Soyuz 11 and Salyut 1
First International Space Docking	1975	Soyuz 19 and US Apollo
First Manned Resupply Mission	1978	Soyuz 26, Soyuz 27, Salyut 6
First Triple Spacecraft Docking	1978	Soyuz 26, Soyuz 27, Salyut 6
First In-space Refueling	1978	Soyuz 26, Progress 1, Salyut 6
First International Crew	1978	Soyuz 28
First Six-month Duration Mission	1979	Soyuz 32

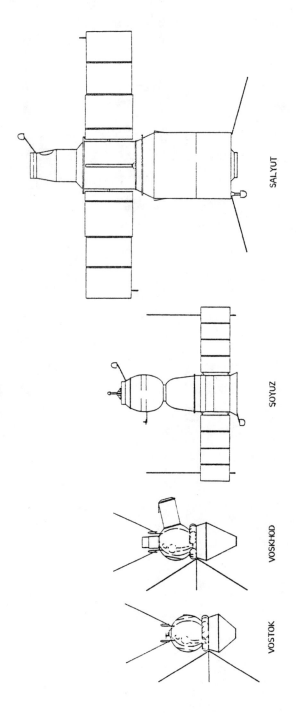

VOSTOK   VOSKHOD   SOYUZ   SALYUT

Figure 2   Comparison of Soviet Manned Spacecraft

425

Appendix IV

LIST OF ILLUSTRATIONS

Appendix IV

LIST OF ILLUSTRATIONS

Following is a list of illustrations as they appear throughout the book. Each item cites figure number, title, page number, and credits where applicable. The author compiled many of the tables and prepared a number of line drawings and graphs. Refer to the page cited for more information.

FRONT COVER, The Soyuz spacecraft in orbit as seen from Apollo during the Apollo-Soyuz Test Project in 1975 (NASA Photo No. 175-H-891)

FRONTISPIECE, Artist's Concept - Soyuz rocket launch from the Baykonur launch complex, USSR, p. iv, (NASA Photo No. 75-H-251)

Section I - VOSTOK

Section V - SOYUZ-SALYUT MISSIONS

BIBLIOGRAPHY

BIBLIOGRAPHY

The following bibliography contains those books and periodicals which contain significant data concerning the Soviet manned space flight and unmanned
lunar and planetary programs. While listing many volumes,this list is by
no means exhaustive, but rather is designed to provide a firm base for any
further study into these programs. Many of the titles have been translated by the US National Technical Information Service or some other department of the US government or government contractor. The number in
parentheses following such works is the NTIS order number by which these
books can be purchased. Both paper and microfiche copies are as a rule
available.

BOOKS, BOOKLETS, ETC.

Aleksandrov, S.G. and Federov, R.Ye., *Soviet Satellites and Space Ships*,
2nd ed., Moscow, 1961, (N63-18430)

Alekseyev, V. and Lebedev, L., *For Lunar Rock*, Mashinostroyeniye Press,
Moscow, 1972, (N73-30801)

Alekseyev, V. and Minchin, S., *Venus Reveals Secrets*, 2nd ed., Mashinostroyeniye Press, Moscow, 1975, (N76-14998)

Andreyanov, V.V., et al., *Automatic Planetary Stations*, Nauka Press,
Moscow, 1973, (N74-29290)

Apollo-Soyuz Mission Evaluation Report, NASA Lyndon B. Johnson Space
Center, Houston, Texas, 1975, (N76-30242)

Apollo-Soyuz Test Project, Academy of Sciences (USSR), Moscow, 1975,
(N75-25985)

*Astronautics and Aeronautics, (year), Chronology of Science Technology,
and Policy*, NASA

Year 1963 - NASA SP-4004	Year 1969 - NASA SP-4014
Year 1964 - NASA SP-4005	Year 1970 - NASA SP-4015
Year 1965 - NASA SP-4006	Year 1971 - NASA SP-4016
Year 1966 - NASA SP-4007	Year 1972 - NASA SP-4017
Year 1967 - NASA SP-4008	Year 1973 - NASA SP-4018
Year 1968 - NASA SP-4010	Year 1974 - NASA SP-4019

Astronauts and Cosmonauts Biographical and Statistical Data, Committee
on Science and Technology, US House of Representatives, 1977

An Atlas of the Moon's Far Side, Interscience Publishers, Sky Publishing Company, Cambridge Mass, 1961

Baker, David, *The Rocket, The History and Development of Rocket and Missile Technology,* Crown Publishers, Inc., New York, 1978

Beard, Robert, *Soviet Cosmonautics, 1957-1967,* privately published, 1970

Beard, Robert, *Soviet Space Failures: A Re-Appraisal,* privately published, 1970

Belyakov, I.T. and Dorisov, YU.D., *Technology in Space,* Mashinostroyeniye Press, Moscow, 1974,   (N75-25982)

Blagonravov, A.A., Chief Editor, *USSR Achievements in Space Research (First Decade in Space, 1957-1967),* Nauka Publishing House, Moscow, 1968,   (JPRS-47311)

Blaine, J.C.D., *The End of an Era in Space Exploration,* Volume 42, Science and Technology Series, American Astronautical Society, 1976

Bono, Phillip and Gatland, Kenneth, *Frontiers of Space,* rev. ed., Macmillan Publishing Company, Inc., New York, 1976

Borisenko, I.G., *In Outer Space,* Mashinostroyeniye Press, Moscow, 1974, (N75-23625)

Borisenko, I.G., *Space Launches and Finishes,* Znaniye Press, Moscow, 1975,   (N77-11076)

Bumshtein, S.I., *Salyut Space Station In Orbit,* Mashinostroyeniye Press, Moscow, 1973,   (JPRS-62201)

Bychkov, V.N., Nazarov, G.A. and Prishchepa, V.I., *Liquid Rocket Space Engines,* "Kosmonavtika, Astronomiya", No. 9, 1976,   (N77-13144)

Caidin, Martin, *Red Star in Space,* Crowell-Collier Press, 1963

Caidin, Martin, *Rendezvous in Space,* E.P. Dutton and Company, Inc., 1962

Clark, Phillip S., *The Proton and Type-G Launch Vehicles,* privately published, January 1977

Supplement 1, June 1977
Supplement 2, January 1978

Clark, Phillip S., *A Review of the Soviet Union's Manned Lunar Programme,* privately published, January 1977

Clark, Phillip S., *Twenty Years of Space Flight, Volumes 1 and 2,* Antares, Volume 2 Special Issue 3, The Bradford Astronomical Society, 1978

Cox, Donald W., *The Space Race,* Chilton Books, Chilton Company, publishers, 1963

Daniloff, Nicholas, *The Kremlin and the Cosmos,* Alfred A. Knopf, New York, 1972

Dimitriyev, A.Yu, et al., *From Spaceships to Orbiting Stations,* Mashino-stroyeniye Press, Moscow, 1971, (N74-15535)

Feoktistov, K.P., *The Salyut 4 Space Laboratory,* Vestinik Akademii Nauk USSR, No. 4, April 1976, (N77-10118)

The First Man in Space, Crosscurrents Press, Inc., New York, 1961

First Panoramic Views of the Lunar Surface, Nauka Publishing House, Moscow, 1966, (N66-38486)

Froehlich, Walter, *Apollo-Soyuz,* NASA EP-109, 1976

Gagarin, Yuri, *Road to the Stars,* Foreign Languages Publishing House, Moscow

Gatland, Kenneth, *Astronautics in the Sixties,* John Wiley and Sons, Inc., 1962

Gatland, Kenneth, *Manned Spacecraft,* Macmillan Publishing Company, Inc., New York, 1976

Gatland, Kenneth, *Missiles and Rockets,* Macmillan Publishing Company, Inc., New York, 1975

Gatland, Kenneth, *Robot Explorers,* Macmillan Company Blandford Press Ltd., London, 1972

Gatland, Kenneth, *Spacecraft and Boosters,* Iliffe Books, Ltd., London, 1964

Gazenko, O.G. and Bjurstedt, H.A., eds. *Man in Space,* Moscow, 1974 (available through Univelt, Inc., San Diego, California)

Gherman Titov, The first Man to Spend a Day in Space, Crosscurrents Press, New York, 1962

Gibney, Frank, and Feldman George J., *The Reluctant Space-Farers,* New American Library, New York, 1966

Glushko, V.P., *Rocket Engines GDL-OKB,* Novosti Press Agency, Moscow, 1975

Gurney, Gene and Gurney, Clare, *Cosmonauts in Orbit,* F. Watta, New York, 1972

Hall, Al, ed., *Petersen's Book of Man in Space, Volumes 1-5,* Petersen Publishing Company, Los Angeles, California, 1974

Hall, R. Cargill, ed., *Essays on the History of Rocketry and Astronauts: Proceedings of the Third through the Sixth History Symposia of the International Academy of Astronautics*

Volume 1 (N77-33030 thru N77-33047)
Volume 2 (N77-33048 thru N77-33070)

Harvey, Dodd L. and Ciccoritti, Linda C., *U.S. - Soviet Cooperation in Space,* Monographs in International Affairs, Center for Advanced International Studies, University of Miami, 1974

James, Peter N., *Soviet Conquest from Space,* Arlington House Publishers, New Rochelle, New York, 1974

Jane's All the World's Aircraft, Jane's Yearbooks, London, annually

Kamanin, N. and Rebrov, M., *An Experimental Space Station in Orbit, 14-18 January 1969,* Izd-vo TsK VLKSM Molodaya Gvardiya, 1969, (AD-718284)

Khodarev, Y.K., et al., *Equipment for Space Research,* NASA TT-F-785, (N75-10988 thru N75-11016)

Krasnov, N.F., ed., *Rocket Aerodynamics,* Vysshaya Shkola Press, Moscow, 1968, (N71-31467)

Korovkin, A.S., *Spacecraft Control Systems,* Military Press, Moscow, 1972, (N73-25903)

Koval, A.D. and Uspenskiy, G.P., *Space is for Man,* 2nd ed., Mashinostroyeniye Press, Moscow, 1974, (N77-11075)

Lebedev, V. and Gagarin, Yuri, *Survival in Space,* Bantom Books, Inc., New York, 1969

Legendary Vostok, Novosti Press Agency Publishing House, Moscow

Leonov, Alexi and Lebedev, Vladimir, *Space and Time Perception by the Cosmonaut,* Mir Publishers, Moscow, 1971

Lewis, Richard S., *From Vineland to Mars, A Thousand Years of Exploration,* Quadrangle/New York Times Book Company, New York, 1976

Ley, Willy, *Events in Space,* Popular Library, New York, 1969

Lipskiy, Yu.N., *Atlas of the Reverse Side of the Moon, Part 2,* Nauka Press, Moscow, 1967, (N69-24206)

Mallan, Lloyd, *Russia's Space Hoax,* Science and Mechanics Publishing Company, New York, 1966

Mandrovsky, Boris, *Soyuz 1. Facts and Speculations,* Aerospace Technology Division, Library of Congress, 1967, (N67-30633)

McGraw-Hill Encyclopedia of Space, McGraw-Hill Book Company, New York, 1968

Moore, Patrick, *Space,* The Natural History Press, 1969

NASA Authorization for Fiscal Year (yearly), Hearings Before the Subcommittee on Science, Technology, and Space of the Committee on Commerce, Science, and Transportation, US Senate; usually contain several references to the Soviet space program

Parry, Albert, *Russia's Rockets and Missiles,* Doubleday and Company, Inc., New York, 1960

Penkovsky, Oleg, *Penkovsky Papers,* Doubleday and Company, Inc., New York, 1965

Peterson, R.W., ed., *Space: From Gemini to the Moon and Beyond,* Facts On File, Inc., New York, 1972

Petrov, G.E., ed., *Conquest of Outer Space in the USSR, 1967-1970,* Amerind Publishing Company Pvt. Ltd., New Delhi, India, 1973

Petrov, V., *Artificial Satellites of the Earth,* Hindustan Publishing Corporation, New Delhi, India, 1960

Petrovich, G.V., ed., *The Soviet Encyclopedia of Space Flight,* Mir Publishers, Moscow, 1969

Ponomarev, A.N., *The Years of the Space Era,* Military Press, Moscow, 1974, (N75-21309)

Rebrov, M. and Khozin, G., *The Moon and Man,* Peace Publishers, Moscow

Riabchikov, Evgeny, *Russians in Space,* Doubleday and Company, Inc., 1971 (Prepared by Novosti Press Agency Publishing House, Moscow)

Romanov, A., *Spacecraft Designer,* Novosti Press Agency Publishing House, Moscow, 1976

Russian Report to the Fifteenth COSPAR Session, Nauka Publishing House, Moscow, 1972, (JPRS-56527)

Sagan, Carl, *The Cosmic Connection,* Dell Publishing Company, Inc., 1975

Sagdeyev, R.Z., ed., *The Conquest of Outer Space in the USSR in 1974,* Nauka Press, Moscow, 1975, (N77-17118)

Salyut Orbital Stations, Novosti Press Agency Publishing House, Moscow, 1975

Schauer, William H., *Politics of Space,* Holmes and Meier, publishers, New York, 1976

Sharpe, Mitchell R., *"It is I, Seagull": Valentina Tereshkova, First Woman in Space*, Thomas Y. Crowell Company, New York, 1975

Sharpe, Mitchell R., *Living in Space, the Astronaut and His Environment*, Doubleday and Company, Inc., New York, 1969

Sheldon, Charles S. II, *United States and Soviet Progress in Space: Summary Data Through 1975 and a Forward Look*, Congressional Research Service, Library of Congress, 1976

Shelton, William, *Soviet Space Exploration: The First Decade*, Washington Square Press, New York, 1968

Shtern, M.I., ed., *Investigations of the Upper Atmosphere and Outer Space Conducted in 1970 in the USSR (14th COSPAR)*, Nauka Press, Moscow, 1971, (N72-17970)

Shtern, M.I., ed., *Space Research Conducted in the USSR in 1973 (17th COSPAR)*, Nauka Publishing House, Moscow, 1974, (JPRS-62861)

Shternfeld, Ari, *Soviet Space Science (Iskustevenniye Sputniki in the USSR)*, Basic Books, Inc., New York, 1959

Sisakyana, N., ed., *Second Group Flight and Certain Results of Flights of Soviet Cosmonauts on the Vostok Ships*, Nauka Publishing House, Moscow, 1965, (AD-619384)

Skuridin, G.A., et al., *Entrance of Mankind into Space (15th Anniversary of the First Manned Flight into Space)*, Znaniye Press, Moscow, 1976, (N77-12082)

Skuridin, G.A., ed., *Mastery of Outer Space in the USSR, 1957-1967*, Nauka Press, Moscow, 1971, (N75-29144)

Smolders, Peter L., *Soviets in Space*, Taplinger Publishing Company, Inc., New York, 1974

Sobel, Lester A., *Space: From Sputnik to Gemini*, Facts On File, Inc., New York, 1965

Sokolov, S.S., *Soviet Automatic Interplanetary Stations Investigate Mars*, Vestnik Akademii Nauk USSR, No. 10, (N75-17272)

Solov'yev, Ts. V. and Tarasov, Ye.V., *Interplanetary Flight Prediction*, Mashinostroyeniye Press, Moscow, 1973, (N74-28312)

"The Soviet Interplanetary Station - Venus 4", Pravda, 22 October 1967, (N70-26751)

Soviet Man in Space, Foreign Languages Publishing House, Moscow; *Soviet Moon Rockets*, rev. ed., Soviet Booklet No. 62, Soviet Booklets, Farleigh Press Ltd., London, 1960

Soviet Space Programs, Committee on Aeronautical and Space Science, US Senate, 1962

Soviet Space Programs, 1962-1965, Committee on Aeronautical and Space Sciences, US Senate, 1966

Soviet Space Programs, 1966-1970, Committee on Aeronautical and Space Sciences, US Senate, 1971

Soviet Space Programs, 1971-1975, Committee on Aeronautical and Space Sciences, US Senate, 1976

Soviet Space Research, Novosti Press Agency Publishing House, Moscow, 1975

Soviet Writings on Earth Satellites and Space Travel, The Citadel Press, New York, 1958

Soyuz and Apollo (in Russian), Moscow, 1976

Stockholm International Peace Research Institute (SIPRI), *Outer Space - Battlefield of the Future?,* Crane, Russak and Company, Inc., New York, 1978

Stoiko, Michael, *Soviet Rocketry: Past, Present, and Future,* Holt, Rinehart, and Winston, New York, 1970

Sykes, Margaret W., *Selected Bibliography on Manned Orbital Space Stations,* Space Sciences Laboratory, General Electric Missile and Space Division, 1963, (N64-21677)

*Table of Earth Satellites, 1957 -   , Royal Aircraft Establishment, Farnborough Hants, England, continually updated

*Table of Space Vehicles, 1958 -   , Royal Aircraft Establishment, Farnborough Hants, England, continually updated

Ten Years of Space Exploration, Novosti Press Agency Publishing House, Moscow

Thomas, John R. and Kruse-Vaucienne, Ursula M., eds., *Soviet Science Technology: Domestic and Foreign Prospectives,* published for the National Science Foundation by George Washington University, 1977, (PB-276968)

Titov, Gherman, *I am Eagle,* The Bobbs-Merrill Company, Inc., New York, 1962

Titov, Gherman, *700,000 km Through Space,* Foreign Languages Publishing House, Moscow

TRW Space Log, TRW Defense and Space Systems Group, TRW Inc., Redondo Beach, California, currently published annually

Tsiolkovskiy, K.E., *Study of Outer Space by Reaction Devices,* Mashino-stroyeniye Press, Moscow, 1967,   (N75-29141)

Turnill, Reginald, *The Observer's Book of Manned Spaceflight,* Frederick Warne and Company Ltd., London, 1975

Turnill, Reginald, *The Observer's Book of Unmanned Spaceflight,* Frederick Warne and Company Ltd., London, 1974

Turnill, Reginald, *The Observer's Spaceflight Directory* (a revised and combined edition of the previous two volumes), Frederick Warne and Company Ltd., London, 1978

Umanskiy, S.P., *Man in Space Orbit,* Mashinostroyeniye Press, Moscow, 1975,   (N75-10688)

USSR Explores the Moon, Novosti Press Agency Publishing House, Moscow

Vassiliev, M., *Sputnik into Space,* The Dial Press, New York, 1958

Vinogradov, A.P., ed., *Lunokhod 1: Mobile Lunar Laboratory,* (N72-12168)

Vladimirov, Leonid, *The Russian Space Bluff,* The Dial Press, New York, 1973

von Braun, Wernher and Ordway, Frederick III, *History of Rocketry and Space Travel,* 3rd ed., Thomas Y. Crowell, 1975

Voskhod 1 and Voskhod 2 Flights, Surveys of Soviet-Bloc Scientific and Technical Literature, Aerospace Technology Division, Library of Congress, (N65-32217)

Wilding-White, T.M., *Jane's Pocket Book of Space Exploration,* Collier Books, New York, 1976

Wukelic, G.E., *Handbook of Soviet Space-Science Research,* Gordon and Breach Science Publishers, New York, 1968

Yefremov, Yu.I., *The Panoramic Views of the Lunar Surface, Volume 2,* Nauka Press, Moscow, 1969,   (N71-19242)

Yefremov, Yu.I., *Space Research Conducted in the USSR in 1974 (18th COSPAR),* Nauka Publishing House, Moscow, 1975,   (JPRS-65778)

Yefremov, Yu.I., *Space Research Performed in USSR in 1972 (16th COSPAR),* Moscow, 1973,   (JPRS-59778)

Zaehringer, Alfred J., *Soviet Space Technology,* Harper and Brothers Publishers, New York, 1961

Zhdanov, G. and Tindo, I., *Space Laboratories,* Foreign Languages Publishing House, Moscow.

PERIODICALS

Individual articles from periodicals have been indicated in the footnotes at the end of each section. Therefore, the following is a list of those periodicals which frequently or occasionally publish articles pertaining to the space programs of the Soviet Union. The country of origin of each periodical is indicated in parentheses.

Astronautics and Aeronautics (USA)

Astronomicheskii Zhurnal (USSR) (available in USA as *Soviet Astronomy*)

Aviation Week and Space Technology (USA)

Aviatsiya i Kosmonavtika (USSR)

Flight International (England)

Flug Revue (West Germany)

Icarus (USA)

Interavia (Switzerland)

Izvestiya (USSR)

Journal of the British Astronomical Association (England)

Journal of the British Interplanetary Society (England)

Journal of Spacecraft and Rockets (USA)

Kosmicheskie Issledovaniya (USSR) (available in USA as *Cosmic Research*)

L-5 News (USA)

Nature (England)

New Scientist (England)

Pravda (USSR)

Science (USA)

Science News (USA)

Sky and Telescope (USA)

Soviet Aeronautics (USSR) (available in USA in English edition)

Soviet Aerospace (USA)

Soviet Physics - Doklady (Translation of Physics Section of the Proceedings of the Academy of Sciences of the USSR)   (USA)

Soviet Life   (USA)

Space/Aeronautics (USA)

Spaceflight   (England)

Space Technology International (USA)

Spaceview (Holland)

Space World   (USA)

Tass   (USSR)

Translations on USSR Science and Technology, Physical Sciences and Technology (Translations of Soviet scientific journals by the Joint Publications Research Service, available from NTIS)

BIBLIOGRAPHIES

Whereas many of the volumes referenced above contain excellent bibliographies, the following four bibliographies are worthy of special note due to their comprehensive nature for selected time periods:

Beard, Robert, *Soviet Cosmonautics, 1957-1969, A Bibliography of Articles Published in British Periodicals and of British and Foreign Books,* privately published

Kendon, Anthony, "A Guide to the Study of the Soviet Space Programme", *Spaceflight,* May 1975, pp. 175-179

TRW Space Log, Winter 1968-1969, TRW Defense and Space Systems Group, Redondo Beach, California, pp. 24-29

TRW Space Log, 1974, TRW Defense and Space Systems Group, Redondo Beach, California, pp. 20-35.

INDEX

INDEX

A

A-4 (V-2) rocket, 3
A-9/A-10 rocket, 3
A-class launch vehicle, 394-400, 404, 410
Akademik Sergei Korolev (ship), 293
Akademik Shirshov (ship), 167
Aksenov, Vladimir, 138, 194-197, 373, 417, 419
Amak-3 analyzer, 246, 311
AN-30 aircraft, 196
Anna III telescope, 230-231, 293, 295
AO-1/AO-2 orienter, 245
Apollo-Soyuz Test Project (ASTP), 84, 94, 95, 99, 105, 107, 123-125, 130,
        132-133, 175-193, 204, 236, 299, 306, 316-318, 335, 348, 409
"April 5th Anomaly", See Soyuz 18A
Artyukhin, Yuri, 215, 301-304, 416, 419
Audio experiment, 354

B

BA-3K camera, 246
B-class launch vehicle, 394, 396-399, 404, 410-411
Belka (dog), 28-29
Belyavev, Pavel, 64, 69, 75-84, 415, 419
Beregovoi, Georgii, 148-150, 201, 415, 419
Berolina experiment, 355
Biogravistat experiment, 196
Bioterm experiments, 246, 310
Brezhnev, Leonid, 75, 219
British Interplanetary Society, ix
BST-1M telescope, 260, 345, 358, 365
Bushuyev, Konstatin, 323
Bykovsky, Valery, 34, 49-53, 55, 138, 194-197, 325, 354-355, 415, 417-419

C

C-class launch vehicle, 394, 396-397, 399, 404, 411
Chernushka (dog), 28, 31
Chibis medical unit, 232, 246, 260, 309, 311
Chlorella experiment, 260, 346
Comet Kohoutek, 174
Cosmonaut deaths, 39, See also Soyuz 1 and Soyuz 11
Crystal experiment, 250
Cygnus X-1, 319
Cytos experiment, 341

D

D-class launch vehicle, 93, 219, 232, 234-235, 262, 381, 394, 396-397,
        399-402, 404, 410, 412
Delta apparatus, 246, 260, 309, 311, 337-338
Demin, Lev, 215, 305-306, 416, 419
Diffusia experiment, 250, 326
Dobrichovsky, Z., 211
Dobrovolskiy, Georgiy, 215, 290-299, 416, 419
Docking failures, See Soyuz: 2/3, 7/8, 10, 15, 23, 25, 33
Docking mechanisms
        1st generation, 107, 123-124, 152-156, 163
        2nd generation, 107, 124, 220, 222, 285-289
        ASTP, 107, 124, 183, 185, 272
Dzhanibekov, Vladimir, 215, 339-341, 347, 417, 419

E

Emissiya experiment, 246, 319
Era experiment, 232, 295-296
Extinctia, 260, 346
Extra-vehicular activity (EVA), 20, 64, 75-83, 156-159, 173, 202, 209,
        240, 253, 255, 258-261, 275, 280, 285, 331-332, 336-337, 342,
        352-353, 361, 371

F

Fakel photometer, 246
Farkas, Bertalan, 373
F-class launch vehicle, 394, 396-397, 401-402, 404
FEK-7 camera, 231
Feoktistov, Konstantin, 64, 73-75, 198, 323, 415, 419
Filin-2 experiment, 245, 309-310, 319
Filipchenko, Anatolii, 138, 160-163, 175-179, 416, 419
FKT experiment, 246, 310
Fractional Orbital Bombardment System (FOBS), 401-402
Freon experiment, 246

G

Gagarin, Yuri, vii, x, 13, 33-40, 44, 50, 54, 139, 143, 209, 291, 415, 419
G-class launch vehicle, 132, 134, 165, 262, 394, 397, 402-403
Glazkov, Yuri, 215, 331-333, 417-419
Gorbatko, Viktor, 138, 160-163, 215, 331-333, 416-417, 419
Grechko, Georgiy, 215, 307-313, 335-347, 385, 416-417, 419
Gubarev, Aleksey, 215, 307-313, 345-346, 385, 416-417, 419

H

Hermaszewski, Miroslaw, 215, 349-351, 418, 420
High altitude biological flights, 3-5

I

Impulse apparatus, 327
In space refueling, 145, 201, 217, 258, 265, 267-268, 323, 326, 342, 344
        347, 352

```
            Kosmos 672 (Soyuz), 130, 133-134, 175, 204
            Kosmos 690 (Vostok), 84
            Kosmos 772 (Soyuz), 130, 134, 382, 386
            Kosmos 782 (Vostok), 85, 323
            Kosmos 881/882, 381
            Kosmos 869 (Soyuz), 130, 134, 382
            Kosmos 929, 381
            Kosmos 997/998, 381
            Kosmos 1001 (Soyuz), 130, 134-135, 382
            Kosmos 1074 (Soyuz), 130, 134-135, 382
            Kosmos 1101/1102, 381
Kosygin, Aleksey, 75, 175
Kovalenok, Vladimir, 215, 333-334, 348-360, 369, 384-385, 417-419
Kristall apparatus, 351, 353, 358, 360-363
KRT-10 radio telescope, 369-371
KSS-2 experiment, 245, 309
Kubasov, Valeriy, 106, 125, 138, 160-163, 180-193, 291, 373, 416-417, 419


        L

Laika (dog), 6-8
Lazarev, Vasiliy, 138, 169-171, 204, 215, 300, 313-316, 416-417, 419
Lebedev, Valentin, 138, 172-175, 416, 419
Leonov, Aleksey, 9, 64, 75-84, 106, 125, 138, 180-193, 291, 415, 417, 419
Levka experiments, 174, 246, 311, 327
LV-1 apparatus, 246
Lyakhov, Vladimir, 215, 360-372, 418-419


        M

Makarov, Oleg, 138, 169-171, 204, 215, 300, 313-316, 339-341, 347,
        416-417, 419
Malyshev, Yuri, 373
Medusa experiment, 260, 338, 352
Meteor weather satellites, 167, 293, 297, 303
MKF-6 camera system, 103, 194-196
MKF-6M camera system, 260, 342, 344, 349-350, 354
MMK-1 detector, 245, 309
Molniya 1 communications satellite, 163, 170, 293
Molniya 3 communications satellite, 316
Morava experiment, 260, 346
Mushka (dog), 28-31


        N

National Technical Information Service (NTIS), ix
Neytral equipment, 246
Nikolayev, Andriyan, 34, 45-49, 51-52, 54, 91, 99, 138, 165-168,
        415-416, 419


        O

Oazis experiments, 173-174, 232, 246, 293, 296, 310, 318
Ocean Surveillance System (OSS), 401-402
Orion-1 telescope, 172, 222, 227-228, 230, 246, 272, 294-296
```

Orion-2 telescope, 171-173
OST-1 experiment, 245-247, 249, 308-310, 319
Oxymeter, 260, 346

P

Palma apparatus, 327
Patseyev, Viktor, 215, 290-299, 416, 419
Pchelka (dog), 28-31
Penguin suits, 231, 293, 303, 358
Plesetsk, 397-398, 409, 411-412
Plotnost monitor, 246, 311
Polynon installations, 246, 260, 311
Popov, Leonid, 373
Popovich, Pavel, 34, 45-49, 55, 91, 215, 301-304, 325, 415, 416, 419
Potek experiment, 250, 326
Praktica EE2 camera, 355
Progress Design, 126, 265-270
Progress spacecraft
        Progress 1, 201, 211, 253, 259-260, 265, 267, 269, 271, 274,
           342-344, 352, 424
        Progress 2, 211, 253-254, 267, 269, 271, 351-355
        Progress 3, 211, 254, 267, 269, 353-355
        Progress 4, 211, 254, 269, 358, 360
        Progress 5, 211, 254, 269-270, 361-363
        Progress 6, 211, 254, 269-270, 366, 368
        Progress 7, 211, 255, 269-270, 369-371
        Progress 8, 211, 373
        Progress 9, 211, 373
Proton launch vehicle, see D-class launch vehicle
Proton satellites, 400

R

Raduga experiment, 260, 342
Reaction experiment, 250, 326
Relaks experiment, 260, 349
Remek, Vladimir, 215, 345-346, 417, 420
Reporter experiment, 355
Resonance experiment, 260, 341
Rezeda-5 recorder, 246, 311, 327
Romanenko, Yuri, 215, 335-347, 417, 419
Rozhdestvenskiy, Valery, 215, 328-330, 417, 420
RSS-2M spectrograph, 250, 326
RT-4 experiment, 245, 309, 319
Rukavishnikov, Nikolay, 138, 175-179, 215, 283, 288, 363-365, 416,
      418, 420
Ryumin, Valery, 215, 333-334, 360-373, 384-385, 417-418, 420

S

S-2 sextant, 246
Salyut design, 112, 209-211, 216-217, 219-263
Salyut, future, 261-263, 377-382

Salyut programs (civilian/military), 213-217, 229, 271, 275
Salyut propulsion system, 224-225, 255, 258-259, 267-268, 362, 396
Salyut prototype, 164, 219
Salyut spacecraft
        Salyut 1, 127, 169, 171-173, 209, 211, 214-216, 220-234,
           236-240, 242, 244, 246, 252, 279, 283-301, 317, 341,
           377, 401, 416, 424
        Salyut 2, 170, 211, 214-215, 234-239, 273, 317, 324, 384, 401
        Salyut 3, 127, 133, 179, 211, 214-215, 236, 239-245, 249,
           252-253, 255, 273, 300-308, 317, 322, 324-325, 329,
           331, 333, 401, 416
        Salyut 4, 127, 133, 170, 188, 194, 204, 211, 214-215, 236, 240,
           244-249, 252, 255, 261, 265, 273, 280, 307-324, 327,
           330, 335, 369, 401, 416-417
        Salyut 5, 127, 194, 211, 214-215, 239-240, 248-252, 255, 261,
           265, 275, 324-333, 401, 417
        Salyut 6, 127, 135, 201, 209, 211, 214-215, 229, 236, 239, 249,
           252-263, 269, 271, 280, 333-373, 379, 385, 401,
           417-418, 424
Sarafanov, Valsilyevich, 215, 305-306, 384, 416, 420
Satellite Interceptor System (SIS), 401-402
Sevast'yanov, Vitalii, 138, 165-168, 215, 249, 275, 317-321, 416-417, 420
Sfera experiment, 250, 325
Shatalov, Vladimir, 138, 151-158, 160-163, 215, 283-284, 306, 329, 332,
        335-337, 373, 415-416, 420
Shonin, Georgii, 138, 160-163, 416, 420
Silya-4 spectrometer, 245, 309, 320
Sirena experiment, 260, 349
"solar warping", 119, 166, 168
Soviet launch vehicles, 393-406
Soviet manned lunar landing program, see Zond lunar landing program
Soviet military rockets, 405
Soviet rocket engines, 396
Soviet space launch facilities, 409-412
Soviet space shuttle, 217, 373, 380-382, 403
Soviet space stamps, 14
Soviet superbooster, see G-class launch vehicle
Soyuz
        Soyuz 1, 84, 97, 125-127, 129, 131, 137-143, 147, 149, 161,
           415, 419
        Soyuz 2, 91, 97, 126-127, 130-131, 138-140, 147-152, 201,
           322, 415
        Soyuz 3, 97, 127, 130-131, 138, 147-152, 201, 415, 419
        Soyuz 4, 97, 107, 127, 132, 138, 148, 151-160, 209, 240, 261,
           279, 283, 285, 415, 420, 424
        Soyuz 5, 97, 107, 127, 132, 138, 148, 151-160, 209, 231, 240,
           261, 279, 283, 285, 324, 331, 416, 419-420, 424
        Soyuz 6, 103, 126-127, 132, 138, 160-165, 219, 263, 279, 283,
           331, 416, 419-420, 424
        Soyuz 7, 97, 127, 132, 138, 160-165, 175, 219, 263, 279, 283,
           290, 331, 416, 419-420, 424
        Soyuz 8, 127, 132, 138, 160-165, 219, 263, 279, 283, 290, 331,
           416, 420, 424

Soyuz 9, 107-108, 124, 127, 132, 138, 231, 279, 296, 313, 317, 339, 416, 419-420
Soyuz 10, 97, 107, 125-127, 169, 175, 211, 215, 220, 232, 244, 280, 283-290, 300, 304, 363, 416, 420
Soyuz 11, 96-98, 124, 127, 132, 169-170, 211, 215, 220, 229, 232-234, 239-240, 244, 252, 269, 280, 289-300, 304, 313, 416, 419-420, 424
Soyuz 12, 125-127, 133, 138, 169-173, 238, 273, 290, 300, 313, 339, 384-385, 416, 419
Soyuz 13, 127, 138, 171-175, 300, 317, 416, 419
Soyuz 14, 127, 133, 211, 215, 239-240, 243-244, 280, 300-305, 307, 325, 416, 419
Soyuz 15, 127, 133, 179, 211, 215, 240, 243-244, 280, 305-308, 329, 331, 416, 419-420
Soyuz 16, 107, 124-127, 138, 175-179, 181, 188, 243, 416, 419-420
Soyuz 17, 127, 211, 215, 245, 247-248, 280, 307-313, 318, 335, 416, 419
Soyuz 18A, 127, 199, 204, 211, 215, 245, 248, 274, 280, 313-318, 339, 417, 419
Soyuz 18B, 127, 133, 188, 194, 211, 215, 217, 245, 247-248, 274, 280, 317-322, 417, 419-420
Soyuz 19, 107, 124, 127, 138, 175, 180-194, 204, 217, 318, 321, 417, 419, 424
Soyuz 20, 91, 127, 211, 245, 248, 280, 306, 322-325, 417
Soyuz 21, 127, 194, 211, 215, 250-251, 275, 280, 324-328, 332, 417, 420
Soyuz 22, 103, 124, 126-127, 138, 194-197, 275, 325, 328, 342, 354, 417, 419
Soyuz 23, 121, 127, 211, 215, 250-251, 280, 328-331, 334, 385, 417, 420
Soyuz 24, 127, 211, 215, 251, 280, 330-333, 417, 419
Soyuz 25, 127, 211, 215, 252-253, 255, 259, 280, 333-334, 337, 348, 360, 384, 417, 419-420
Soyuz 26, 127, 201, 211, 215, 229, 253, 255, 259, 261, 269, 274, 280, 333, 335, 348, 355, 359-360, 372, 387, 417, 419, 424
Soyuz 27, 127, 211, 215, 229, 253, 259, 280, 339-341, 343, 345, 347, 417, 419, 424
Soyuz 28, 127, 211, 215, 229, 253, 271, 280, 345-347, 417, 419, 424
Soyuz 29, 127, 211, 215, 229, 253-254, 261, 269-270, 274-275, 280, 348-360, 362, 368-369, 372, 385, 387, 418-419
Soyuz 30, 127, 211, 215, 229, 253, 271, 280, 349-351, 354, 418-419
Soyuz 31, 127, 211, 215, 229, 254, 271, 275, 280, 354-357, 359, 387, 418-419
Soyuz 32, 127, 211, 215, 254, 261, 269-270, 274, 280-281, 360-372, 385, 418-420, 424
Soyuz 33, 127, 211, 215, 254, 271, 280, 363-366, 418, 420
Soyuz 34, 91, 127, 211, 254, 280, 366, 368, 372, 418
Soyuz 35, 373
Soyuz 36, 373